Lost Landscapes of
Plymouth

Maps, Charts and Plans to 1800

Lost Landscapes of
Plymouth

Maps, Charts and Plans to 1800

ELISABETH STUART

ALAN SUTTON
in association with
MAP COLLECTOR PUBLICATIONS LIMITED

First published in the United Kingdom in 1991 by
Alan Sutton Publishing Ltd · Phoenix Mill · Far Thrupp · Stroud · Gloucestershire
in association with Map Collector Publications Limited

First published in the United States of America in 1991 by
Alan Sutton Publishing Inc · Wolfeboro Falls · NH 03896-0848

British Library Cataloguing in Publication Data

Stuart, Elisabeth *1949–*
    Lost landscapes of Plymouth: maps, charts and plans to 1800.
    1. Devon (England). Maps, history
    I. Title
    912.42358

    ISBN 0–86299–772–0

Library of Congress Cataloging in Publication Data applied for

*Cover illustration: Detail of Plymouth Sound from harbour chart of south-west England,
c. 1539 (by permission of the British Library)*

Typesetting and origination by
Alan Sutton Publishing Limited.
Printed in Great Britain by
The Bath Press Ltd., Avon.

To my mother
Pamela Irene Elisabeth Stuart

Contents

List of Colour Plates   ix

Acknowledgements   xi

Introduction   1
  The Tradition of Map-making: Types and Content of Maps   5
  Cartographers   45
  Cartography   49
  The Mapping of Particular Places   53
  Conclusion   65
  Notes   68

Maps, Charts and Plans of Plymouth to 1800: A CATALOGUE   73
  Supplement I: Additional Maps, Charts and Plans   162
  Supplement II: Articles Worthy of Mention   164

Appendix I: Institutions Holding Maps of Plymouth   167

Appendix II: Index of Maps by Location   169

Appendix III: Biographical Notes on Selected Map-makers   187

Appendix IV: Features Within the Town of Plymouth   193

Appendix V: Features Around Plymouth Sound   201

Appendix VI: Rocks, Sandbanks and Shoals around Plymouth Sound   209

Bibliography   211

List of Colour Plates

Between pp. 52 and 53

1 Detail of Plymouth Sound from harbour chart of south-west England (*c.* 1539)

2 'Plat of Plymo[uth]' (? pre–1549)

6 'discriptio[n] of a Tow[n]', depicting the landscape around Plymouth Sound (*c.* 1591)

8 Map of the landscape north of Plymouth Sound (*c.* 1591)

10 'Sa[in]t Nicholas Ilande by Plimmouthe' (Robert Adams, 1592)

17 Thematic map showing the water system, mills and streams at the north-west edge of the town of Plymouth (early seventeenth century)

11 'Plat of Plymoth' (? 1592)

38 Decorative plan of Plymouth Citadel (Sir Bernard de Gomme, 1672)

43 'The Plain or Plott of Plymouth Sound Ham Oaze and Cattwater' (? copy by Edmund Dummer of original by Jerome Roch, August 1682)

68 'A VIEW of Plymouth Sound & ye River HAMOUZE & CATWATER taken from ye Riseing Land above Mount Edgecomb opposite Mount Wise wch shews yt St Nicholas Island is ye Principal gaurd [sic] to ye New Dock and ye SHIPS In this Harbour D[E]LINEATED 1697'

87 Manuscript copy (1779) of 'A Correct Draught of PLYMOUTH SOUND CATT WATER and HAM OWSE' (inset) on 'A NEW and CORRECT CHART of the CHANNEL between ENGLAND & FRANCE with considerable Improvements not extant in any Draughts hitherto Publish'd; shewing the Sands, Shoals, depths of Water and Anchorage, with ye flowing of the Tydes, and setting of the Current; as observ'd by the learned Dr Halley' (Greenvile Collins, 1723)

107 Manuscript copy (*c.* 1779) of 'A PLAN of the TOWN and CITADEL of PLYMOUTH' (inset) on 'An ACCURATE MAP OF DEVON SHIRE Divided into its HUNDREDS' (Emmanuel Bowen, April 1754)

135 'Plan de la Ville, des Ports, de la Citadelle et des Chantiers de Plymouth' (? M. de Beville, September 1768)

Maps **1**, **43** and **68** are reproduced by permission of the British Library; maps **2**, **6**, **8**, **10** and **11** by permission of the Marquess of Salisbury; map **38** by permission of the National Maritime Museum; maps **87** and **107** by permission of the Archivo Histórico Nacional, Madrid; map **135** by permission of the Public Record Office.

Acknowledgements

Publication of this book has been made possible with the help of two grants from the Marc Fitch Fund, Oxford, in 1985 and 1989, and one grant from the Barbican Association, Plymouth, in 1988. Their help is gratefully acknowledged. I also owe an enormous debt to the staff of the British Library Map Library, particularly Tony Campbell, Map Librarian, for reading through the work in draft and making extremely constructive criticisms and Peter Barber, Deputy Map Librarian, for his most helpful suggestions, which have been acknowledged in the text. Francis Herbert of the Royal Geographical Society kindly read the catalogue in draft and made a number of corrections. Graham Haslam of the Duchy of Cornwall has also been particularly helpful and Susan Martin of the same institution drew the charts of Sutton Pool and Plymouth Sound. Brian Harley first suggested that I should write this book.

Thanks are also due to the institutions and private owners mentioned in the text. It seems invidious to mention names, but the following have been helpful: James Barber, Geraldine Beech, Rose Bell, Camilla Blackman, Mark Brayshay, J.G. Coad, Betty Fathers, Gareth Fitzpatrick, Harold Fox, Crispin Gill, Basil Greenhill, Robin Harcourt-Williams, Kate Harris, Susan Healy, Roger Morriss, Brian Thynne, Pierre Waksman, Elizabeth Wiggans, Freddy Woodward, John Worsley, Kees Zandlivet and colleagues within Devon Record Office and the University of Exeter.

Finally, Richard Bryant and Roger Thorp of Alan Sutton, my publishers, have been a delight to work with and Mr T. Driscoll of the Driscoll House Hotel, London, provided ideal accommodation for anyone undertaking a task of this nature.

Introduction

Because of its importance for the defence of the realm, the modern city of Plymouth has a rich legacy of historical maps, charts and plans. Very few of these maps survive locally; rather, they lie scattered between the major research institutions in this country and abroad (see Appendix I). The *raison d'être* of this catalogue is to draw together this source material on paper for the benefit of scholars: both those interested in the history of cartography and those working on the history of Plymouth. This treasury of maps constitutes a local heritage of national importance which lies dispersed.

The place-name 'Plymouth' can be interpreted in three senses. In its narrowest sense, it means the original town. In a broader sense, the modern city of Plymouth consists of the Three Towns of Plymouth, Devonport (called Dock until it was renamed in 1824) and Stonehouse, which were united in 1914. However, in the broadest sense, 'Plymouth' is often used to describe the whole area around Plymouth Sound running from Rame Head in the west to the Yealm estuary in the east, and the coastline around this area. In this book, in contexts where confusion might arise, these three areas have been distinguished as 'the town of Plymouth', 'the city of Plymouth' and 'the countryside around Plymouth Sound' respectively.

Each of the Three Towns has a distinct pattern of growth which is discussed below (pp. 34–8). Although the original town of Plymouth retained its central importance throughout this period because of its mercantile trade operating from Sutton Pool, the maps reveal how Dock grew within one lifespan from 'the barton of Mount Wise',[1] little more than a field, in 1689, to a town rivalling Plymouth by 1765.[2] Stonehouse, on the other hand, despite the efforts of the Mount Edgcumbe family in the seventeenth century to create a borough which would rival the town of Plymouth, did not really develop from a small fishing town in the sixteenth century until the late eighteenth century. At that date, it became the home for several elegant naval and military establishments which remain to this day: the Royal Naval Hospital, the Long Room, the Royal Marine Barracks and the Military Hospital.

The countryside around Plymouth Sound was described by John Leland in the 1530s as 'creekes from the mouth of Plym and Tamar'.[3] Why has this area been mapped so often? Undoubtedly the clue lies in its distinctive situation as an outer harbour (the Sound) enclosing a series of inner harbours, thus opening up the land to influences from abroad, whether benign, in times of peace, or hostile, in times of war. Plymouth's geographical position, remote from the heart of national government but accessible to the world outside, especially France and Spain, has made it at times an ideal target for invasion. From the eighteenth century, when the theatre of war began to shift west towards America, Plymouth's significance grew yet greater, and this too was reflected in an increased number of charts at this date.

By analysing the information to be found in this catalogue of maps from the sixteenth until the end of the eighteenth century when this survey ends, it is possible to reconstruct the Plymouth landscape, at least on paper. At times, the picture is

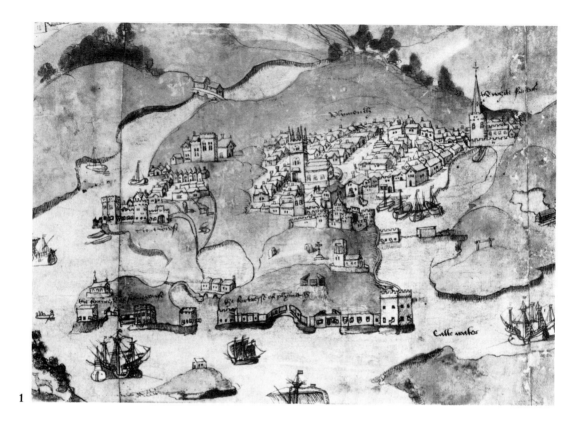

1

incomplete: we know little of what the seventeenth-century town of Plymouth looked like, for instance. Yet, for all that, the sources exist for a unique record, such as can be found for few modern English towns. Ironically, the picture is all the more important because throughout this period and indeed even until our own day, there is only one landmark which has remained constant and enduring from the earliest map (a chart of *c.* 1539): St Andrew's Church.

One feature of this landscape is the sharp contrast between the town of Plymouth, which was constantly changing, and the countryside around the Sound, which has changed relatively little apart from the intrusive expansion of the Dockyard and town, and of Stonehouse. Mount Edgcumbe Park, too, changed during the period covered by these maps but in this case, unlike the towns, the changes represent a self-consciously man-made landscape rather than haphazard growth.

Place-names for the countryside around Plymouth Sound changed little throughout this period. The landscape of the late twentieth-century city of Plymouth, like so much of Britain, is littered with names whose relevance must escape many of those who use them in everyday speech. Milehouse, for instance, is represented as a house a mile away from the centre of the town on map **113**, while Old Mills gave their name to Millbay, and Millbridge was precisely that: a mill standing on a bridge. Similarly, in the countryside around Plymouth Sound map **50** shows the salt-mill above Saltash. To the modern reader, place-names on these maps have two functions: besides the obvious one, that is, acting as a marker, they are a wonderful shorthand way of recording associations, often long after the original features they related to have disappeared.

A few place-names have become obsolete, however: West Comfer (referring to Anthony), for example, occurs from time to time on printed charts, but is no longer used. Likewise, throughout the period of this catalogue, Drake's Island was known as St Nicholas Island or occasionally Francis Island (**38**, **45**) and on one occasion (**2**) as Trystram's Island. In general, however, it is not difficult to equate the place-names given on even the earliest maps with the modern Ordnance Survey 1:50,000 map, and for this reason it has not been thought necessary to draw attention to place-names in the catalogue entries unless for a specific reason.

The earliest of the maps in this catalogue, a chart of the south-west peninsula, can be dated *c*. 1539 from internal evidence and the latest is a printed chart of 1799 (a few nineteenth-century copies of earlier maps have been noticed for comparative purposes). The end of the eighteenth century presents a convenient stopping-point. These two-and-a-half centuries are particularly interesting in terms of the development of the town and countryside around Plymouth and the growth of the Dockyard and town which grew up around it as a direct result of the eighteenth-century wars.

What is a map? The definition suggested in the *Glossary of Technical Terms in Cartography* (Royal Society, 1966) is broad: 'A conventional representation, normally to scale and usually on a flat medium, of a selection of material or abstract features on or in relation to the surface of the Earth, or of a heavenly body.' Some maps, however, are more properly described as charts or plans. A chart is a map primarily designed for navigation, [4] hence many of the examples in this catalogue indicating the outline of coasts, position of the rocks, sandbanks, channels, anchorages and so on. The word 'plan' is also included in the title of this book: cartographically, this means a map drawn exactly to scale.

In practice, however, many of the maps in this catalogue defy rigid definition, and boundary lines are not so neat as the above would suggest. Many sixteenth-century maps are best described as picture-maps, and have been included here. Prints, views and prospects dating from the eighteenth century, however, have been excluded in virtually every case unless there is a map element or other very good reason for including them. Broadly speaking, the maps in this catalogue can be divided into three categories: maps of the town of Plymouth and surrounding area; charts of Plymouth Sound; and plans of the fortifications. Plymouth's cartographic legacy is a rag-bag of maps, uneven in quality, ranging from the line-sketch (**7**), probably drawn about the time of the Armada and barely recognizable as the outline of the Sound were it not for the place-names 'plomowth' and 'stonhouse', to the fine manuscript surveys and charts of Gardner and Mackenzie (**155**, **159**, **164–6**, **179–82**). Most of these maps were made for a reason, and their makers would not have been self-conscious about their artistry. The word used most often by contemporaries to describe these maps is 'plot', 'plat', 'platt': 'in Tudor usage . . . a true ground plan of which details of features were often shown in perspective'.[5]

Likewise, criteria for inclusion and exclusion in the catalogue have been decided on practical grounds. In general, maps which merely note Plymouth's existence and give no significant detail have been omitted. However, while all of the maps in this book include the whole or part of this area, they vary in scale from maps covering the whole of the south-west peninsula (**1**, **5**) to plans focussing on a small area such as the Citadel, Dockyard or St Nicholas (now Drake's) Island. Plans showing the whole Dockyard or

Citadel have been included, but not those showing part only or individual buildings. Likewise, even after analysing the knowledge gleaned from the maps, some maps remain impossible to date and have been placed at the end of the catalogue. Maps, like any other form of historical evidence, should be approached with caution. This is dealt with in detail below in the section on cartography.

Note: References to catalogue entries are printed in bold figures.

8 (detail)

The Tradition of Map-making: Types and Content of Maps

Military Maps

Sir Niklaus Pevsner described Plymouth as 'the only British city whose existence appears to be centred on war'.[6] The remarkable legacy of maps, charts and plans that has survived for this town and the surrounding countryside before 1800 bears out this comment. Although not all the maps can be dated precisely, the main concentrations of maps in this catalogue show a correlation with the years when England was either at war or lay under foreign threat: the late sixteenth century, the 1690s and the second half of the eighteenth century.

1 Drawing Room Maps

Despite Plymouth's wartime significance, however, only a small proportion of the maps in this catalogue are 'military maps' in the strictest sense. The Tower of London Drawing Room did not begin until 1717 and intensive mapping of the area around Plymouth does not occur until the American War of Independence (1775–83).

Before these late eighteenth-century surveys made on the spot began, the Tower draughtsmen in London had to work from maps and sketches drawn in Plymouth but with no detail of the surroundings.[7] As a consequence, maps emanating from this source can be easily identified because the draughtsmen use the same background detail, for example, limestone kilns and quarries, Borough House and Underhill Farm at Stoke Damerel. In some instances, these details continue to be shown even after they have become out of date: for instance, Stonehouse passage occurs on maps recording the 1779–82 encampments (**168–9**) although the bridge had been built over ten years earlier!

The earliest of this little group of maps was drawn by Colonel Desmaretz, undated but probably made between 1756 and 1767. Another tell-tale clue in the case of this map is the number of copies which has survived alongside it at the Public Record Office.[8] Copying earlier maps was part of the routine training within the Board of Ordnance.

2 Plymouth's Military Significance Throughout This Period: Localization of the Theatre of War

William Roy, appointed Surveyor-General of Coasts and Engineer for Making and Directing Military Surveys in Great Britain in 1765, commented that if a country had not yet been surveyed, the state of warfare generally produced the first improvements in its geography.[9] Certainly the mapping of Plymouth improved significantly during the American War of Independence. In addition to the immensely detailed surveys of

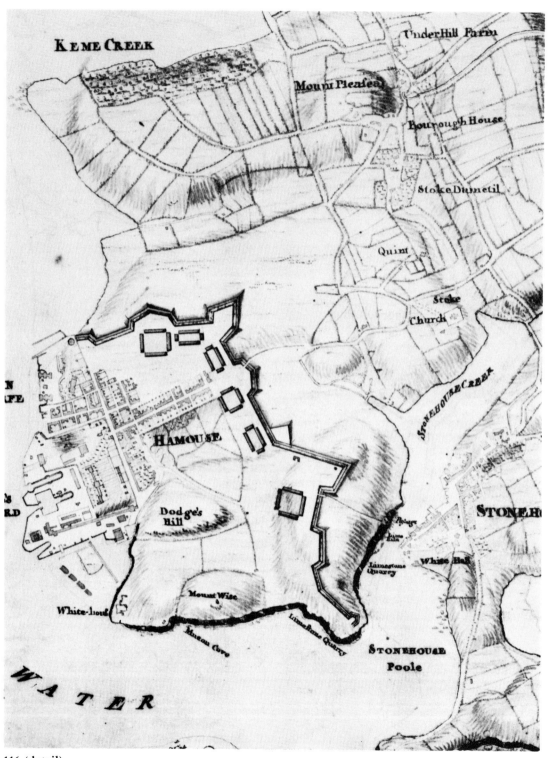

116 (detail)

William Gardner (**179–82**), there are the carefully measured distances between the batteries on rising grounds drawn by R. Sturt in 1788 (**186**). Heights above sea-level, distances across water and across land all make their appearance for the first time in the late eighteenth century (see below, pp. 28–30, 39).

To appreciate Pevsner's comment, however, it is necessary to understand that throughout the whole period covered by these maps the area around Plymouth Sound was vulnerable. After the building of the Dockyard in the late seventeenth century, it became a military landscape. Previously, the threat from abroad had been generalized: from the early eighteenth century, the theatre of war became much more localized. Arguably, therefore, although only a small proportion of the maps in this catalogue are military in the strictest sense, yet war or the threat of war was the prime motivation for the majority of them.

The little town of Plymouth, clustered around the northern and western edges of Sutton Pool, was an Achilles' heel of all England from at least the reign of Henry VIII onwards because of its accessibility to the wider world. Noted as 'Plemme' as early as *c.* 1321 on a portolan chart,[10] it became a pilgrimage port later in the fourteenth century and suffered at various times during the fifteenth century from burning by the Bretons and French. By the sixteenth century, it was a prime target for a would-be invader, its distance from the capital leaving it open to attack, slow and costly to defend.

Indeed, the earliest of the maps in this catalogue was inspired by war. Made *c.* 1539, when the country was in danger of invasion from Francis I and Charles V, it shows Plymouth in considerable detail. However, because the threat of war has not yet become localized, it covers the whole of the south-west peninsula. In February 1539 Henry VIII had commissioned

> sadde and expert men of every shire in Ingland beyng nere the sea . . . to viewe all the places alongest the secost wher any daunger of invasions ys like to be and to certifie the sayd daungers and also best advises for the fortificacion therof.[11]

The next cluster of maps occurs in the last two decades of the sixteenth century when the Spanish threat loomed large despite the dispersal of the Spanish Armada in 1588 (see below, pp. 30–2). This group peaks in 1592, with plans of fortifications designed for self-defence against invasion. One effect of the Spanish Armada and, more importantly, the continuing danger from Spain throughout the 1590s was that the threat of attack became more specific to the area around Plymouth. The building of the fort upon the Hoe at the end of the sixteenth century should be seen as a response to this threat.

The building of the Dockyard in the late seventeenth century (Plymouth was not the only site to be considered) converted a weak point into a stronghold. This meant that the theatre of war became far more localized to the Plymouth area in the eighteenth century and this is reflected on the maps in this book in three details: fortifications, guns and encampments.

3 Fortifications, Guns and Encampments

Lilly's surveys (**80–1, 84**) of the Crown fortifications in the countryside around Plymouth Sound in 1714–17 and 1718 are useful because they include several military or quasi-military installations not previously mentioned on maps, such as the Naval Powder House at Oreston, the Naval Brewhouse at Southdown and Mount Wise Gun Wharf. The problem was always that while expenditure on fortifications might have seemed justifiable in time of war, in peace-time it was another matter! Lilly's survey was carried out soon after a period of war (the War of the Spanish Succession, 1701–13). Even then, Lilly's comments on the gunners are not such as to inspire confidence:

> most of them are old and infirm persons or else Tradesmen or Alehouse Keepers in the Town of Plymouth who as they have been placed there by favour are negligent of their duty and thinks themselves above their Master Gunners Command or Discipline.[12]

In the second half of the eighteenth century, by contrast, the country was often either at war or under its threat, and as a result military detail in maps became both more prominent and much more precise. For example, an undated but mid-eighteenth-century volume of plans of fortifications (**101–3**) gives precise details of the guns at the Citadel, St Nicholas Island and the gun wharf at Dock. The defensive capability of the Sound is again shown clearly on two virtually identical maps made by Drawing Room draughtsmen in 1756 (the outbreak of the Seven Years War) (**114–15**).

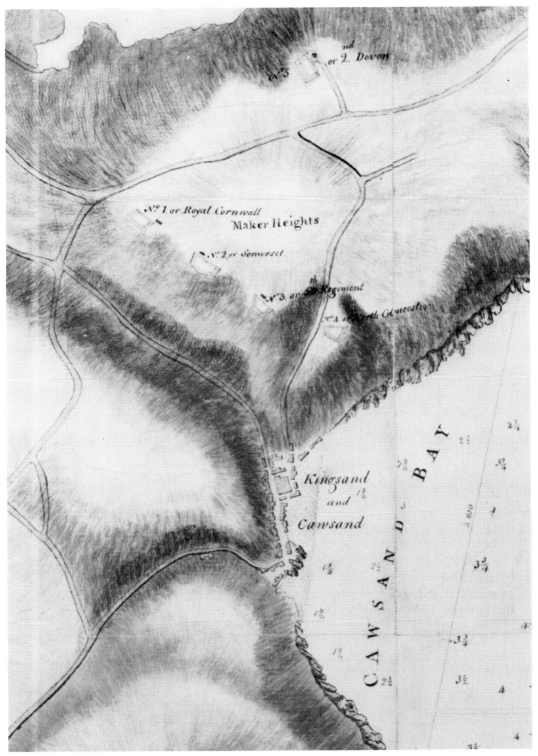

186 (detail: Maker encampments)

But the greatest motivation for producing military maps was undoubtedly the American War of Independence. Because of its westerly situation, Plymouth's importance as a naval base was enhanced during the American War of Independence and this is reflected on the maps. Murdoch Mackenzie's chart of 1777–9 supplies details of the guns at Stoke blockhouse from its commanding position north of the Dockyard besides those of the coastal batteries (**159**). These are also shown on printed maps. Another map of 1780, while providing similar information on guns, includes a scheme for fifteen floating batteries intended to protect various stretches of water in Plymouth Sound (**170**). Likewise, some of the maps include details of encampments, particularly at Maker (**172, 174**), but also at Dock town, on Roborough Down and at Buckland (**168–9**).

The above maps are obviously military. In addition, it is possible that some of the other maps, now divorced from their documentary context, may have been made for military reasons. The survey of Devonport leat made by Matthew Dixon, a Colonel of Engineers (**195**), almost certainly represents a realization of the advantages to be gained from providing water for not just Dock but also the fleet based there.

Spy Maps

Just as military maps of Plymouth become more intensive in the second half of the eighteenth century, so, too, are spy maps more evident during this period. Even when England was not actually at war with France, there was a cold war. The Duke of Choiseul,[13] drawing up instructions in August 1768 for a French spy sent to England, paid lip-service to the French king's desire to keep the peace between the two countries but regretted that England's overweaning ambition had led her to adopt less equitable and moderate principles.[14] Yet the Seven Years War, in which France and England opposed each other, had been concluded in 1763, and the two countries were not nominally at war again until February 1778, when France concluded an offensive and defensive alliance with the United States during the American War of Independence. Despite the fact that the projected Franco-Spanish invasion of Plymouth in August 1779 never landed, and despite the subsequent peace in 1783, the cold war continued until the next outbreak of war, and indeed into the next century.

The French spy who received the instructions of 1768 was the Seigneur de Béville, a lieutenant-colonel of Dragoons who came to England in September and October 1768.[15] His detailed account of his journeys, including twenty-three plans of ports and towns on the south coast of England (besides Windsor and London), has survived in the Public Record Office. Among them is a plan of Plymouth and Dock drawn from memory on 24/5 September (**135**); detached copies of this plan are also to be found in the Archives du Génie and the Service Historique de L'Armée de Terre (**136–7**).

De Béville's plan gives a valuable insight into the problems of attacking the area from an invader's point of view. In the accompanying text he notes the need for special pilotage to reach the port because of the rocks and sandbanks, while the plan shows the passage taken by warships (east of St Nicholas Island) and by frigates and small boats (west of St Nicholas Island). Lines of unmasted warships are ranged up the port entrance to Dock. On land there are references to several recently-built features, for example, the stone bridge at Stonehouse (the Act for the bridge was passed in 1767), Stonehouse Baths and the Royal Naval Hospital for sick soldiers and seamen, which, when finished, would hold up to 1,500 patients. De Béville's plan also made suggestions for adapting existing batteries and erecting new ones in order to ensure French control of the port, and especially the Dockyard. The highest and lowest points along the Dock lines have been noted and the best spot at which to attack. However, rather than burn the Dockyard, he suggested it would be better to evacuate it. In order to achieve this, he proposed taking the Citadel first. The Citadel could best be attacked from the Victualling Office beneath it, but would probably require a siege.

Another perspective on Plymouth from a spy's point of view is provided by Robert, Count of Paradès,[16] ten years later. Unlike de Béville, he does not seem to have enjoyed the confidence of his government at a high level. His secret memoirs,[17] written after his release from the Bastille, cover the period 1778–82 and purport to explain 'the failure of the ever memorable expedition against Plymouth in 1779'. An interesting map showing the entry to the Channel with the manoeuvres of the combined armies of France and Spain during the month of August 1779 has survived to illustrate this account (**A3**).

Paradès took his orders from M. de Sartine,[18] who advised him to set up a local intelligence system in England:

> I formed an acquaintance in every sea port, with some officer in the marine department, in order to render my correspondence more general. They all engaged to send me once or twice a week, an exact journal of what passed in the port in which they were employed, as well as of the orders they might receive, each making his own terms according as his ambition led him.

But it is Paradès's account of his inspection of the Citadel which is particularly interesting. Having picked up a local man whom he had met upon the quay, they walked inside the Citadel unchallenged and Paradès was able to examine every part of the fortifications. He then sat down on a wall overlooking the harbour and began making sketches. An hour later he was spotted by the sentinel in front of the guardhouse, who was surprised at seeing two strangers walking along the rampart so early in the morning (there had been no sentinels around the ramparts). Challenged by the guard,

> I found it necessary to be bold on this occasion accordingly I went down to meet him as if my walk was over. We met at the bottom of the slope. He asked me, What business I had in the fort; and said I ought to know that nobody was allowed to come there. I answered, that being a stranger, I did not know that; but that the person who brought me, should have told me of it, since, living in the town, he ought to have been acquainted with the regulations. Seize this rascal, said the serjeant, and take him to the guard-house. The soldiers seized my guide by the collar, and carried him off. I immediately took ten guineas from my pocket, and offered them to the serjeant, and said, 'Let the poor fellow go, if he has done wrong, it was certainly without knowing it.' He accepted the money, and said to the soldiers, 'Turn him out, and don't let him come in any more'; then addressing himself to me in a milder tone of voice, 'Perhaps, Sir, you wish to see the fort . . .'.

Left unattended for a moment, Paradès was able to stuff his incriminating sketches into the mouth of a cannon, which he pretended to be examining, but he need not have feared since the serjeant showed him round the Citadel several times.

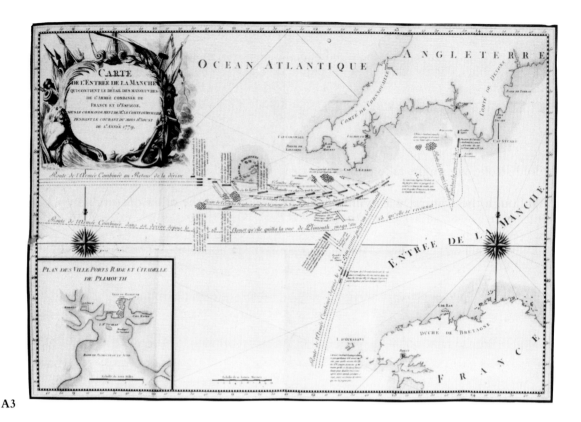

A3

Meanwhile, Paradès's chief agent had found a ship's captain, out of work, dissatisfied with the government and encumbered with debts, who was prepared to enter his service for the pay he would get as commander of the ship which the French minister intended to obtain. Not trusting to the post, Paradès now had a messenger from every port to London, and from London to Calais. He also decided to draw up plans for invading the different English ports: 'I began with Plymouth, and drew a very minute plan of it, and of its different harbours and roads, which I sounded carefully . . .'.[19]

Despite Paradès's sophisticated intelligence network, however, there was suspicion of him among the French ministers. His recommendation that the French and Spanish should invade swiftly while the English were unprepared went unheeded. He joined the combined fleet on 7 August 1779, and on 15 August land was sighted:

The admiral[20] began now to inquire for the pilots with which I was to provide the combined fleet; I told him that after they had remained at sea for six weeks, in sight of Ushant, they were obliged to put back to Plymouth, from whence they would come and join us whenever sent for. I then put into his hands an exact description of this port, which had been sold to France, and of which we could take possession without striking a blow. In the meantime I proposed to get on board some of the English fishermen, who being well acquainted with the coast, would, on being sufficiently paid, act as pilots to the fleet . . .

On 17 August four ships were sighted. The combined fleet agreed they must be Spanish, but Paradès, using an excellent telescope, could spot that they were English, a piece of information for which he was reprimanded! Paradès now again recommended invasion,

> urging . . . that the fort [Citadel] was only guarded by a hundred invalids, and that there were not any other soldiers either in the town or the neighbourhood: that all the batteries were unfit to be used, that the garrison of St Nicholas amounted only to fifty men, and that the harbour was defended by a single frigate only; so that by one bold stroke we might take possession of it.

Although the admiral was willing to listen to Paradès, the other officers reminded him that he had no such orders from France, and that if the enterprise failed, he would be severely reprimanded. They also pointed to the encampments at Maker and on the opposite coastline, and suggested that the English fleet might be lurking nearby. Privately telling Paradès that his youth and the fact that he was a land-officer were the officers' true grounds for objection, the admiral gave way to their arguments:

> Count D'Orvilliers, to the qualifications of a good Admiral, united a degree of weakness which is often observed in great men. As he had too much diffidence in his abilities, he never maintained with sufficient firmness, his own opinion, though it was the best; nor enforced his first orders, though they were always judicious; he was too easily persuaded that he was mistaken.

Paradès felt particular frustration because the French court was aware of the defenceless state of Plymouth: 'What then must they have thought of the Admiral upon receiving his dispatches, which stated that the enemy's fleet was blocked up; they must have supposed he was out of his senses.' He vents his fury, however, upon the faulty reconnaissance of the Sound:

> . . . these officers therefore ought to have been tried for the false accounts they gave, and . . . should have received all the blame, instead of the Admiral. Thus I saw the object, to attain which I had been engaged for 18 months, and which had been attended with great fatigues, unceasing cares, and extreme dangers, and upon which the king had expended above 120,000 livres at once irretrievably lost.

Was he right? Both in the opinion of contemporaries and of historians enjoying hindsight, he was.[21] 'Never had perhaps so great a naval force been assembled on the seas. Never any by which less was done,' commented *The Annual Register* in 1780.[22] John Harris, writing in 1806, gives a graphic picture of the situation in 1779:

> The Town was thrown into Great alarm by the appearance of the combined fleet of France and Spain. Taking advantage of the Strong easterly wind and the absence of the British fleet, w[h]ich, att that time were att westwards of lands end, it was na[t]urally expected the[y] would make a Descent here and Destroy the Town and Dockyard with the Arsenals – as to the state of the Garrison, and the Millatary [military] force it was very weak, of w[h]ich there is every reason to believe the[y] were to[o] well inform'd by a Spy . . . in the pay of France. . . . The Townsmen

armed and formd themselves in companys, and assisted the removal of 1300 French Prisoners here to Exeter. Thousands of men came to Plymouth to see the Enemy, principally out of curiosity. Rame Head and the opposite Heights were lined with spectators from Daylight until Dark. Thousands of women and children left the Town in great confusion.

Moreover, the allies had considerable advantages: Plymouth's defences were in disrepair and there was a divided command to defend the town. But the need to get back to Spain before the onset of winter (the French fleet under D'Orvilliers had not set sail until July 30) and the distance from Brest meant that the situation was never fully exploited. Furthermore, there can be little doubt that England was saved partly by the divided motivations of the allies. If France's chief concern was to reduce English maritime supremacy while a large part of her navy was 3,000 miles away across the Atlantic, Spain had not declared war on England until June 1779, stating categorically that she would give effective aid only to an invasion on the mainland.

Both French and Spanish archives contain a number of maps drawn up with the proposed invasion of 1779 in mind. Apart from a sketch drawn to accompany a letter from M. de la Luzerne to the Comte de Broglie on 23 June 1779 (**163**), these manuscript maps are copies of English printed charts. Thus there are copies of Greenvile Collins in the Bibliothèque Nationale (**56–8**) and of another printed map, 'Plymouth Sound, Hamoaze and Catwater surveyed in 1770', in both the Archives du Génie and the Archives Nationales (in the catalogue the printed map is **141**, the copies are **143–5**); there is also a copy of the Citadel extracted from Donn's map in the Archives du Génie (**132**). However, as so often with maps, the value of these copies is greatly reduced because they have been divorced from accompanying documentation.

What greatly enhances the significance of the manuscript copies of printed maps which have survived in the Spanish archives is that they have not been so divorced and retain their connection with a bundle of correspondence relating to the war with England, 1779–83.[23] Though the correspondence sheds no further clues, it is likely that all the copies were made by a Frenchman since the annotations are in French. The maps comprise three copies of Emmanuel Bowen's 'AN ACCURATE MAP OF DEVONSHIRE' (**105–7**) and two copies of Greenvile Collins's charts (**54, 87**). In addition to these are three sketches in ink on paper of Dock ('*Dique de Plymouth*'); these show only part of the Dock.[24]

The first question which arises in considering these manuscript copies of English printed maps and charts is why such old-fashioned prints were chosen. But, in fact, although Captain Greenvile Collins was first commissioned by Charles II to survey the coasts of Great Britain in 1681, his charts continued to be used throughout the eighteenth century until 1792. It therefore seems likely that they would have been reasonably easy to get sight of and copy, particularly since a French edition of Collins's *Coasting Pilot* had been published in 1757.[25] The same considerations apply to Emmanuel Bowen's map which had appeared in editions of the standard *Large English Atlas*. The usefulness of the Bowen map rather than, say, that of Benjamin Donn, to a would-be invader is that the inset plan of Plymouth on the former includes a lengthy key to the Citadel.

The accompanying correspondence makes it clear that the allies considered Plymouth to be relatively defenceless, apart from the Citadel: '*Plimouth . . . est entièrement découverte par l'intérieur de la terre, et le Port, et ses établissements restent à la merci des arrivants.*' An attack on Plymouth was considered a good prospect by the French since the invaders could be supplied from Brest while the English town could be cut off from the centre of the kingdom. The Citadel was regarded as the chief obstacle to invasion, so it would have to be either taken or razed, so that the allies could establish themselves in Plymouth, taking over the port, or else destroy it in four days and re-embark at their leisure. Another proposal of August 1779 was that St Nicholas Island should be taken and an attack launched on Dock from Mount Edgcumbe.

Several points emerge from the correspondence. Firstly, that the main invasion plan was to attack Portsmouth and the Isle of Wight. Attacking Plymouth and Falmouth was only a secondary option. Secondly, that the invasion plans were extremely fluid, with proposals and counter-proposals abounding. One plan was to attack Plymouth but another suggested that, since the English under Admiral Hardy would be expecting this, it might be more advantageous to attack Falmouth instead. Its distance from London meant the English would have problems drafting in reinforcements, while the land round about was fertile. Yet another possibility was that Dartmouth, Plymouth and Falmouth should be attacked from Portsmouth.

In addition to these well-documented maps, the Dépôt des Cartes et Plans in Paris holds an interesting but undated collection of maps of Plymouth (**76, 203–6, 209–11**). Divorced from any accompanying documentation, it is impossible to be certain of the

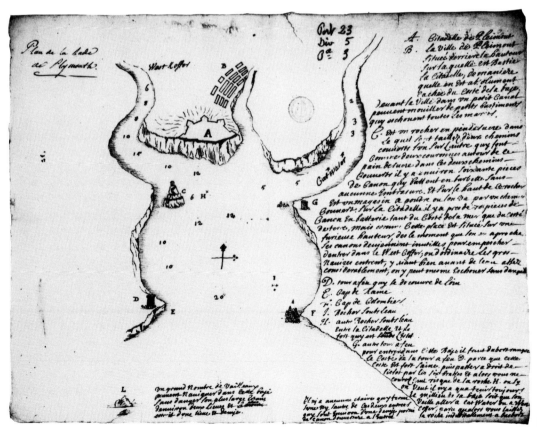

203

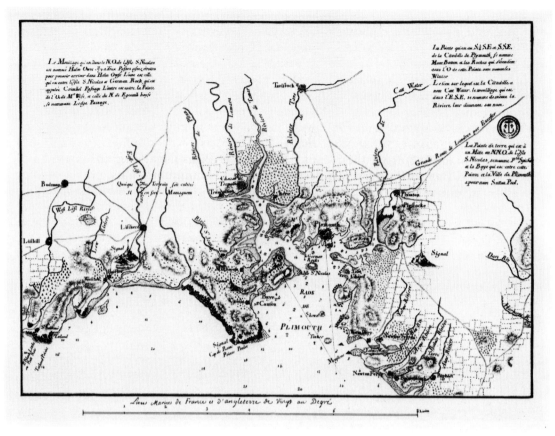

211

circumstances in which they were produced. Nevertheless, all the maps in this group include details of gunnery and navigation, suggesting that they were made with hostile intentions in mind.

A feature of many of these spy maps is their vagueness, possibly because they were drawn later from memory. Map **203**, for example, is merely a brief sketch but with lengthy notes describing how Plymouth is situated behind the hill on which the Citadel is built, thus completely hiding it from the Sound, besides details of the guns held on St Nicholas Island and the Citadel. The point is made that the Citadel stands so high above the sea that as soon as a ship approaches, the guns become useless to prevent entry into the Hamoaze. The sketch-map itself highlights defensive features such as the Citadel, the fort on St Nicholas Island, Mount Batten Tower and Penlee Tower. Maps **210** and **204** are similarly vague, map **210** noting that the Sound is a league across and that the English warships lie up the Hamoaze because the anchorage is better there. Mount Edgcumbe house is described as '*Maison blanche ou du Duc Dyorck*'. The rather attractive but aptly titled 'Idée du Port de Plymout En Angleterre' (**206**) again includes details of gunnery around the Sound in its key: Pigg's Point is described as a battery of seven cannons, Mount Batten as a gun-tower, St Nicholas Island as having a perimeter wall with two rows of guns and Stonehouse as a fishing village with eighteen cannons. Map **76** has considerably more local detail, since much of it has been copied from Greenvile Collins, although not all: for instance, the road leading from Stonehouse to Plymouth.

One of the most interesting maps in this group (**205**) is a bird's-eye-view pictorial map of the landscape around the Sound as seen from beyond Stoke Church. The town of Plymouth is shown surrounded by a wall, and the town gates and 'broad quay' mentioned by Celia Fiennes clearly depicted. The Dockyard is much in evidence, also gun batteries and the blockhouse at Cawsand, suggesting that this map was drawn for military reasons. A key to the map notes two prisons beyond the town of Plymouth to the north-east; while Millbay prison is frequently referred to on maps, these two prisons are not recorded on other maps.[26] Stonehouse is described here as '*ville franc*' and Mount Edgcumbe house as '*maison de Cromwel*'.

Another map (**211**) from the Dépôt des Cartes et Plans illustrating the coastal area from Talland Bay to Bigbury was designed to show communications, probably with invasion in mind. The map highlights river estuaries and their course inland, and includes some significant mistakes. The River Tiddy has been wrongly marked as the Plym, while the River Plym is described as Catt Water River, and two non-existent estuaries (the Rivers Bott and Balmer) have been inserted between the Yealm and the Avon. But for all this, the map is interesting. Two signal-posts are noted: one between Liskeard and Looe, another above the River Yealm. The countryside north of Liskeard is described as cultivated but mountainous; boggy ground ('*terre humide*') is recorded near Bigbury. The instructions on entrance to the Hamoaze are garbled.

There is no integral connection between the maps in this group. The foundation of the Dépôt des Cartes et Plans as early as 1720 makes it likely that the survival rate of individual maps is higher than if no such institution had existed. The likelihood is that these maps were made at various times during the eighteenth century against the interests of France's neighbour and (often) enemy, England. Yet they remain an intriguing enigma.

In time of war there was always a risk that the enemy might obtain copies of printed charts to use against the interest of the makers. The confiscation of Richard Cowl's 'Plan of Plymouth and Country adjacent' in 1783 with its details concerning 'Fortification, Bays, Harbours, Soundings &c' has been described elsewhere.[27]

Charts

1 Recording the Sea-bed

Hydrographie requireth a particular Register of certain Landmarks (where marks may be had) from the sea, well able to be skried, in what point of the Sea compasse they appear, and what apparent form, situation and bigness they have, in respect of any dangerous place in the sea, or neer unto it, assigned . . . And in all Coasts, what Moon maketh full Sea, and what way, the Tides and Ebbs, come and go, the Hydrographer ought to record. The sounding likewise: and the Chanels wayes: their number and depths ordinarily, at ebbe and floud, ought the Hydrographer, by observation and diligence of Measuring, to have certainly known . . .

(Dr John Dee, 1571)[28]

The earliest charts in this catalogue draw a distinction between waters navigable by ship and those suitable only for boats by depicting appropriate vessels. Throughout the period the extent of hydrographic detail about Plymouth Sound shown on the charts increases: firstly rocks, then inter-tidal areas, soundings, fathom lines and finally the sea-bed. But this is not a uniform progression, and much of the detail, particularly on printed charts, is suspect. The accurate and detailed surveys of Plymouth Sound by Murdoch Mackenzie junior in the 1770s are exceptional.

i Rocks

Rocks appearing above the surface of the sea are obvious, so it is hardly surprising that they occur early on charts. Depths under water of individual rocks are shown from the late sixteenth century (**4**). There are minor variations according to time and tide; thus Shovel Rock varies between 15 ft (**94**) and 17 ft (**157, 183**), while Winter Rock varies between 11 ft (**157**) and 14 ft (**94**). In general, cartographers rarely stated tidal conditions at the time of their survey until the eighteenth century (**134**).[29]

Although individual rocks in the Sound are often shown on charts, the range of rocks known as 'the Bridge' running from St Nicholas Island to the Maker peninsula, is shown much less regularly.[30] Sailing instructions for Plymouth note that 'to the Westward of [St Nicholas] Island is all foul Ground, and sunken Rocks, that the Passage is very difficult, except in small Vessels, or those that are well acquainted'.[31] It seems likely that since this channel between the island and Mount Edgcumbe was rarely used for navigational purposes, little attention was devoted to it on charts.

Not until the detailed surveys of Murdoch Mackenzie in the 1770s does hydrographic information appear to be shown for its own sake rather than for navigational purposes. He was sufficiently self-confident of his work to be able to say: 'the whole of the Survey has been so circumspectly taken, that there is great reason to believe there [are] no shoals or foul Ground, which have escaped observation' (**164**). The sophistication of his survey is shown by the following distinctions on this map: 'rocks always above water', 'rocks covered and uncovered alternately by the tide', 'rocks dry with the spring tide only' and 'rocky shoals always under water on which the least water is put down'.

Mackenzie was the first person to put a name to the Knap Rock during his survey of 1777–9 (**159**), and he had a black buoy put upon it. This was a practical way to alert mariners to the existence of underwater rocks. One map explains how Cloudesly or Shovel Rock was 'call'd so from Sir Cloudesly Shovel, who order'd a Buoy to be upon it' (**93**).[32] At the time Mackenzie began his survey of 1777–9 there was apparently '1 Swinging Beacon on the Tinker, 1 white buoy on the North end of the Shovel and 1 red buoy on the North end of the Panther'. The swinging beacon was apparently a 'White perch, Buoy or Beacon with an Iron Vane' (**149**), while Mackenzie's buoy on the Knap consisted of a 'Black Beacon with a White Globe'.

ii Sandbanks

Plymouth Sound was hazardous to navigate, and it is clear from these maps that it was considered essential to employ coastal pilots. The French spy, de Béville, in making this point drew attention to the sandbanks (**135**).[33] The sandbank Beggar's Island in St German's River first occurs on late sixteenth-century maps (**8–9**), although (like the Bridge) it is only shown rarely (**81, 159, 178**). Sandbanks are shown on de Béville's map and also on a chart by Murdoch Mackenzie (**159**), but they are unusual. A printed chart of 1784 includes their depth under water (**177**).

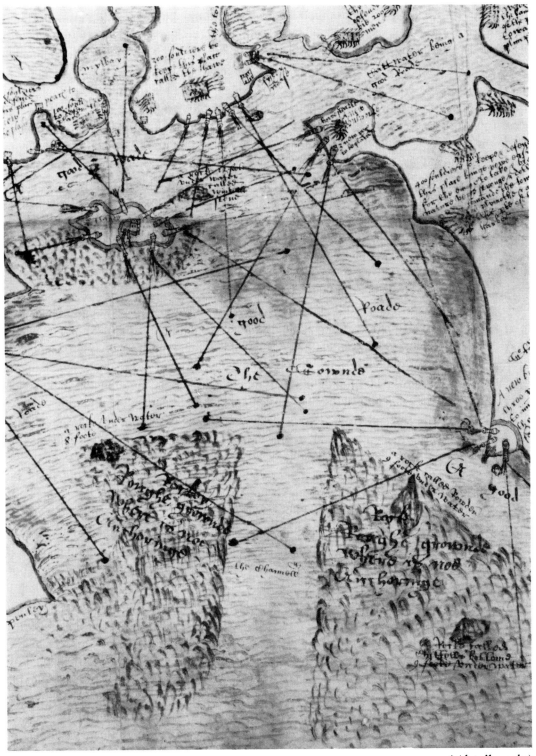

4 (detail: rocks)

iii Inter-tidal Areas

A recurrent phrase on these maps is 'all owse and dry at low water', often depicting the inter-tidal area around the coastline. 'Ooze' is noted as early as the late sixteenth century (**2**). Several charts record that Sutton Pool was 'dry at low water' (**81**, **84**, **91**). However, more detailed information on tides is not supplied until the late eighteenth century. A chart of 1774 refers to the need for 'great attention to ye Rapid Tide which at different times . . . shutes in different Directions' (**154**) and a chart of 1779 by Mackenzie (**164**) shows the time of high water at new and full moon, also the speed in knots of the streams at spring or neap tides, and the direction of the stream of flood. Darts to show the direction of the currents are also given on a printed chart of 1777 (**157**).

iv Soundings

The usefulness of soundings to mariners was that by letting down their lead and line to obtain evidence of the nature of the sea-bed, they could gain an indication of the ship's position relative to the coast and hence the course to be steered. Since much navigation

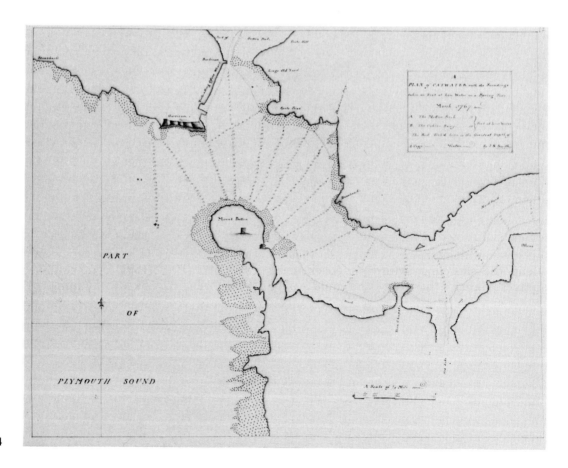

must have been coastal during the period of these maps, this would have been extremely useful. However, the earliest of the manuscript charts here (**22**) which shows soundings does not occur until the mid-seventeenth century, which is relatively late.[34] They are still by no means commonplace on early eighteenth- century manuscript charts in this catalogue, although much more frequent on printed charts.

The reliability of soundings on the printed charts has to be called into question, however. Much more convincing are the soundings shown on a survey of the Cattewater at low water on a spring tide in 1767 (**134**). The bench-mark in terms of accurate soundings is the work of Murdoch Mackenzie junior. By applying a new survey technique of fixing by sextant angles and plotting by station pointer, Mackenzie and his assistant Graeme Spence were able to survey harbours such as Plymouth Sound in immense detail.[35] Several of Mackenzie's charts included in this catalogue were working documents, not the finished article, and the soundings are densely recorded.[36] Yet Mackenzie was well aware of the indigestibility of too much information. A note on **164** shows that such a sophisticated cartographer realized the value of leaving out as well as putting in, although he expected his hard research work to be recognized as not so effortless:

> to prevent that confusion which a multiplicity of Soundings and Marks would occasion, numbers of them are omitted . . . tho' spaces in this Chart where no Soundings are inserted, have been examined as well as those parts where they are put down

v Fathom Lines or Isobaths

Fathom lines or isobaths[37] are shown on a few late eighteenth-century charts. A chart which can be dated *c.* 1770 (**139**) shows a 3-fathom line, and Murdoch Mackenzie's charts depict red danger-lines around rocks, 2-fathom lines, 4-fathom lines showing 'how near Ships may stand to the shore' (**164**) and sometimes 5-fathom lines (**159**). These examples are relatively late considering that an English naval officer first attempted to show fathom lines on a sea-chart of 1715.[38]

vi The Sea-bed

A few charts give detailed information as to the nature of the sea-bed. The chart of the Cattewater made in 1767 (**134**) distinguishes between 'ouse', 'beach', and 'hard sand' along the shoreline. Murdoch Mackenzie's chart of 1777–9 (**159**) found 'stones', 'gravel', 'beach', 'hardway' and 'mud', and a slightly later chart of 1779 by him (**164**) noted muddy, rocky and sandy bottoms. A chart of 1788 by James Fraser attempted a similar description of 'clay', 'mud', 'rocky ground', and 'sandy bottom'.

vii Coastal Change

It is clear from the municipal records that there was some degree of coastal change during this period. In 1635 commissioners investigating Sutton Pool complained that it had recently become silted up with gravel, sand, stones and ballast.[39] This was apparently due to the activities of the tinners on Dartmoor, to the failure by the mayor and burgesses of Saltash to clear a wreck and to sand carried down the Cattewater from the rivers Plym and Meavy. It was feared that 'a necke of land called how sterte [Mount Batten] deviding the said harbour from the mayne sea [was] much fretted and worne away with the breach of the sea, soe that the sea without timely prevencon is likly to make a passage through it'. Fortunately, however, this never happened. Only one chart in the catalogue (**178**) makes a detailed attempt at a coastal survey.

2 Navigation

i Navigation Channels

Another feature of the Cattewater chart is a deep-water channel marked by a red dotted-line. This type of information occurs occasionally on English charts: for example, a map of 1784 (**179**) notes 'the course of vessels going up the Hamoaze'. It is significant that this type of information occurs on French charts of Plymouth too: the course of vessels entering Plymouth Sound is marked on the chart made by the spy de Béville (**135**) and on a reconnaissance chart of 1786 (**184**).[40]

ii Anchorages

Anchorages appear quite frequently on the printed charts of Plymouth Sound, but, like soundings, their reliability must often be suspect. Specific statements such as 'Anchoring Place above Millbrooke R[iver]' (**90**) suggest a higher degree of credibility, and the detailed anchorages up the Hamoaze supplied on manuscript prototypes (**139–40**) for a chart of 1770 which was frequently resurveyed and reprinted (**141, 147–9**) until the end of the eighteenth century can surely be taken at face value.

iii Wrecks

A few charts record the hulks lurking in the waters of Plymouth Sound. The *Berwick* hulk is shown on a chart of 1747 (**99**), and the *Sheer* hulk opposite Dock and the *Temeraire* off Cremyll are recorded on a chart by Mackenzie of 1777–9 (**159**).

It is clear from the municipal records[41] and contemporary diaries that shipwreck was common at this date. John Allan referred to 'great shipwreck in many places' in September 1671. James Yonge noted 'A great storm this Christmas Day [1690] cast away the *Henrietta* and *Centurion* and a great deal men-of-war' and in 1691 'the *Coronation* and *Harwich* lost, and all the rest in danger'. Defoe recorded the great storms of 26 November 1703 and August 1704.[42] The latter blew up suddenly, illustrating the risks of riding on Plymouth Sound:

> This very Mistake was the Ruin of a whole Fleet of Merchants Ships homeward bound from Barbadoes, and deep loaden . . . when putting into the Sound in fine weather, with an Easterly Wind and almost calm, [they] forebore to go into the Ham Oaze as they ought to have done; and by a sudden Storm were all dash'd to pieces against the Rocks, or founder'd as they rode in the Sound, the third Night after they arriv'd and most of the People lost; only one Ship was saved by running, or rather driving into Catwater in the dark, and in the height of the Tempest.

3 Landmarks Seen From at Sea

The land as viewed from the sea is represented on many of these charts, both manuscript and printed. Few charts are as ambitious as map **68**, which shows Brent Tor (about 20 miles north of Plymouth) in the distance, though church towers nearer the coast made obvious landmarks for fixing positions at sea. Wembury occurs regularly, and its position near the mouth of the Yealm estuary is reflected in the fact that it is often referred to as Wembury Yealm Church (**141**) or even just Yealm Church (**157**, **183**, **201**). Maker Church is shown on later charts with signals or a telegraph (**198**). In the town of Plymouth, it seems natural that the tower of St Andrew's Church (the only constant landmark throughout this period) should be referred to simply as Plymouth Tower or 'Old Church' while Charles Church, differentiated by its steeple, becomes 'New Church' (**139**). Both churches are frequently mentioned in sailing directions.

Other common landmarks in the immediate vicinity of Plymouth Sound were natural features such as the Withy Hedge at Staddon Heights, the White Patch on the Hoe and occasionally trees in the far distance, for example, Mutley Firs (**155**, **164**). Tall buildings such as obelisks and public buildings such as the Citadel, Mill Prison and the Royal Naval Hospital at Stonehouse are quite common. But some charts also pick purely idiosyncratic buildings: 'Mrs Cormick's', 'Harris's', 'Dr Polby's', 'Mr Winn's', 'Captain Bertie's', 'the Agent's house near Mill Prison' and 'the tavern'. These give a delightful sense of the returning sailor keenly scanning the horizon:

> Oh dream of joy! is this indeed
> The lighthouse top I see?
> Is this the hill? Is this the kirk?
> Is this mine own countree?
>
> (Coleridge *The Rime of the Ancient Mariner*)

4 Sea Journals

No account of the charts of Plymouth during this period would be complete which ignored one minor yet intriguing theme: Plymouth as a port of call. The need to put into port for fresh water is borne out by frequent notes on the charts that fresh water ('Vars Water') was obtainable at Staddon Point. As we have already seen, the need to provide fresh water for mariners was one reason behind the building of the Plymouth leat in the late sixteenth century.

Three very different seventeenth-century charts (**22**, **43** and **45** respectively) illustrate this theme. Charles Wilde was returning from a round-the-world voyage, Plymouth being the first port of call after Mozambique. His chart of the area is inaccurate and confused. Edmund Dummer, a midshipman extraordinary on board HM *Woolwich* bound for Tangier and the Mediterranean in 1685, had better reason to remember Plymouth Sound since it was while anchored here that a violent scuffle broke out between two Moors on board. The third chart was made on board the Good Ship *Benjamin*, an East India Company vessel whose crew, hearing rumours of war with France in May 1689, insisted the captain travel with a convoy. When they set sail from Plymouth on 26 June, it was in company with the Dutch fleet.

What motivated the making of a sea journal? Despite the occasional excitements described above, there must have been long hours of boredom at sea and making charts or keeping a journal could be a means of distraction. Edmund Dummer wrote:

> considering Time might be emproved if I began with it, I Resolved to hedge in all Occurrences of my Voyage (appearing worth a Notice) by perticular Views, as well as relation, and to make ye whole Progress a lineall, visible Demonstration . . .[43]

Special-purpose Maps

These maps were made for a number of reasons, often quite specific. The most important single reason was military planning, particularly self-defence against the threat of invasion. But other maps were made as evidence in lawsuits, for special projects such as laying moorings or building a breakwater to protect ships in the Sound against the dangerous winds, for setting out the route of a leat to provide water for the towns of Plymouth and Devonport in the late sixteenth and eighteenth centuries respectively. Route-finding, the purpose for which most people use maps in the twentieth century, does not appear much on these maps.

1 Lawsuits

A number of the maps in this catalogue were intended as evidence in legal disputes and enquiries. These particularly relate to prime sites near the water's edge and the old town of Plymouth such as the Lambhay, the land above it upon which the Citadel was built in the mid-1660s and Sutton Pool.

A common practice throughout Western Europe during the period covered by these maps was the employment of painters in making plots or plats at legal disputes.[44] A view-day would be held for judges and contestants to inspect the subject of the litigation: the judge would then ask the painter to fairly depict the scene, and ask the respective parties if they accepted the picture as an accurate record. If they did, the judge would ask the parties what they had to say, statements would be taken, witnesses heard and interrogated, and finally judgement entered.

At the Lambhay, the enquiry held in 1672 by Richard Edgcumbe and John Skelton into the ownership and worth of the land along the water's edge gave rise to two of the maps in this catalogue (**37** and **39**).[45] By 1672 this land must have appeared particularly valuable because the Citadel had just been completed. But, in fact, the municipal records suggest that this had long been a prime site: as early as January 1594, nearly a century earlier, commissioners had been appointed to inquire into the Strode family's building activities at the Lambhay, and whether they would prejudice the town.[46] This earlier inquiry does not appear to have generated any maps.

This land formed the subject of a dispute again in 1758, between the Victualling Office (which had subsequently been built on this site – see Appendix IV, entry 32) and Plymouth Corporation. Map **36** is probably an eighteenth-century copy made at this date of a map used during the 1672 enquiry. A letter in the eighteenth-century dispute refers back to Edgcumbe and Skelton's enquiry and how 'they had caused a Land Meater [surveyor] to take an Exact measure of the said Lambhay and had transmitted a draught thereof with their said letter'.[47]

This characteristic of legal disputes, namely their tendency to lie dormant for decades, even centuries, before being resurrected, is responsible for the 1812–14 copies of the seventeenth-century Citadel plans (**31–2**, **34–5**). The Crown's appropriation of land on the Hoe for building the Citadel in 1666 had affected a number of parties. A map of 1671 (**30**) distinguishes between land as 'bought' and 'not bought'. Plymouth Corporation brought the matter to a head in the early nineteenth century when the Assistant Solicitor to the Ordnance was forced to admit that the Eastern Hoe belonged to the Corporation.[48]

Edmund Bayntun's plan of Sutton Pool (**125**) was an official view and survey in the presence of both parties to the dispute: Thomas Veale, as lessee of the Pool from the Duchy of Cornwall (to whom it belonged) on the one hand, and a committee of the mayor and commonalty on the other. Veale had complained to the duchy about this latter party's encroachments. The plan is that of the mayor and commonalty. Although the duchy archives do include a survey of Sutton Pool,[49] this appears to be nineteenth-century, so the presumption must be that the duchy's copy of the official view and survey no longer survives.

2 Proposals for Laying Moorings in the Hamoaze and for a Breakwater at Cawsand

An interesting chart of 1747 (**99**) was prepared as a preliminary for laying chain moorings up the Hamoaze. The accompanying letter to the Navy Office notes in detail

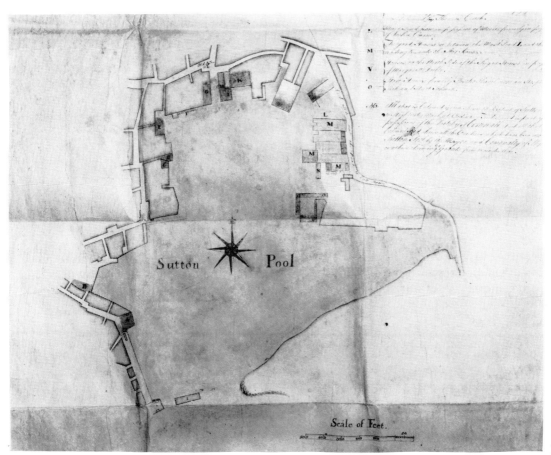

the moorings already laid below the *Berwick* hulk and the places where chain moorings and transporting anchors are proposed to be laid for conducting ships out of and into Hamoaze, and in and out of the south channel. By 1774 there were forty-six moorings for ships of the line and nine for frigates (**154**).

Another proposal at the end of the eighteenth century was for a pier to be built from Penlee Point. J.B. Warren, in a letter of July 1798 accompanying map **200**, argued that Cawsand was the best anchorage for ships of war because it had the greatest depth of water in that area and lay further west than any other place in the Channel for bringing squadrons or convoys. Unfortunately, however, its capacity was restricted to eight or nine ships of a high rating for fear of being exposed to the south-west winds. What Warren proposed was that a pier be run out from Penlee Point for three-quarters of a mile or so in a curve so that the impact of the sea would be broken. He suggested the pier be built of rough stone, seaweed and, in deepest water, old hulks filled with sand and sunk; a pier of masonry surmounting the whole might or might not be necessary. The work could be done either by troops from the barracks at Maker Heights or by convicts at a cost of between £20,000 and £30,000. When completed, it would enable a fleet of twenty sail of the line to lie in safety.

Although neither this nor an alternative proposal of Warren's to close the water between St Nicholas Island and Mount Edgcumbe was implemented, the plans are interesting because they prove how long it took between realization that there was a problem and the finding of a solution. Another precursor of Plymouth Breakwater (which was eventually begun in 1812) occurs in a letter of 1806 accompanying map **189**. Besides a breakwater, it suggested a pier leading out from Andurn Point on the opposite side of the Sound, below Staddon Heights.

3 Leats

The lack of a freshwater source within a mile of the town of Plymouth was a serious inconvenience to mariners in the sixteenth century because in fetching water for their ships they might lose good winds. The need for a freshwater source had been registered as urgent by the Corporation of Plymouth as early as 1559/60,[50] although the leat built by Francis Drake was not completed until 1591. The map depicting the leat (**8**; now at Hatfield House) and its copy (**9**; at the British Library) were probably made about this date, although possibly earlier since the Plymouth Water Act had been passed in 1585. William Parker, mayor of the town in 1601, wrote: '. . . if our water be taken away, our town is not able to live, neither are her Majesty's nor her subjects' ships able to be supplied with water, nor her army to be so well fitted with bread and beer'.[51]

Likewise, the late eighteenth-century map (**195**) prepared by Matthew Dixon, Colonel of Engineers, to show the route to be followed by the proposed leat to supply water for Dock is undated. The Act for the building of Devonport leat to supply the needs of Dock, Stoke Damerel and Stonehouse was passed in 1793, so it was probably made about this time. Unlike the sixteenth-century leat map, which is a picture map with a wealth of information about the countryside traversed and the difficulties of building the leat, the late eighteenth-century map is a line-drawing giving landmarks along the route such as tors, brooks and houses.

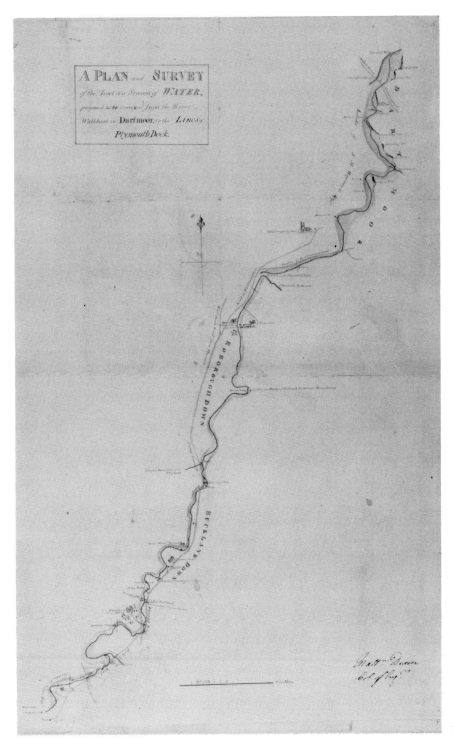

195

4 Communications

As previously mentioned, route-finding does not appear much on these maps. Where roads are given (leading out of Plymouth, for example), although they are often described as the road to a particular place, there is little attempt to describe the route along the way.

An exception to this is the late sixteenth-century leat map (**8**), which does show the roads or ways running from one small community to another, often crossing considerable natural obstacles such as rivers (using bridges), estuaries (using passage points), marshes and moors. But this map really proves the point with its cryptic message, 'There are many ways more which are not made in this platt.' Roads are much less clearly shown than rivers and other means of water transport.

This is not really surprising if we think about the landscape of Plymouth Sound during this period. One of its most striking features is the inaccessibility of communications by land. Unless approached from the north, via Tavistock (one sixteenth-century map (**3**) does show the type of traffic encountered along this road), Plymouth was virtually inaccessible except by a water-crossing. Some of the ferries appear to be ancient: the Cremyll, Saltash and Oreston ferries are shown from the earliest of these maps. But until the building of Stonehouse Bridge in 1767 and Torpoint ferry in 1790 – both as a result of the increased traffic from Dock – it seems likely that water transport was much more important throughout this period, both for long and short distances. The use of water for long-distance transport is exemplified by an account on the back of one of the Citadel plans (**27**) showing how the stone for building the gate was brought from Portland by water.

In terms of local travel, the catalogue includes one or two interesting river maps. Jerome Roche's map of the Rivers Tamar and Tavy (**50**) depicts all the little settlements by the water's edge, including mills, salt-mills and even a silver mine. Map **51** shows the same landscape but as a mass of grassy hills punctuated by hamlets and villages distinguishable only by their place-names.

Passage-points across rivers and estuaries occur fairly frequently on these maps as we might expect. In the case of the Cattedown–Oreston passage, and the Stonehouse passage (until the bridge was built in 1767), these ferries apparently consisted of boats being towed across by means of a rope fastened to each shore.[52] The Cremyll ferry across the Hamoaze estuary also occurs regularly on maps, and sometimes the passage-house too. Celia Fiennes, writing in 1698, found this crossing 'very hazardous . . . by reason of 3 tydes meeting' but admitted that it saved several miles' riding.[53] An interesting note on map **174** is a record of the distances between various points at sea: 3 miles across Plymouth Sound, 500 yds from Cremyll to Mount Wise, 1,400 yds from Southdown to Dock, 800 yds from Torpoint to Dock and 500 yds across the Tamar from Saltash.

Roads are not shown as significant features on the landscape until the eighteenth century on the maps in this catalogue. The only road map as such (**113**) was intended for a road-widening scheme. The proposal was to construct a new road leading out of Plymouth and to widen the roads to Plympton, Oreston, Dock, Saltash and Stonehouse. The map draws a distinction between main roads and 'cross roads' or minor roads, which are mostly very narrow and deep.[54] The date of this map is 1756, just a year or two before the Exeter Turnpike Act was passed in 1757/8. Apart from this, roads are also shown as important for military communications. Mileages

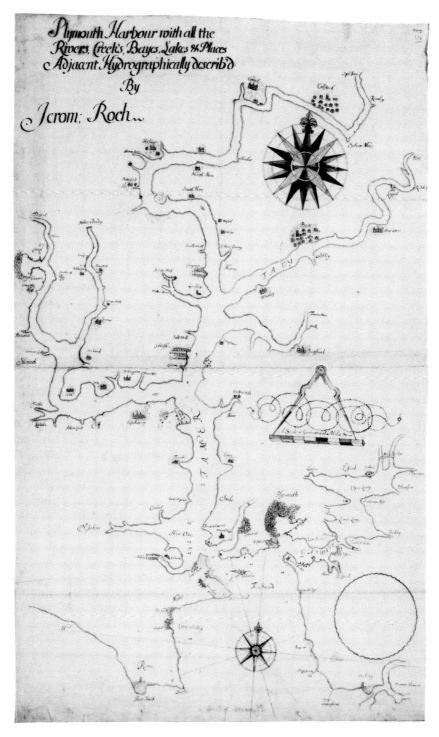

between towns in this area, for instance, from Plymouth to Tavistock, Ivybridge and Modbury (this last shown as a turnpike road) and from Liskeard to Saltash and Cremyll are given on map **174**. Turnpike roads are stained brown on map **194** and turnpike gates marked on map **195**.

Maps Depicting Particular Events

On three occasions during this period Plymouth came under particular pressure. On two of these, enemy fleets lay in Plymouth Sound, poised to invade: the Spanish Armada in the late sixteenth century, and the Franco-Spanish allies in 1779 during the American War of Independence.[55] The third occasion was rather different: in 1643 the town of Plymouth was besieged by the Royalists during the Civil War. Each of these events gave rise to a group of maps, though in several instances maps were made after, rather than before, the worst of the danger, possibly to commemorate the event.

1 The Armada

Maps drawn up in connection with the Armada make it clear that until the 1590s, the threat was perceived as general rather than specific to Plymouth Sound.

Robert Adams's set of eleven charts (**WM2**) engraved by Augustine Ryther and published by him in 1590 to accompany an English translation of Petruccio Ubaldini's *Discourse of the Spanish Fleet invading England* covers the course taken by the Armada round the British Isles. Although four of the charts include Plymouth, it is not highlighted as lying under any particular threat as yet.

Likewise, 'A Plott of all the Coast of Cornwall and Devonshire as they were to bee fortyfied in 1588 against the landing of any Enemy' (**5**) covers the whole of the south-west peninsula.[56] Although it notes various inlets and estuaries, proposing armed men and barricades to counter the hostile threat from abroad, the proposals are not specific.

The exception to these, and the first map to suggest that somebody was aware of the particular threat to Plymouth Sound, is Richard Grenville's (**4**), made probably between 1586 and 1588, when he was heavily involved in arranging for the defence of the south-western counties. This is an interesting chart covering the whole of the Sound. The town of Plymouth is mentioned only *en passant*, the cartographer's main thrust being to show the number of men and armaments necessary to defend any potential landing place. Particularly significant is the attempt to depict rocks beneath the water (the earliest extant chart to show this detail) and the shipping channel running between them. Another point illustrated by the chart is the dependence upon local landowners as pillars of the community in mustering defences. Christopher Harris of Radford House, for example, is recorded on the map as 'a sufficient gentillman to take charge to defend this quarter w[i]th thinhabitants of Plimpton hundred'. Added together, the number of men considered necessary to defend the Sound amounts to 2,100 – not much less than half the total mobilization of the county of Devon (5,000 according to an annotated copy of the map of Devon in the Saxton-Burghley atlas).[57] But perhaps most striking of all on this chart are the guns located at various points around the Sound: Cawsand, Cremyll, Stonehouse, the Hoe, Mount Batten, Staddon Heights and, most important of all, St Nicholas Island.

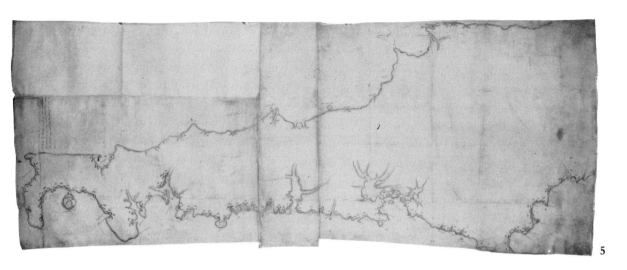

5

Yet despite the significance of the year 1588 in our history books, documentary sources make it clear that contemporaries continued, with good reason, to regard the threat of invasion from Spain as serious throughout the decade following the Armada. Moreover, the town of Plymouth felt particularly vulnerable and this is reflected in a number of maps made during the final decade of the sixteenth century.

Thus, in May 1590 Sir Francis Drake and the Mayor of Plymouth wrote to the Privy Council beseeching the queen's help in building a fort upon the Hoe:

> . . . the harboure, lying without anie defence to make long resistance, the town [was recently] stricken with such feare, that some of [the townspeople] had convaied their goods out of the towne, and others, no doubt, would have followed if they had not ben stopped by the cominge of Sir Francis Drake who, the more to assure them, brought his wife and familie thither.[58]

Early in 1592 Robert Adams was sent by the Privy Council to advise on strengthening the town's fortifications. A plan of St Nicholas Island made by him in that year, and of the fort upon the Hoe a year later, have survived (**10** and **12**). So too has his letter to William Cecil, Lord Burghley, of 31 May 1593, complaining of the 'small [financial] meanes' of the town and 'cold charitie of their smalle fellow feeling neighbours'. Yet despite the difficulties of raising the money to pay for the fort and of actually building it – 'the hardnesse of this rock hath been so extreme painfull' – Adams was convinced of the necessity for 'the garde of so wourthie and perelesse a westerne porte, as in my poore knowledge I know not his equall in England'.[59]

A plot of the fort and the Hoe for which Spry was paid 6s. 8d. in 1595/6 according to the municipal records,[60] has not survived, and the next extant plan is that of Sir Ferdinando Gorges endorsed March 1596.[61] Gorges (1565–1647) was a soldier who had fought with Elizabeth I's forces on behalf of the Dutch against their Spanish rulers; in 1595 he was appointed to the command of Plymouth fort and St Nicholas Island. His plan concentrates upon the defensive powers of the fort, emphasizing the number of guns, and is interesting in showing how the fort had developed out of the 1593 plan by Robert Adams (who had died in 1595).

In 1601, Gorges lost his command of the Plymouth fort until 1603, due to his involvement in the Earl of Essex's rebellion against the queen. During this period, he was replaced by Sir John Gilbert. The latter noticed various defects in the fort and St Nicholas Island, and pressed the Privy Council for them to be put right. The Privy Council clearly considered he had overstated his case, but agreed to send the Italian engineer, Federico Genibelli, to look into the defects on the proviso that Gilbert 'must understand that the meaninge is not to make any Royall or extraordinary peece of fortification, or such as the State may relye on in any sort for itselfe but only such as may serve the country for Recourse and Reliefe upon any sodeine attempt'.[62] Genibelli, however, considered that the town lay in real danger of falling into enemy hands, and proposed that to avoid this the town should be fortified by a wall with nine ravelins and joined to the fort (**15–16**).[63] His second plan of the fort itself includes section drawings of both the fort and St Nicholas Island.

Genibelli's report was not ignored: £1,405 was spent on repairs to the fortifications. Moreover, a further survey of the fort in 1623 (part of a general survey of castles, forts and blockhouses in this country) agreed that it should be kept in repair.[64] However, once the invasion threat from Spain had disappeared, the importance of the fort declined. The peace between the two countries concluded in 1604 and the switch to domestic preoccupations meant that a body of engineers to maintain coastal fortifications was never established. The 1623 report had pointed out that the fort was not so well placed as it might have been for the defence of the Cattewater, and after the building of the Citadel fifty years later, the fort's usefulness was superseded.

2 The Siege

A town is more than a mere plot of ground, it is a living entity. As such, the scars of its history may need to be recorded upon the map whether or not they leave any visible remains. The Siege must have been a traumatic event in the life of the town's inhabitants, just as the Blitz during the Second World War three hundred years later. Unlike the Blitz, however, the Siege left few visible remains, apart from the demolition of the castle and erection of the Citadel twenty years later 'for a checke to the Rebellious Spirits of the Neighbourhood'.[65]

Despite this lack of visible remains upon the landscape, the Siege must have been very real in the minds of the townspeople. The town had declared itself for Parliament and cast up earthworks around the castle and town; between 15 September and 21 December 1643 it was besieged by Prince Maurice of the Rhine.

From the town's point of view, the Siege was successful in that it never surrendered, despite hunger, treachery and a ship lying at Laira Point which 'stood Newters' during the Battle of Freedom Fields until it had decided which was the winning side![66] The town was hard to defend, however, because its earthworks were so far apart and the ground so uneven that the enemy could sometimes approach without being seen. Given the circumstances of the time, it is not surprising that the Parliamentarians should have felt that God was on their side, particularly when, at the very height of the famine, a great quantity of pilchards was caught in Sutton Pool. The plate of the Siege by Wenceslas Hollar (**18**) occurs in a contemporary Parliamentarian tract written in 1643 and published in 1644: *A True NARRATION of the . . . Seige* [sic] *of PLYMOUTH . . . wherein is manifested to the World the handy-work of God, and his gracious assistance to the United Forces of that Towne and Garrison.*

18

Though it looks relatively straightforward and many of the places on it are well authenticated from other maps, the Siege map raises a number of interesting questions. In addition to the authentic features – the late sixteenth-century fort, the castle, the churches at Plymstock, Egg Buckland, Stoke, St Budeaux, the mills at Pomphlett, Lipson, Weston Mills – there is the 'hidden' military landscape. 'Hidden' because it is actually very difficult to trace satisfactorily on the ground.

To begin with, was the town wall shown on the Siege map ever built?[67] An order in the Black Book for 5 July 1643 refers to the erection of a wall 'for the better defence and safetie of this towne ag[ains]t the Enemyes nowe in armes ag[ains]t the Parliam[en]t'.[68] The Siege pamphlet refers to the town walls, 'which then were not fully finished, and could not long have been defended'. The town wall occurs only rarely on maps (**11**, **15**, **18–21**, **206**), and, as we have seen elsewhere in this study, it is not unusual for a feature to be projected on maps during this period; that is, shown 'as if' it were there, although the evidence tells us that it was not. In this case, the truth probably lies somewhere in the middle: part of the town wall is shown on a reliable map of 1725 (**91**), and the likelihood is that this is the answer: part only of the town wall was built.[69]

The Siege map is interesting from the point of view of map history too. Although it is usually to be found as part of the tract, detached copies have also survived. A note on a copy of the Siege pamphlet in the Ashmolean Museum, Oxford, runs: 'This Copy has the very rare plate by Hollar, so difficult to find that it sells for five or six guineas.' Perhaps this scarcity value is the reason why there are as many as three manuscript copies of the Siege map, all made much later. One is an eighteenth-century copy in the Gough collection at the Bodleian Library (possibly by Richard Gough, the antiquary), another is a beautifully executed copy now in the National Maritime Museum, made no earlier than 1828 (the paper is watermarked), and there is a further nineteenth-century copy in the Hydrographic Department at Taunton.

Town Plans

1 Plymouth

Of the Three Towns which form the modern city of Plymouth, the oldest and best documented by maps is the town of Plymouth, which grew up round Sutton Pool.[70]

Sixteenth-century maps afford a good picture of what the town of Plymouth looked like at that date, given that the emphasis and accuracy of each map varies.[71] Three elements occur regularly: St Andrew's Church, the market-cross and the castle. One map also names streets and shows the town gates (**11**).

After this relatively clear picture of sixteenth-century Plymouth, there is a tantalizing gap in the maps recorded in this catalogue until the detailed town plan of 1725. The fact that the town is virtually a palimpsest – with the exception of St Andrew's Church, there are virtually no permanent landmarks shown on the maps throughout this period – does not help. Yet fortunately documentary evidence, particularly the descriptions of contemporaries, do much to help supply the missing pieces in the jigsaw and to explain how the town had developed by the eighteenth century into 'a large, populous and wealthy Town' (**93**).

Of the three key features of the sixteenth-century town, only one remains: St Andrew's Church. The market-cross has been superseded by the Town Hall or Guildhall, built in 1605/6.[72] The castle was pulled down in 1665/6, although its site continued to be referred to as 'the place of the ould Castle' on several maps made soon after it had disappeared on the ground (**28–30**, **38**). No doubt the loss of a feature which had served so long to guard and defend the town must have required considerable mental adjustment. The friary, another prominent landmark on the earliest map in this catalogue, was much less important in the town's life by the eighteenth century: in 1794, it was converted into a Hospital for Sick Soldiers.[73]

By the eighteenth century, at least three more town gates[74] are shown than on map **11**. The town's seven gates are documented throughout the eighteenth century, although it is obvious from the municipal records that the gates were not static, unchanging features but, rather, modified throughout the period. The 1725 map also shows the Shambles and fish market[75] and the water conduits.

Comparison of the street plans of the late sixteenth-century maps with those of the early eighteenth century show that the town has grown, spreading out north and west beyond St Andrew's. (Why did it never spread east round Sutton Pool?) Documentary evidence makes clear that the town had a minor population explosion during the seventeenth century. The preamble to the Act for building Charles Church in 1640 states that St Andrew's, the parish church, was not large enough for the congregation to hear divine service 'because the said Town has so much increased of late'.[76]

What did the eighteenth-century town look like? Although maps of this date are much less informative about this than the sixteenth-century picture maps, there are clues to fill in the gaps. Celia Fiennes tells us that at the end of the seventeenth century the town lacked great houses, and that the narrow streets were mostly inhabited by seamen. The French spy, the Seigneur de Béville, writing in 1768, gives a similar impression: large, open, perched on the edge of a hill, the town was well defended by

161

its Citadel but ill-built, ill-paved and with extremely narrow streets. These contemporary descriptions are the more valuable because the eighteenth-century town plans of Bowen and Donn (**104** and **131**) with their street plans and main civic buildings give little sense of the town's uniqueness even allowing for the fact that they were merely insets on the county maps of Devon. The town plan of 1725 (**91**), though itself manuscript, set the pattern for the details to be shown on the eighteenth-century printed town plans which appear stereotyped and lifeless.

For corporate pride, a sense of the town's identity, we need to look at a map made by one of its sons, Richard Cowl, in 1778 (**160**). The fascination of Cowl's plan is its wealth of detail, enabling us to reconstruct the social and economic life of the townspeople in some detail. While pinpointing the two Anglican churches by drawing them on the map, Cowl includes in his key references to all the foreign and Nonconformist places of worship, hardly surprising when we remember that this was a polyglot port, but, nevertheless, something that had not been done before. Then there are all the buildings of a modern eighteenth-century town – the workhouse, poorhouse, hospital, prison, burial grounds – not fashionable perhaps, but realistic and raising the question of for whom the plan was intended. The social buildings are here too: the market, theatre, public houses. The plan seems to bustle with life when compared with the static plans of Bowen and Donn.

2 Stonehouse and Dock

There are no town plans as such for Stonehouse unless we count the plan by Jerome Roche (**44**). Nevertheless, it is interesting to contrast the way in which the two relatively modern towns of Stonehouse and Dock were represented on the maps with the manner in which Plymouth was treated.

The picture of Stonehouse that emerges is that of a small fishing settlement built of limestone.[77] The little town was concentrated midway up the peninsula. Its main building was White Hall and there was also a chapel and an almshouse. The Roche map makes clear that much of the area belonged to the king.

Until the mid-eighteenth century, Stonehouse peninsula was largely cut off from other settlements in the area, apart from Cremyll passage. Despite the efforts of the Mount Edgcumbe family to set up a borough there, the peninsula did not really develop until the second half of the eighteenth century, and then as a consequence of the growth of the Dockyard. In 1767, traffic between Dock and Stonehouse was such that it was decided to build a bridge in place of the former passage across the water. Soon after, several important naval and military buildings were erected.

The first of these was the Royal Naval Hospital. Intended to accommodate up to 1,500 sick when finished (**135**), the hospital must have been sufficiently large to dominate the landscape. Its cupola and water engine feature sometimes on sailing charts because of their visibility from the sea. Other buildings in this area included the Military Hospital, shown on a map of 1784 (**179**) and, less importantly, Stonehouse Baths,[78] probably constructed in the mid-1760s, and the Long Room, shown on a map of 1770.

By contrast with Plymouth, which does not appear to have expanded greatly during the eighteenth century, successive town plans of Dock illustrate how very fast the new town grew, particularly during the latter half of the century. Unlike Sutton Pool, which was a natural deep-water harbour, the site for the future dockyard was by no

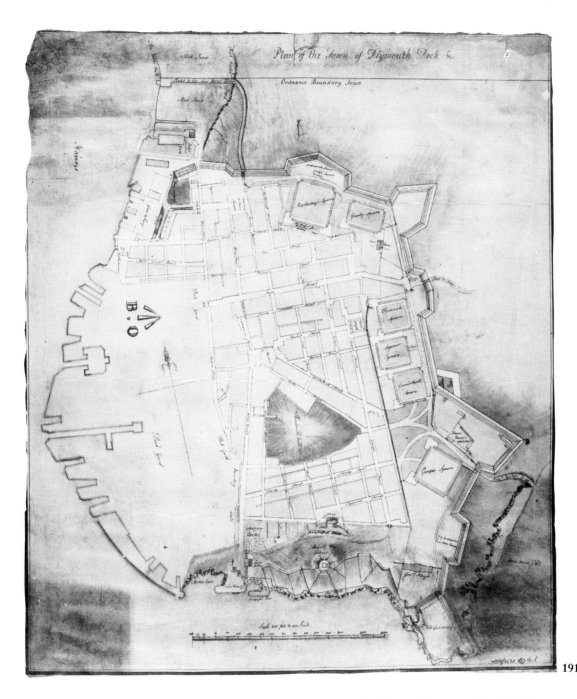

191

means a foregone conclusion. Building a deep-water harbour there required shifting four acres of land.

Yet the rapid development of the new town was facilitated by the fact that the whole of it was held by leases on three lives for ninety-nine years (at first from the Morice family, later from the St Aubyns). Despite private ownership, however, the town was not consciously planned.

It is interesting to note that the name Devonport occurs on a map of 1784 (**179**), although the town was not officially so called until the early nineteenth century.

Countryside on the Maps

1 Natural Features

i Rocks on Land

There is little information on the maps about the rocks on land, although we know from documentation associated with the maps that they were important and, at times, awkward features. Robert Adams, in building Plymouth fort upon the Hoe, commented that 'the hardnesse of this rock hath been so extreme painfull' in a letter to Lord Burghley of 31 May 1593.[79] Edmund Dummer, engaged in building Plymouth Dock, mentioned 'the lofty and Irregular riseing of the land from whence may be Conceived what a prodigious Labour and Charge it was to levell those Rocks down to a plain Superfices'.[80] Christian Lilly referred to 'the Ditch cutt out of the Solid Rock' at the Citadel (**83**). On only one of the earliest maps, Drake's leat map, is there any serious attempt to depict the rocks occurring above ground, to illustrate the point made on the

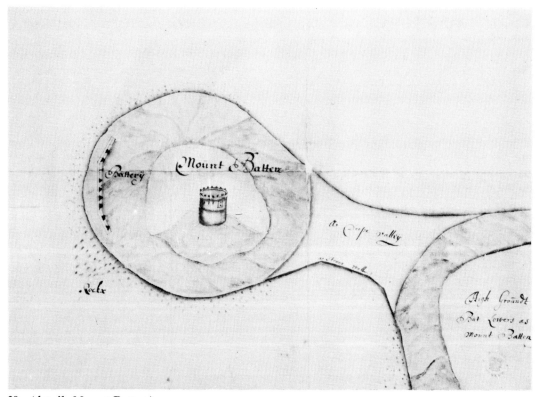

29   (detail: Mount Batten)

map: 'Here the river [Meavy] is taken out of the old river and carried 448 paces through mightie rockes which was thought impossible to carrie water through' (**8**). More often, however, when the rock was underground, no attempt was made to define where it occurred.

ii Hills

Although hills are shown on several of these maps, there is little attempt at precision except where this is important for military reasons.

Shown as seen from the sea, the town of Plymouth often appears hidden behind the hills.[81] One chart (**192**) actually refers to Plymouth as 'Moorend hills', yet no detailed information about these hills is supplied, presumably because mariners did not need it.

The varying heights of the hill on which the sixteenth-century fort was built are referred to on map **11**.[82] Likewise, Bernard de Gomme gives us an indication of high and low ground at Mount Batten on map **29**, though he does not attempt precise measurement (as when he gives the height of the stone wall around the Citadel). De Béville's map describes places in terms of height ('*hauteur*', '*élevé*'), but this is necessarily in general terms because the map was drawn from memory (**135**). For a potential invasion, it was important to establish how easy it might be to attack the Citadel and Dock.

Heights above sea-level are given for the first time on maps made during the American War of Independence (**170**, **174**). They are repeated on a map of 1788 (**187**), while another of that year supplies the distances between the batteries on rising grounds (**186**). Three of these are military maps, made by engineers; the fourth is by James Fraser, a naval officer, and it was dedicated to Pitt.

Although fathom lines or isobaths occur on charts in this catalogue, contouring of hills is beyond the scope of the maps; hills are often represented by hachures on eighteenth-century military maps.

iii Trees

Individual trees or groups of trees are rarely shown on the maps unless they have a particular significance. Map **91** shows the Great Tree in Plymouth town, but this is unusual. The Withy-Hedge ('withy' = willow) is often shown on charts because it was a landmark; some charts (such as **155** and **164**) show Mutley Firs for the same reason, but this is less common and one chart (**187**) shows the Eastern Trees near Tor House. Some of the late eighteenth-century surveys, with their detailed field patterns, inspire credibility for the trees depicted; map **159**, for instance, is so reliable that the nursery at Lower Anderton no doubt existed although it is not marked anywhere else. Printed maps, on the other hand, and less frequently manuscript maps, sometimes give trees alongside houses merely to indicate a settlement; there is no attempt to reproduce what actually stood on the ground.[83]

iv The Salt-marsh

An interesting feature shown on many of the eighteenth-century maps is the salt-marsh which stretched in a triangle from Millbay to Stonehouse and on to the

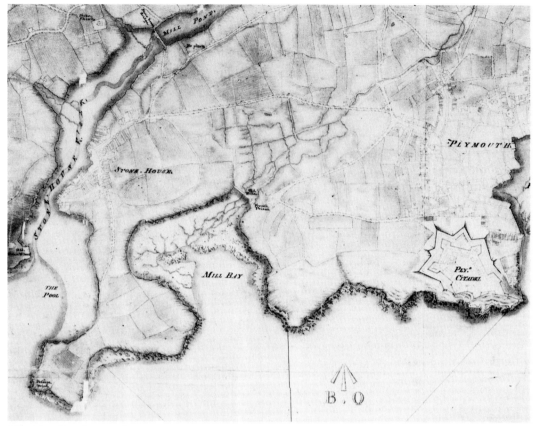

90   (detail: salt-marsh)

western edge of Plymouth (**89, 114, 116, 130, 187–9, 196**). A note on map **11** records: 'This was plimmouth milpoole before the River was brought there by Sir Fraunses Drake . . . and this poole was made drie for a medow.' Although the salt-marsh is *shown* on map **89**, it is not *marked* as such until map **114**. Despite the considerable area occupied by the salt-marsh – 26½ acres according to a map of 1794 (**196**) – there is little evidence to suggest its exploitation as an economic resource. A 'salt-house' on the edge of Sutton Pool is shown on map **125**, but other than that the only map to show salt-mills is the river map by Jerome Roche (**50**), which also illustrates a silver-mine.[84]

2 Man-made or Economic Features

i Tinworks

Tinworks are only shown on one late sixteenth-century map (**8**). A serious conflict of interest between the tinners on Roborough Down and the town arose *c.* 1600 when a certain Mr Crimes, a local magistrate, erected clash-mills on the Down to work the tin. Without the clash-mills, the tinworks would not have been able to operate, but the townsmen were furious and brought the case to the Star Chamber.

ii Mills

The Crimes case is interesting because it highlights the town's dependence upon the mills erected by Drake in the late sixteenth century, when he built the Plymouth leat. William Stallenge, writing to Cecil on 3 November 1601 on behalf of the town, stated:

> As the estate of the town is now, with the help of the mills I can, if need require, provide within 2 months 1,000 tons of provision for her Majesty's service. But if these mills be taken away, and I forced as I must be . . . to send corn and malt 3 or 4 miles to be ground at those gentlemen's mills, the like quantity of provisions or much less will not be made in a far longer time.[85]

Both town and country mills are shown on these maps. The town mills built by Drake are shown on map **17** and are distinguished as a tucking mill,[86] a malt-mill, and the Higher, Middle and Lower Mills. Account books in West Devon Record Office prove that the latter were used for grinding wheat and barley.[87] In addition to these town mills, the Millbay mills were being used for paper by 1794 (**196**).

Mills are also frequently shown throughout this period in the country areas surrounding Plymouth: Weston Mills, Lipson Mill, Marsh Mills, Pomphlett Mill, Radford Mill are particularly common.[88]

Most of these mills would have been powered by water, but it is worth noting horsemills and windmills at Dock (**114**), and a windmill is shown on the Hoe on some maps.

iii Limestone Kilns and Quarries

Limestone kilns and quarries in and around Plymouth are shown quite frequently, particularly on eighteenth-century maps. Limestone quarries are marked at Stonehouse Pool and Mount Wise (**116**); there are limestone kilns and a quarry at Dock (**191**), a quarry on the Hoe (**187**) and also a kiln (**26**) and a kiln at the Citadel (**26**, **28–9**, **33**). All this suggests very localized exploitation, dotted here and there about the landscape.

Much of the coastline in this area is Middle Devonian, that is, limestone at lower and higher horizons separated by grey slate, and this would have determined the appearance of the Three Towns at this date. Stonehouse was occasionally referred to as 'limehouse' as we have seen, while Celia Fiennes mentioned that the houses in Plymouth were built of 'this sort of stone which is a sort of marble'. Dock, she adds, had 'fine slate on the rooffs, and at a little distance it makes all the houses shew as if they were cover'd with snow and glisters in the sunn which adds to their beauty'.[89]

iv Fishing

Fishing is referred to only incidentally on the maps. Several maps (**67** and **91**) show the 'Fish House' on the causeway at the entrance to Sutton Pool which served as a breakwater until it was washed away in a very bad storm. Cowl's map (**160**) gives a Fish Cage just off the north-eastern edge of Sutton Pool.

Yet it is clear from other sources that fishing must have been a principal occupation in the area throughout the period covered by the maps. Thomas Cox in a letter to his uncle Macro in 1700 wrote: 'They have Fish in great Plenty, you may buy a Couple of large Cods for a shilling and half a Dozen Whitings for a Penny and Generally what is ye Product of the Country hereabouts is very cheap.'[90] John Harris in the early nineteenth century stated: 'No town surpasses Plymouth in abundance and variety of its Fish-Market, and the fish trade of Plymouth, after the great quantity sold in the three large towns, and from thence also to numerous villages.'[91]

3 Land Use

In general, there is little detailed information on land use on the maps in this catalogue with the exception of surveys by William Gardner, the military engineer, in the 1780s (**179–82**).

Several of the maps show field boundaries;[92] some also give formal gardens such as Mount Edgcumbe and even the gardens on the outskirts of Plymouth town (**84, 89–90**). Others attempt to distinguish between cultivated and uncultivated land (**116, 135**); but few of these maps achieve the credibility inspired by Gardner's surveys with their immensely detailed field boundaries and wooded areas depicted in different shades of green to distinguish land use.

Gardner's problem, however, like that of Murdoch Mackenzie junior at sea, was how to communicate clearly a multiplicity of information. Showing hills in relief may leave little space for distinguishing land use.

4 Acreages

Only one of the maps in this catalogue could properly be described as an estate map (**44**). This is Jerome Roche's map of the manor of Stonehouse which belonged to the Mount Edgcumbe family. The map gives acreages for the plots of ground, which are numbered within the borough, but allotted letters beyond it.

Acreages are also sometimes given on plans, particularly those where ownership may have been important to establish for legal reasons. It is shown on a sketch-map (**37**) of the Lambhay used in the 1672 enquiry, for example. The acreages of the East Hoe, upon which the Citadel was built, and the West Hoe are given on two seventeenth-century maps (**30** and **33**), though there is a slight discrepancy between them.[93] The acreage of the East Hoe is noted again on a late eighteenth-century map (**197**), although by then it was considerably less than at the time the Citadel was built over a century before.

Another map giving acreages is the plan of Mount Wise showing the newly built Dockyard (**65**); around the yard are fields, whose names and acreage are given in a key. A detailed note concerning the measurement of footpaths and roads adjoining the Dockyard is given on an early eighteenth-century map (**79**), while a map of January 1774 (**151**) gives the extent of the Dockyard.

A plan of the salt-marsh (**196**) records it as $26\frac{1}{2}$ acres statute measure, hedges not included, and an estimate of the extent of Sutton Pool (**28**) records it as 31 acres and 146 perches.

5 Ownership

Ownership is shown from time to time on the maps, particularly when land either had been or was likely to be the subject of dispute. A seventeenth-century map (**30**) tells us which parcels of land on the Hoe were bought when the Citadel was built, for example, and also gives boundary stones between the East Hoe and the Lambhay. Edward Bayntun's mid-eighteenth-century map of Sutton Pool (**125**) distinguishes by colour Duchy of Cornwall property (in green) from the illegal erections made by the mayor and commonalty or their lessees (in red).

The early seventeenth-century mills map (**17**) draws a distinction between land belonging to the town and that belonging to named individuals, but it is less easy to understand the reference to 'Mr Gloynes Field being the beanes and Charters land' on map **33**.

6 Gentry Houses

In the sixteenth century, marking the houses of the gentry on a map had a practical function. These were the people around whom the defence of the land would be organized. Hence map **4**, drawn up when the country was under threat from Spain, noted:

East Anthonie: Mr Ric Carewe his howse; Radforde Mr [Christo]pher Harrys his howse and he a sufficient gentillman to take charge to defend this quarter with thinhabitants of Plimpton hundred.

4   (detail: Radford)

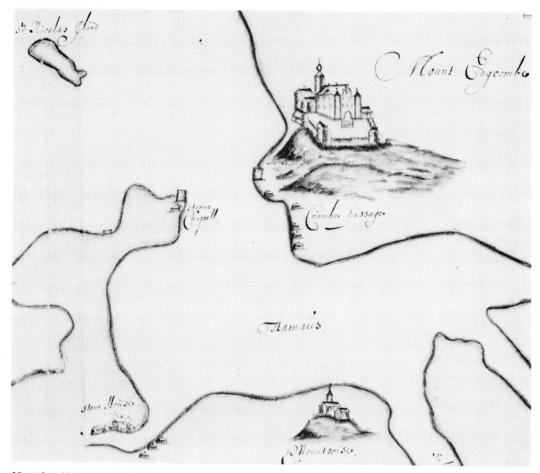

25 (detail: Mount Edgcumbe house)

In a relatively feudal society, the large houses of the gentry would have dominated the landscape and provided an obvious landmark for miles around. In some cases the cartographer has emphasized an already conspicuous feature out of all proportion. Mount Edgcumbe house dominates the entrance to the Hamoaze on a seventeenth-century map (**25**) in much the same way as paintings of the sixteenth or seventeenth century will sometimes show the king or queen as physically larger than his or her subjects, although we know from historical records that this was not factually the case.

The houses of the gentry are again used as landmarks on the road-widening map (**113**), while owners' names have been marked in red ink on a military communications map (**174**) and they have been noted (when known) along the course of the proposed Devonport leat (**195**). In the case of printed maps, there might be something of a status symbol in a subscriber having his or her name on the map, thus enhancing its sales. Cowl's map of 1780 (**171**) contains a veritable roll-call of names.

Finally, the distinction between the counties of Devon and Cornwall is very rare, although it does occur on copies of the Siege map (**19**).

Cartographers

Although manuscript maps were relatively straightforward, production of early printed maps may have involved as many as five functions, [94] though often more than one of these was undertaken by the same person (for example, a publisher sometimes acted as engraver and seller). Firstly, there was the cartographer or hydrographer. Secondly, the draughtsman, whose job was to compile the finished map; he was a copyist or compiler and sometimes described himself as delineator (*del., delin.*). Thirdly, the engraver, whose task was to transfer the finished manuscript to copperplate (*sc., sculp.* for *sculpsit*; *scrip.* for *scripsit*). Several engravers combined engraving with publishing and selling; one was even a jeweller. [95] Fourthly, publishers, who sometimes initiated charts (though there is no proof this happened for the Plymouth maps) and, of course, financed the publication. Fifthly, printed map-sellers, many of whom were situated around Cornhill in London. In the catalogue entries, the names of those performing any of these functions have been recorded. In this introduction, attention will be focused on the cartographers and surveyors.

If we study the cartographers of these maps of Plymouth, certain characteristics emerge. Very few of them were local, Richard Cowl being one exception and Granville Smith another. [96] Granville Smith described himself as 'Teacher of the Mathematicks and Land Surveyor'. Benjamin Donn, who came from Bideford, referred to himself and his son as 'TEACHERS of the Mathematics and Natural Philosophy'. No doubt their mathematical skills proved very useful for surveying. But local schoolteachers were the exception rather than the rule: most of these cartographers had worked in other parts of the country and some abroad as well.

Despite this, however, documentary sources do throw some light on local mapmakers during this period, although the results of their work do not appear to have survived in most instances. [97] Mention is frequently made among the Plymouth municipal records of members of the Spry family. John Spry, for instance, made a 'platt' for 13s. 4d. in 1546/7, [98] and haven 'platts', while 'Robert Spry the Paynter' engraved a basin and ewer of silver-gilt with 'a mapp of the Towne' in 1622. [99] The death of Morris Spry, painter, aged fifty-two, on 7 May 1752 is also recorded. [100] Were the Spry family map-makers to the town, official or unofficial, during this period? Another person who occurs in the municipal records is 'Pearse the painter'; he was paid £2 in 1671/2 for nine maps of the town and harbour (none of which appear to have survived). [101] He may be the same person as William Pearse the painter who was paid £1 15s. in 1674/5 'for makeing of Mr Lanyons armes'.

Many of the cartographers were of high standing, including: Robert Adams, Surveyor of Queen's Buildings; Bernard de Gomme, Surveyor of Ordnance to Charles II; Edmund Dummer, Surveyor of the Navy; Greenvile Collins, Hydrographer to the King and Queen. Several were foreigners: Genibelli, the Italian engineer; de Gomme, the Dutch engineer; Christian Lilly, a naturalized Englishman who received his training at Celle and Hanover; besides a few Frenchmen such as the spy, de Béville. Several of the earliest printed charts of Plymouth Sound are Dutch and it has been commented that Dutch knowledge in the seventeenth century of the English coastline was probably greater than that of some natives.[102] This is borne out by the fact that Dutch names for the rocks in the Sound 'Coaxbroot Meuston', 'Mewstone of Meeuwe Steen of Roks Broodt' (both referring to the Mewstone) and 'Idestone Mieusteen' (Eddystone) are sometimes repeated on English charts.

An interesting example of a Dutch surveyor at work in Sutton Pool and the ambivalent attitudes towards him occurs in 1596. Peter Fecke of Rotterdam, master of a ship called the *Black Eagle*, was engaged in taking soundings of the Pool when he was apprehended. Ferdinando Gorges, Governor of Plymouth Fort, reported it thus to Sir Robert Cecil:

> What his meaning was therein I know not, but the time being such as is [the Spanish threat] cannot but be suspicious. [However,] . . . I have examined divers that have known him a long time . . . and they all . . . protest much for his honesty and simple intent, as having a desire only to acquaint himself with the harbour, taking it to be a thing belonging unto him as he was a mariner, not thinking he had committed any offence.[103]

Although the cartographers of the area consisted of a variety of people from different occupations, nevertheless there was a preponderance of military and naval men. The military men include: Bernard de Gomme, the Dutch engineer; Christian Lilly, Third Engineer of the Plymouth Division; Desmaretz, an engineer and captain in the Royal Artillery; Matthew Dixon, Chief Engineer of the Plymouth Division; William Gardner, Surveyor of Ordnance; Elias Durnford, Lieutenant-Colonel and Commanding Royal Engineer and William Test, Chief Royal Military Surveyor and Draughtsman. Among the naval men are: Edmund Dummer, Midshipman Extraordinary, later to become Surveyor of the Navy; Joseph Gilbert, Master of the Pearl; Murdoch Mackenzie junior, a naval lieutenant later to succeed his uncle and namesake as Maritime Surveyor at the Admiralty and James Fraser and William Price, Masters in His Majesty's Navy.

In the cases of both military and naval cartographers, the reason for this preponderance was a mix of needs, expertise and capital outlay which must have limited those who could undertake hydrographic surveys. Until 1800 the British Navy had no proper chart production and the charts that did exist were so poor that the Navy encouraged ordinary serving officers to obtain information on depths, sea-marks, times and tides, setting of currents, and so on as part of their duties.[104]

The Navy's backing was crucial because the chief obstacle to accurate hydrographic surveying was expense. Greenvile Collins had estimated that it would cost him £600 to survey the sea-coasts of the British Isles as he was ordered to do in 1681; by 1688, he was £1,400 in arrears on the payment owed him, and felt that it was beyond his means to do the work thoroughly in view of the poor public response.[105]

To carry out an accurate survey, much expensive equipment and manpower was necessary. Murdoch Mackenzie senior, in his *A Treatise on Marine Surveying*, first published in 1774, included among the list of instruments and other necessaries for taking a coastal survey a survey-boat or six-oared cutter, a vessel of about 120 tons burden, with a crew consisting of master, purser, mate, midshipman, carpenter, sail-maker, boatswain, cook, fourteen able seamen before the mast, and a coastal pilot, besides the surveyor, his assistant and the two servants. It is ironic that Mackenzie himself should have commented: '. . . most of the books that treat on nautical surveying, give a numerous list of requisite instruments, which few young officers can procure'!

Hydrographic surveying could also take a very long time if done properly. Map **159** bears a note:

This Survey was begun in the year 1777, indeed some angles were taken in the year 1774 and some work begun but we were ordered to the North coast of Kent which stop'd this Survey till 1777 . . . 1778 when this Survey was finished and in part of 1779.

The proper way of constructing charts was from sea-journals of courses and distances, but this might take so long that a bad navigator was tempted to skimp and adopt instead 'a method, by which he surveys more coast in one year, than he could travel over in three; surveying a little himself, and copying a great deal from others, without distinguishing the *certain* from the *uncertain*'. As a result, 'some places have been surveyed again and again, yet in process of time are found to require it anew . . . so few draughts are to be met with, that answer the end for which they are intended, viz. to direct ships into safe anchorage without a pilot'. This is an interesting comment in view of the fact that it was generally considered that anyone entering Plymouth Sound required the services of a coastal pilot. The implication of what has been said above is that coastal pilots relied upon their own tradition and that the majority of these charts probably had little practical relevance for them.

On land, too, expense might be a problem, though on a less grand scale. William Blackmore, surveying Buckland Down outside Plymouth during the War of American Independence[106] noted:

I should have been much happier to have made a regular Survey and finished plan of the whole, but the price you fixed was not Sufficient for the expense of Self and Assistants in taking such a plan in a proper manner. I took the most early Oppertunity [sic] as you required it with speed, the weather being very uncertain made it expensive, but hope your future favours will make it up.

In at least one instance, there seems to have been lack of cooperation between the military engineer and the hydrographic surveyor. General Roy wrote in October 1783: 'We have only further to observe that during our stay in Plymouth, we received no information whatever from the Admiralty, relating to the coasts near Plymouth and to the westward as your Lordship's letter of the 4th October gave us hope to expect.'[107]

Cartography

Explicit Information

1 Scales

Scales are rare among the earliest manuscript maps (late sixteenth century), with the exception of maps by Robert Adams (such as **10**). From the turn of the seventeenth century they became increasingly frequent, however, until by its end it was rare to find a map without a scale. In a few cases, a scale was not practical because of the circumstances under which surveying was undertaken, such as the spy maps of de Béville and others.[108] Virtually all the printed maps have scales.

2 Measures

The two most usual land measures for these maps are feet and miles. Yet even these apparently straightforward measures have their pitfalls. Although the mile was standardized as 1,760 yds as early as 1591, this was not generally adopted for a long time and even as late as 1800 a mile was described as 2,040 yds (**201**). Likewise, a perch could vary between anything from 16 ft to $25\frac{1}{2}$ ft. Surveyors usually got round this by clarifying the number of feet to a perch in that instance. Thus Robert Adams specifies in map **12**: 'The Scale of Perches, every perche conteyninge 18 foote'; while map **33** states: 'This scale of Equall partes is after $16\frac{1}{2}$ foote to the perch stattut Measure.' Small discrepancies are also to be found: a French map notes that, *'le pied Anglois vaut 11 pouces 3 lignes du pied Francois'* (**56**).

Some individuals and institutions had their own favourite measures. The Italian engineer, Federico Genibelli, working in the very early seventeenth century, expresses his scale as *'passi geometrii'*. This is clarified in a map of 1677 (**41**) as 'A Scale of Geometrical Paces or of 5 Foot to a Pace'. An early eighteenth-century French cartographer used a scale of *'1250 Pas Geometriques, qui font un mille d'Angleterre'* (**74**). Several maps produced by the Drawing Room had a scale of 800 (or occasionally 400) feet to the inch, while William Gardner expressed his scale in terms of '80 Gunter Chains or One Mile' when not using a six inch to the mile scale.

Charts naturally used nautical measures. Fathoms (6 ft) are not uncommon: 1,000 fathoms, 1,014 fathoms or 1 nautical mile and 1,200 fathoms. French maps sometimes employed the *toise*, which was $6\frac{1}{2}$ ft (**163**, **184**). Murdoch Mackenzie in one instance used a scale of three cables' length, a cable being approximately 600 ft or a tenth of a nautical mile (**159**). An interesting note on map **1** reads: 'ffrom Dudman to Rame hedde a kenyng'. A kenning is the distance that bounds the range of ordinary vision, especially at sea; hence a marine measure of about 20 or 21 miles.

3 Latitude and Longitude

An interesting note on latitude and longitude occurs on map **187** by James Fraser:

I have deduced the longitude of St Nicholas Island from my observations on the Solar Eclipse in June 1788, having previously determined the error of the Lunar Tables at that time, by a rigorous calculation founded on the observations of Alexander Aubant Esq at Loampit Hill near Greenwich. The Latitude of the island has been settled by Mr Willm Bayly Head Master of the Royal Academy at Portsmouth with an Astronomical Quadrant before he sailed with Captain Cook, in the year 1772.

Generally, however, references to latitude and longitude are extremely rare on these maps.

4 Orientation

Most of the maps in this catalogue are oriented north, although this is not an invariable rule, particularly during the earlier period. Harbour charts of the Sound, for instance, are quite often oriented south and occasionally east. Plans of the Dockyard are usually oriented east. St Nicholas Island charts are sometimes oriented south, but occasionally west, likewise plans of the Citadel. The compass rose suggests orientation east on map **25**, but it should be south; likewise orientation is west on map **163** despite the directional arrow. These maps show that even renowned engineers such as Robert Adams (**10**) and Sir Bernard de Gomme did not always orient their maps north.

5 Colouring

On the earliest charts, the sea is represented by the colour blue (**2**), by blue wavy lines (**4**), by navy-blue lines on a white ground (**8**) or just by wavy lines (**15** and **16**); later, it is shown by a green wash (**163**). Rocks are shown in various ways: by dark blue strokes (**4**), or painted in grey (**6**) or blue (**10**).

On land different shades of green are used on some maps to distinguish land use. Colour is also sometimes used to distinguish between actual and planned improvements, for instance, on maps **150** and **151** 'the lines in Black is the Yard in its present State and those in Yellow are agreeable to the General Plan of Improvement'.

6 Conventional Signs

For much of this period the conventions in map-making were fluid though the role of printing in encouraging standardized signs should not be overlooked. Although usually represented by colour on the earliest manuscript maps, rocks are later often depicted by crosses. Inter-tidal areas are often denoted by black dots, as explained in a note on map **11**: 'Note alway that where it is full of prickes, theire it is drie at lowe water, when the springe is at hiest [highest].' Dots were easier to reproduce on printed maps than pink shading (**69**) or yellow wash (**114**). Dots were also used on map **177** to represent a sandbank and dots on a yellow wash denote a sandy bay (on **173**). Towards the end of the period covered, two of the printed maps (**164** and **177**) have keys for conventional signs.

7 *Dedication*

Most of the printed maps bear a dedication. What was the function of the dedicatee? Although dedications do not necessarily imply financial help or even approval,[109] dedicatees do appear to have been chosen with regard to the suitability of their office for the purposes of the map. For example, charts have been dedicated to the First Lord of the Admiralty, the 'Admiral of the Blew C-in-C in present Expedition', Prince William Henry, and the Master, Wardens and Elder Brethren of Trinity House (**53, 67, 183** and **198** respectively). A printed plan of the Citadel is dedicated to the Governor of Plymouth, town plans to the Lord High Steward of Plymouth and the Prince of Wales, a county map to the Lord Lieutenant, and Dockyard plans to Sir John St Aubyn and Viscount Parker (**95, 104, 110, 112, 160**). Was dedication merely a token of respect?

Only in the case of Benjamin Donn is there any explicit recognition of financial patronage. He dedicated his map of 1765 to John Baring and Matthew Lee from Exeter 'as a grateful Acknowledgment of the great and generous Assistance which they have given thereto' (**131**). His map of 1784 (**177**) was dedicated to a group of people: 'For Favours received and To the rest of the Subscribers . . . this Map is humbly Inscribed'.

An interesting example of how the subscription system might have worked is afforded by an advertisement in *The London Journal* for 21 March 1723/4 headed 'PROPOSALS for Printing a compleat SEA ATLAS'. The price was set at three guineas, 'one to be paid down . . . Subscribers Names to be printed and their Arms engraven'. There follows a list of booksellers who would take in subscriptions. It seems likely that this atlas was primarily aimed at merchants since the gloss described it as 'a new Undertaking calculated for the further Improvement of Navigation, and the universal Benefit of Commerce'.

Internal Evidence

1 *Charts*

How accurate were these charts? In the early seventeenth century there appears to have been some debate as to the relative accuracy of printed and manuscript charts. The publisher's point of view is put forcefully in *The Light of Navigation* published in 1620.[110] Playing devil's advocate, the writer suggests first that many coastal pilots preferred manuscript charts because they were regularly updated, in contrast to the printed charts, which never were:

> but herein they are not a little deceived, for the printed mappes in each respect are as good, yea and better then the written, for that the printed mapps are once in everie point with all the care and diligence made perfect, in regard that they serve for many, for that being once well made, all the rest may with as little labour be made good, as well as badde.

Manuscript maps, on the other hand, had to be laboriously copied out, often by copyists with no specialist knowledge of charts.

How far do these comments ring true? Most of the early printed charts in this catalogue do not inspire confidence. Partly it may have been that commercial pressures such as the expense of altering plates may have discouraged updating them[111] and partly that the original surveys seem to have left much to be desired. Samuel Pepys, for instance, was suspicious as to the accuracy of charts: 'It is clear . . . that rather than show their differences, for fear of showing their mistakes, masters will conceal their differences, and so let the charts remain for ever as they be.'[112] This degree of suspicion may be explained by Pepys's experiences on board ship when soundings were being taken: 'we [cast our log] but every two [hours] and God knows that done by some very ignorant and unskillful hand, especially in the night'. Certainly the soundings on some of the early printed charts of Plymouth appear to justify a high degree of scepticism.

Another cynic as to the reliability of printed charts was Murdoch Mackenzie senior. His *Treatise on Marine Surveying* noted that:

> the merits of the draughts to which seamen trust their lives and fortunes are seldom judged by any other rules than the recency of the publication, the neatness of the engraving, the Authority under which the survey was executed; or, sometimes, by the rank and reputation of the persons to whom they are inscribed.

Hence the function of the dedications described earlier, perhaps!

Manuscript charts, on the other hand, inspire a degree of confidence, dependent on their maker. A benchmark in the history of charting Plymouth Sound is the work of Murdoch Mackenzie junior in the 1770s. His printed chart of 1779 (**165**) was reprinted by the Hydrographical Office in 1810 with 'a few alterations and additions since made'. Likewise, his assistant Graeme Spence used his original angles from a survey of 1774 again in 1807 to show that 'the Compass Bearings of the Handeeps given by the Masters attendant to the Navy Board in the year 1791, are wrong, and ought to be corrected'.[113]

2 Maps

i Errors and Inconsistencies

In the case of maps, there are a few errors and inconsistencies, and sometimes features are shown on a map which in reality were never there. More often, however, features which did exist on the landscape have been ignored on the maps, and this element of selectivity is discussed in some detail below.

A map should not be totally discounted because of some errors and inconsistencies. Place-names transposed or misspelt may tell us something about the cartographer and his perception of the landscape. Map **22**, for example, shows us obvious and important features about the town, such as the group of houses and church tower on the western edge of Sutton Pool, Mount Edgcumbe house, the houses at Cawsand, but the details are wrong: Cawsand is called Gosson, and the names of Mount Wise and Stonehouse have been transposed. This becomes less surprising when we learn that the chart was drawn by a mariner on a round trip to the East Indies in 1646. Plymouth was merely one of the numerous ports of call.

ii The Need for Caution

Internal evidence on the maps should at times be treated with caution. In some cases, names were actually changed to different places; 'Stonehouse bridge', for instance, refers to Millbridge until the erection of a stone bridge between Stonehouse and Dock in 1767. On other occasions, the maps tell us what might have been but never was, such as the 'land fitting for a docke' at Hooe in the late seventeenth century or the proposed new gun wharf at Stonehouse in 1718 (**25** and **84**).

iii Selectivity

Selectivity is crucial to the cartographer's mental map: what he has chosen to record, what is ignored and what is emphasized out of all proportion.[114] This may be determined both by his particular sensitivities and by the purpose for which the map was made, especially if this was done under some pressure. For example, very few of these maps show the town of Plymouth surrounded by a wall, yet of those that do, one was drawn up about the time of the Armada, another during the Siege and another by a potential French invader. Can we afford to discount them? [115]

Likewise, the cartographer's sensitivities come into play in determining what is recorded. Eighteenth-century maps of Plymouth frequently record the existence of the two Anglican churches, St Andrew's and Charles. If it were not for the plans of Richard Cowl, we might be totally unaware that there was a multiplicity of places of worship at this date: a Quaker meeting-house, two Presbyterian meeting-houses, a tabernacle, Baptist and Moravian meeting-houses, a Jewish synagogue and a French Protestant meeting-house (**160–61**).[116] Yet, while earning credit for noting their existence, Cowl, too, provides drawings only of the Anglican churches, thus showing their central function on his mental map of Plymouth as landmarks.

Mental maps differ according to the cartographer's sensitivities, and it is not surprising that it should be a French map which draws attention to the existence of a colony of religious refugees at Saltash.[117] It is clear from other sources that such colonies existed in the town of Plymouth and its environs, yet this is the only reference on the maps.[118]

iv Landmarks

Some landmarks are obvious and common to all those familiar with a landscape. Church towers, for example, are often drawn to represent a community because they are such a conspicuous feature; sometimes, it is not even felt necessary to depict the cluster of houses gathered around them. Other deliberately placed landmarks are beacons and obelisks, such as those on Staddon Heights and at Mount Edgcumbe, which are frequently shown on these maps.

Yet landscapes evolve their own landmarks too. This landscape is defined in terms of certain familiar landmarks repeated again and again: the Old Mills, the Mill Prison, the parsonage house at Stoke, the New Bridge over the River Plym and the houses of the large country landowners.

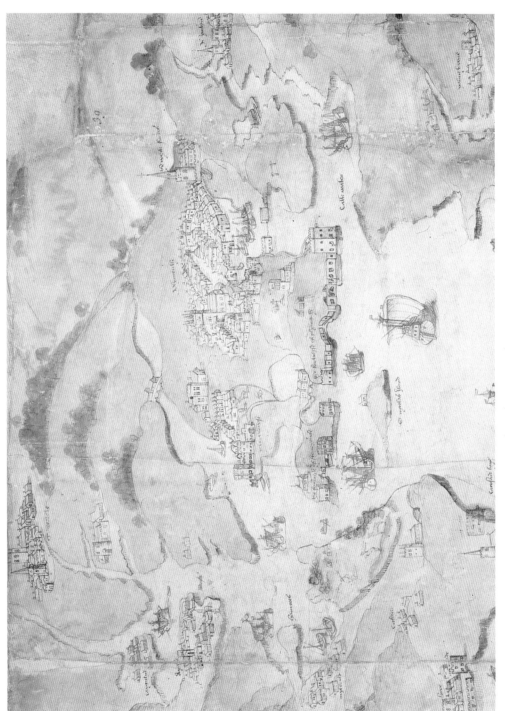

1 Detail of Plymouth Sound from harbour chart of south-west England (c. 1539)

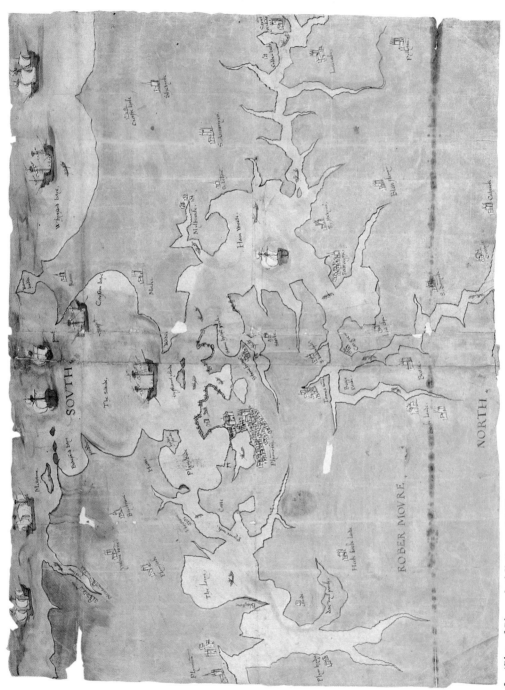

2 'Plat of Plymo[uth]' (? pre-1549)

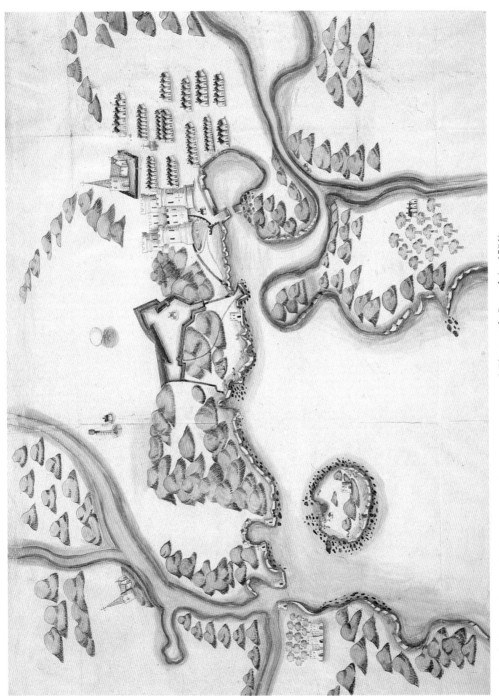

6 'discriptio[n] of a Tow[n]', depicting the landscape around Plymouth Sound (c. 1591)

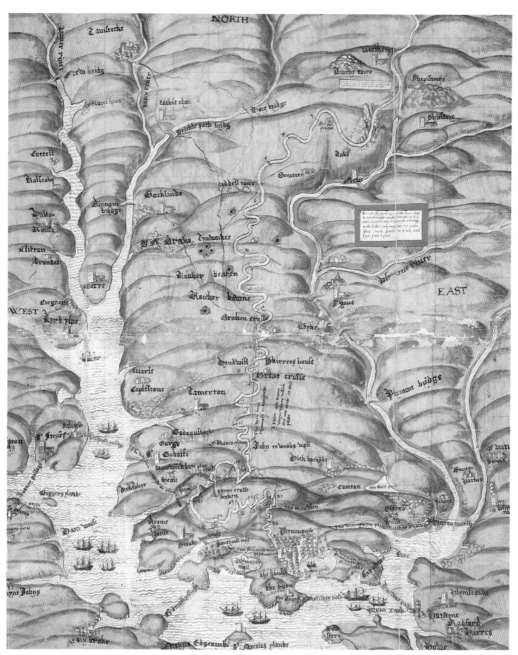

8 Map of the landscape north of Plymouth Sound (*c.* 1591)

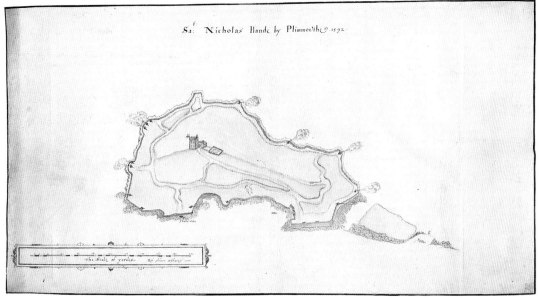

10 'Sa[in]t Nicholas Ilande by Plimmouthe' (Robert Adams, 1592)

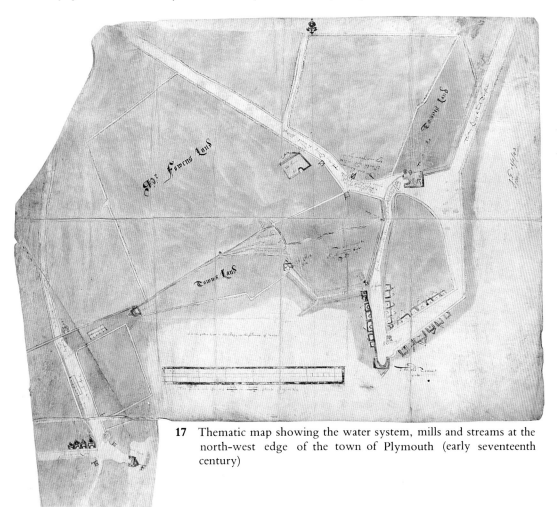

17 Thematic map showing the water system, mills and streams at the north-west edge of the town of Plymouth (early seventeenth century)

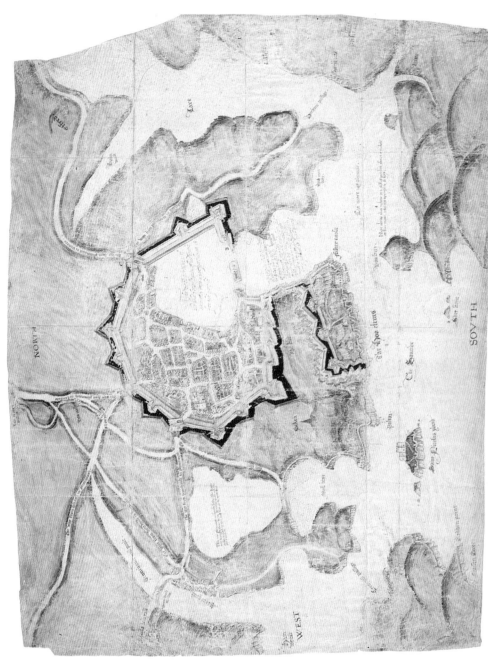

11 'Plat of Plymoth' (? 1592)

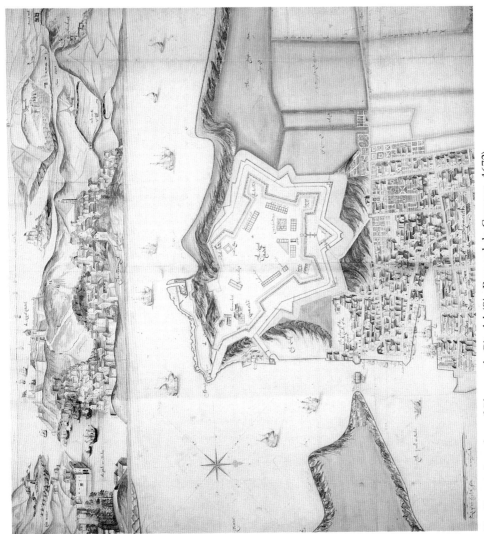

38 Decorative plan of Plymouth Citadel (Sir Bernard de Gomme, 1672)

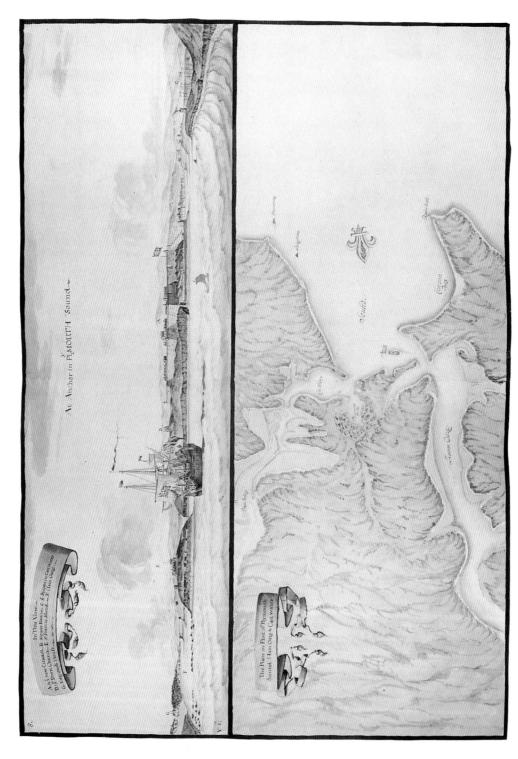

In This View.
A At y^e new Cittadel. B Mount Batten. C y^e Ships in Cattwater.
D y^e Town Church. E y^e Francis Illand. —F Lan Oaze.
G y^e St Nicholas Illand. —

At Anchor in PLIMOUTH Sound.

The Plain or Plott of Plymouth
Sound. Ham Oaze & Catt water

43 'The Plain or Plott of Plymouth Sound Ham Oaze and Catt water' (? copy by Edmund Dummer of original by Jerome Roch, August 1682)

68 'A VIEW of Plymouth Sound & ye River HAMOUZE & CATWATER taken from ye Riseing Land above Mount Edgecomb opposite Mount Wise wch shews yt St Nicholas Island is ye Principal gaurd [sic] to ye New Dock and ye SHIPS In this Harbour D[E]LINEATED 1697'

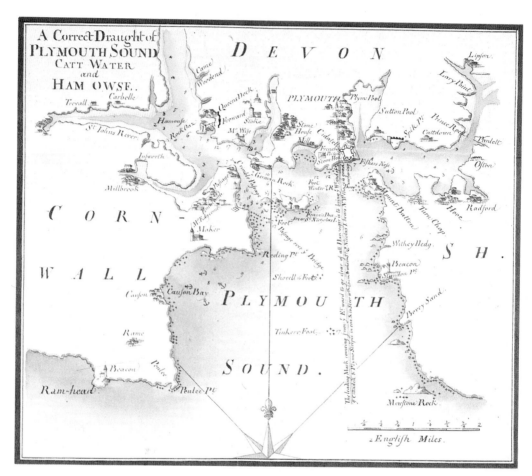

87 Manuscript copy (1779) of 'A Correct Draught of PLYMOUTH SOUND CATT WATER and HAM OWSE' (inset) on 'A NEW and CORRECT CHART of the CHANNEL between ENGLAND & FRANCE with considerable Improvements not extant in any Draughts hitherto Publish'd; shewing the Sands, Shoals, depths of Water and Anchorage, with ye flowing of the Tydes, and setting of the Current; as observ'd by the learned Dr Halley' (Greenvile Collins, 1723)

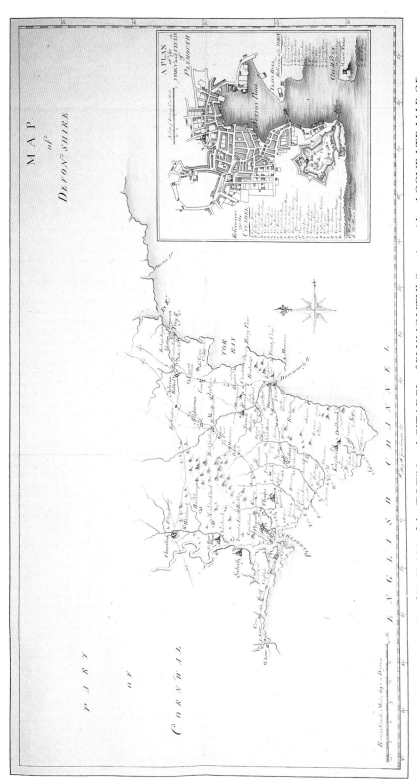

107 Manuscript copy (c. 1779) of 'A PLAN of the TOWN and CITADEL of PLYMOUTH' (inset) on 'An ACCURATE MAP OF DEVON SHIRE Divided into its HUNDREDS' (Emmanuel Bowen, April 1754)

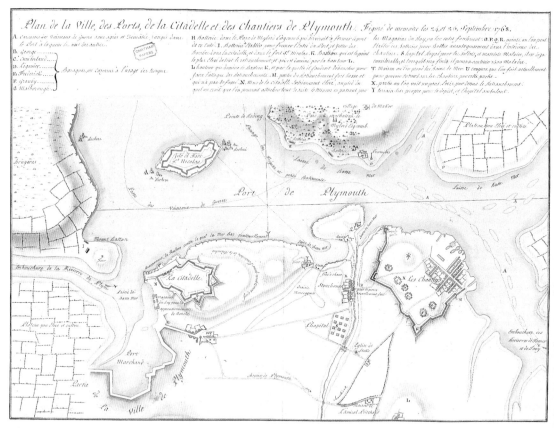

135 'Plan de la Ville, des Ports, de la Citadelle et des Chantiers de Plymouth' (? M. de Beville, September 1768)

The Mapping of Particular Places

The maps in this catalogue cover the whole area around Plymouth Sound. Within that area, some places have a particular significance. These include: Sutton Pool, which was the heart of the old town of Plymouth; St Nicholas (or Drake's) Island, because of its importance for defending the Sound; the Citadel; the Dockyard; and Cawsand, because of its potential as a harbour. In this section, the light shed by the maps on these particular places is discussed.

Sutton Pool

Sutton Pool formed the heart of the old town of Plymouth. Its convenience in allowing even relatively large ships right up to the centre of the town is the main reason why the town grew up around it. The earliest map in this catalogue (which is one of the most informative) shows tall ships lying at anchor in Sutton Pool, emphasizing its role as a merchant port in the mid-sixteenth century.

Soon after this earliest map was compiled, the town's importance grew. From the municipal records, we know that three main quays were built during the Elizabethan period: South Quay in 1572, Smart's Quay in 1601, and New Quay probably at the same time.[119]

Nearly a century later, Celia Fiennes writing in 1698 described the main quay as 'a broad space which leads you up into the broade streete and is used in manner of an exchange for the merchants meeting, for in this streete also is a fine stone Crosse and alsoe a long Market House set on stone pillars'.[120]

The small quays which grew up around Sutton Pool are shown on two maps, one being the map of 1757 drawn up in the dispute between the Duchy of Cornwall, who owned the land, and the mayor and commonalty who had encroached upon it (**125**). The other map is William Simpson's survey of 1786 (**A4**), which gives a detailed account of the quays, slips and streets around the Pool.

Sutton Pool must have been often at risk in the later Middle Ages. As we saw above,[121] on several occasions it was attacked or burnt because it was not enclosed or walled. From at least the time of Leland in the 1530s, the mouth of the Pool could be chained over in time of need, and as late as 1760 this was still the case.[122]

The early town's sense of its own vulnerability must have been heightened by the fact that on occasions it was difficult to distinguish between friend and foe. In an interesting letter to the Privy Council of July 1599 the Mayor of Plymouth, John Blytheman, explained the town's reaction when a fleet of Flemish ships, rumoured to be one hundred but in fact not more than sixty-three, had put into port. Two flyboats preceding the fleet had advised the town that the fleet were merchants intending to go to La Rochelle; a Scotsman entering the harbour at the same time had confirmed this.

Whereupon the fleet, bearing into the sea towards the West, with full intent, as appeared, to have proceeded in their intended course, we forebore for the present to put our men in arms, which we would otherwise have done. But the wind and weather altering, these ships put back with[in] the harbour, which occasioned the town to put themselves in so great a readiness as they saw the cause require: and so they mean to do, whatsoever shall be inveighed against them, noting this by the way, that a man of war which was of these ships' company as they came with[in] our harbour, did in dutiful sort strike sail before her Majesty's island here, which were sufficient tokens that they entered not proudly into the harbour, as appears it was inveighed.[123]

The episode is interesting because it highlights the town's confused reaction to the incoming fleet.

St Nicholas Island (Drake's Island)

The strategic importance of St Nicholas Island for controlling Plymouth Sound is a recurrent theme throughout these maps.

The fort, converted from a chapel in 1547/8, is a prominent feature on the first map we have of the island: a plan made by Robert Adams in 1592 (**10**). A survey of 1623 made the point that the island was virtually impregnable provided its fortifications were maintained and it was kept manned: the only way it could be attacked was by small boats which could easily be repelled.[124] Edmund Dummer in the late seventeenth century thought similarly that, if sufficiently stocked with men and provisions, the island could withstand the greatest force that might decide to attack it. Christian Lilly, writing in 1714–17 shared this view: 'I am of opinion that no Expence should be spared for putting this Island into the best posture of Defence, it being capable of recoiveing every strong [force] though but a Smal fortification.'[125]

Maps **68** and **81** describe the island as the best guard for the Dockyard, although it should be noted that de Béville (**135**), looking at the island from an invader's point of view, thought the Citadel should be captured first, after which it would be easy to crush the fort on the island.

Christian Lilly, in the report accompanying his map, described the island in some detail. In length 880 ft, in breadth about 400, its inaccessible precipes crowned with platforms of cannon, besides the entrenchments running around the island, meant that it was very hard to attack, even though its fortifications had been allowed to fall into disrepair. A French map (**203**) described the island as a sugar loaf ('*pin de sucre*').

Two maps showing the island in 1725 and 1781 respectively (**92** and **175**), differ little in their representation of it, illustrating its perimeter wall with the ten gun-platforms (named), gatehouse, guardhouse, powderhouses, carriage house and barracks. Another map of the mid-eighteenth century (**102**) tells us that the island's establishment at that date consisted of a master gunner paid 2s. a day besides gunners from Plymouth and thirty-five guns on the platforms, thirty of which were 32-pounders.

The island's role in defending the Sound would have been enhanced by the presence of the combined Franco-Spanish fleet in 1779. It is not surprising that soon afterwards we find Lieutenant-Colonel Dixon, Chief Engineer of the Plymouth Division, carrying out various works there. He erected a battery of twenty-one 32-pounders on the summit of the island, 67 ft above sea-level, with four 18-pounders and two 13-inch mortars to the right and left of it. He felt that the existing batteries along the lower line, close to the rocks and about 20 ft above sea-level, could be commanded by musketry

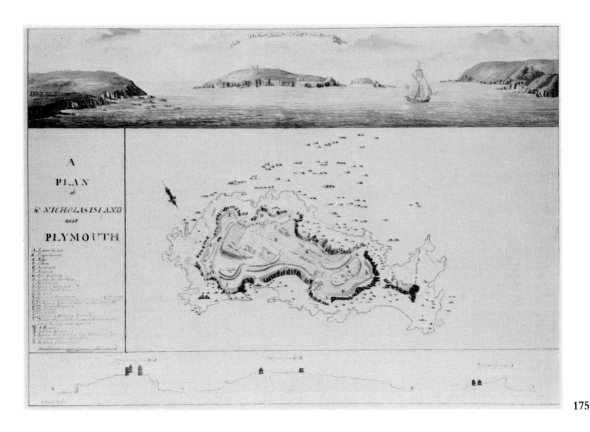

175

from the round tops of ships of war. In addition, he removed the guns looking inwards to the harbour so that there was no possibility of Wester Kings battery or the ship moored between the island and the coastline being attacked. Map **173** illustrates his proposals.

The Citadel

The maps and plans illustrating the Citadel serve as a record of its construction, give details of the intended occupants of the various buildings, provide clues as to its defensive capability, and were themselves used as evidence in the early nineteenth-century dispute as to the ownership of the land upon which it was built.

The commission for building the Citadel was issued in November 1665, and Sir Bernard de Gomme, the Dutch engineer, began work on it in 1666. His five plans of the Citadel were made as working documents to record its building between 1665 and 1672 (**26–30**). The extent of his involvement can be judged by the fact that another of the maps has an account in his hand for building the sentry-house, including the bringing of seventeen tons of timber and Portland stone by sea at a cost of £21 5s.(**27**).

The plans give detailed information about the building of the Citadel, including the changes as it progressed. Thus the first plan of 1665 (**26**) provides detailed measurements in feet of the space along the bastion wall and plots the individual

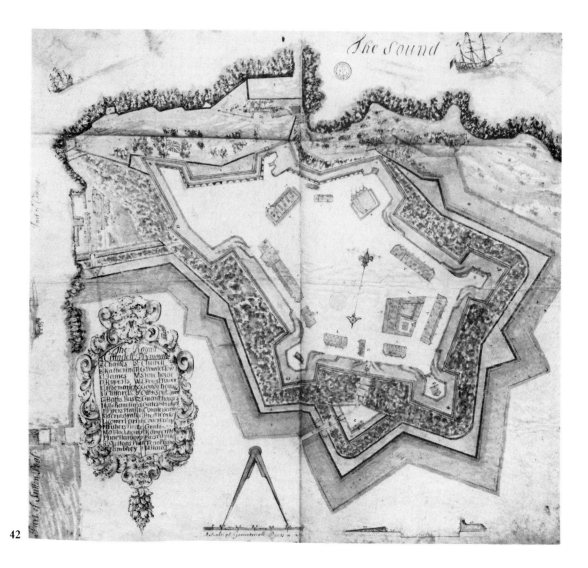

42

buildings within the Citadel. A later plan (**28**) suggests the intended occupants of the buildings. By 1668, when the next map (**29**) was made, the position of the chapel had changed and there are suggestions for alterations in the Citadel wall above the Lower Fort and near Rupert's bastion. This map also gives the height of the stone wall around the Citadel at the various bastions. By 1672, de Gomme's last extant plan (**38**) shows that several buildings have different sites from the preceding plans: the deputy governor's house, suttler's house, storekeeper's house and the great storehouse. A French plan of the Citadel (**40**), undated but made probably a year or two later, notes the canteen within the Citadel for the first time, as well as distances to Mount Batten tower and St Nicholas Island respectively.

The plans suggest that a number of changes were made in the course of the Citadel's construction. A detailed plan of 1677 (**41**) shows the following bastions have now changed their names: Albemarle to Bath, Bath to Clifford and Rupert to Albemarle.[126]

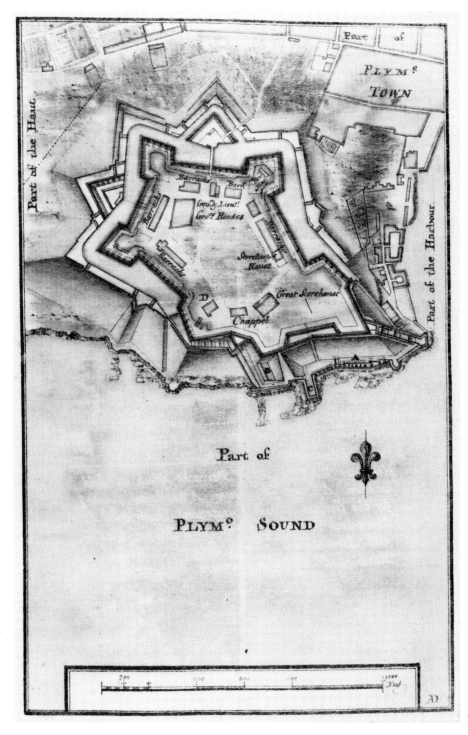

Part of the Haut.

Part of PLYM? TOWN

Part of the Harbour.

Barracks

Barracks

Govr Lieut.^t Gov.^t Houses

Barracks

Barracks

Storekeeper Hous:

Great Storehouse

D

Chappel

Part of

PLYM? SOUND

101

In addition, the chapel has been built on a different site to that originally planned. The alterations suggested in the 1668 plan (**29**) have now materialized as a terrace-walk, and a water-gate and water-tower are shown for the first time. By 1715, the former water-tower is apparently known as New Harbour Tower (**83**), and by 1725 has been renamed again as Wilhen's Tower (**91**). This latter map identifies the houses of the fort major and chaplain within the Citadel. Little new material is shown on a plan of 1776 (**156**), which does, however, include a profile of the fortifications taken from north to south of the Citadel.

Although the plans of the Citadel in this catalogue were mostly produced in the seventeenth century, documentary evidence shows that it remained important throughout the eighteenth century because of its role in defending the Sound. It was built soon after the Restoration, and contemporaries believed that it was intended partly to subdue the (Parliamentarian) town of Plymouth. Christian Lilly repeated this view half a century later, writing that it was to act 'for a checke to the Rebellious Spirits of the Neighbourhood'. By this date (*c.* 1717), it had been allowed to fall into disrepair and Lilly was asked to estimate how much it would cost to put things right (**80**).

Opinions, English and French, vary as to its defensive capacity. An undated but probably early eighteenth-century French cartographer pointed out that it stood so high above the sea that its guns became useless to prevent entry up the Hamoaze once a ship came close (**203**). On the other hand, its height above sea-level meant that it could not be taken from the sea, and would have to be besieged. The Seigneur de Béville, writing in 1768, thought this a viable proposition since taking the Citadel would mean mastery of the port: '*La Citadelle prise, on écraserait facilement le fort qui est dans l'Isle St Nicolas, et on seroit pours lors maître de l'entrée du port*' (**135**). Lilly, too, had considered that the Citadel represented the key to control of the Sound, in view of its position commanding not only the sea but the Cattewater estuary, the town and the chief passage into the Hamoaze. Lieutenant-Colonel Dixon, however, writing *c.* 1780, considered that the Citadel's defences were not sufficient to defend the north and west channels without the aid of other batteries on high ground.[127]

Ownership of the land upon which the Citadel was built is shown on a plan of 1671 (in de Gomme's hand though unsigned) (**30**). A very late eighteenth-century plan (**197**) distinguishes boundaries and occupation on the Hoe, noting that the lieutenant-governor and commanding engineer occupied the area within the fences surrounding the Citadel, while the governor occupied the fields, gardens and East Hoe. Both of these plans presage the dispute between the government and Plymouth Corporation over the former's acquisition of the land on which the Citadel was built (see above, pp. 24–5).

The Dockyard

Plymouth was not automatically chosen as the location for the Dockyard. In September 1689, the choice facing Edmund Dummer was between Dartmouth and Plymouth. By this date the dockyards at Woolwich and Deptford had been in existence for nearly two centuries, those at Portsmouth and Chatham for over one. A survey of English dockyards in 1698 makes clear the purpose for which the Plymouth yard was designed: 'as the most Convenient Refuge to the Westward for Repairing and Refiting the Ships of the Navy Royall in the time of that Late Bloody and Long Warr with France which Comenced the same year'.[128]

Various sources exist for the cartographic history of Plymouth Dockyard. Edmund Dummer drew up eight early draughts of the yard in an account which he presented to the Navy Commissioners in December 1694.[129] A printed version of this with a few minor variations and a key has survived[130] and there are further manuscript copies of the printed version in existence.[131] The first draught in this account showing the plot of ground at Point Froward illustrates the original track of the seashore before work on building the dock began, a cove out of which the basin was built. Dotted lines show the subsequent works, including the limits of the level ground. The survey of 1698 explains that the yard was:

> Erected upon a very Irregular part of Riseing Rockey ground as may more plainly appear by Viewing the first Draught . . . which shews . . . also the severall Sections which Discover the Lofty and Irregular riseing of the land from whence may be Conceived what a Prodigious Labour and Charge it was to Levell those Rocks down to a Plain Superfices a little above high water Mark.

To get a deep-water approach meant disposing of the rubbish from levelling the

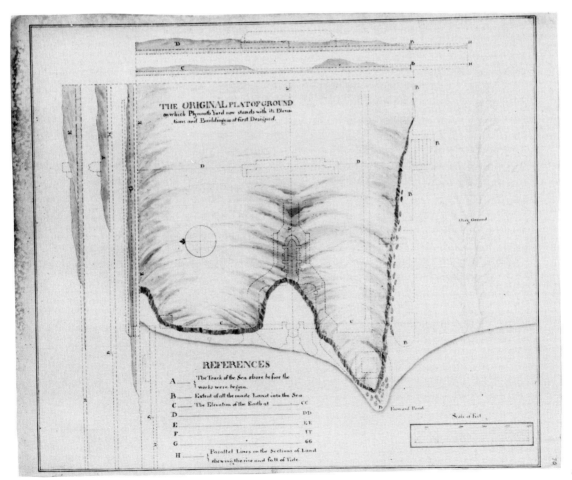

46

docks: about 4 acres of land was gained in this way. Later, the contractor Robert Waters complained that he was much out of pocket, if not ruined, by the arrears of money due to him.[132]

The second draught in Dummer's account shows the embryo Dockyard including the hemphouse, white-yarn house, ropehouse, slips, timber wharf, sawpits, pitch kettles, shipwrights' sheds, anchor forge, crane, officers' dwelling houses and clerks' offices. By 1698, it was possible to write that: ' . . . this is not only the most Regular but also the most Convenient of all the other Yards in England . . . by being soe Disposed that each Officer may Dispatch his Buseness without Incomoding any other Person whatsoever in his Duty'.

1698 was a good date to review the improvements to the country's dockyards since the revolution of 1689. The Peace of Ryswick had been concluded in September 1697, and this detailed account covering Chatham, Sheerness, Woolwich, Deptford and Portsmouth besides Plymouth is an invaluable source of information on the state of each yard in 1689 and 1698 respectively (**47, 49, 71–2**).

Despite its excellent layout, this account makes clear that the new Dockyard was not without its disadvantages. Among these were the crooked passage to the Hamoaze, the false current, the rapid tides, the foul soundings, the dangerous rocks and the fact that both entrance and exit were 'too much Comanded by the Western Winds'. Neverthe-less, in a sense these very difficulties were advantageous, or so argued the persuasive Dummer in 1694:

. . . Naturall Impediments have in this place their proper Virtues And this Super eminent Treasure of the Nation, the Navy and its Stores must never bee easy to come at and Wee must . . . beare with some Difficulties that . . . Wee may never lye at the mercy of an insulting Enemy.[133]

Furthermore, it was considered that all these disadvantages could be overcome by good pilotage, laying buoys and erecting beacons. St Nicholas Island, if stocked with men and provisions, could fend off a force against it, and Winstanley's lighthouse[134] would be helpful as a guide into Plymouth Sound.[135]

Another significant factor in the development of the Dockyard was the fact that the land on which it was built formed part of the manor of Stoke Damerel. The Ninth Draught in Dummer's series 'The Barton of Mount Wise' shows the newly-built Dockyard and its perimeter wall (**65**). Around it, somewhat incongruously, are fields whose names and acreages are given in a key. This land passed from Sir Edward Wise into the hands of the Morice family after the Restoration. The latter was extremely reluctant to sell the land to the government, which was forced to rent it from them. This may well explain an unusual feature on map **79**: the roads, footpaths and bridlepaths leading to the Dockyard together with their measurements. Attention has been drawn to roads in existence before the building of the yard. The yard itself shows various additions since the 1698 plan, in particular a chapel.

There follows a long gap chronologically until the next plan of the yard in 1748 (the year in which the War of the Austrian Succession ended). A number of buildings have been added: the armourer's and plumber's shops, houses for topping of hemp, powder houses, pumphouses, houses of ease, pounds for slabb quarters, the sailmakers' tarring house, stoving kilns (**100**).

The first printed plan of the yard which is dated in this catalogue was published in

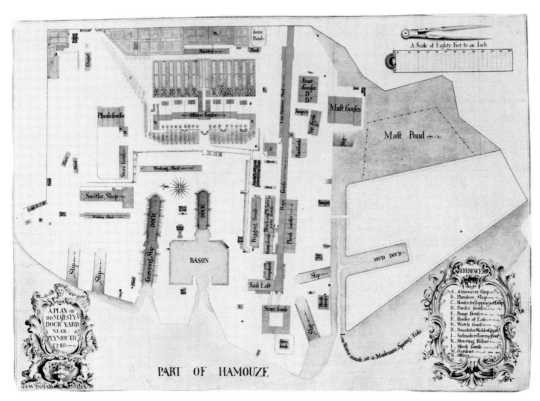

100

1756, the year in which the Seven Years War broke out (**112**). There have been only slight changes since 1748: a new mast house adjacent to the timber ground and sawpits nearby, an officer's garden beyond the pond. However, the Ordnance Wharf is included for the first time with its magazines, storehouses, workshops, officers' houses and gardens. An interesting feature of this plan is its richly decorated border with cartouches of ships: one is noted as 'Burnt to the Water's Edge', another 'Blown up'.

Early reservations as to the development of the Plymouth yard were never entirely overcome. A plan of 1761 (**127**) with proposed additions and alterations should be considered alongside another which gives a detailed estimate for all these. This was the Navy Commissioners' plan of *c.* 1764 (**128**). But a later plan of January 1774 (**151**) shows that only some of these improvements (mainly on the eastern side of the yard) were ever carried out: two out of the proposed four hemphouses, the laying house and spinning house, white-yarn house, tarring house, black-yarn house, locks for stowing rough masts, mast houses, sawpits, smith's shop and slips. The plan also shows how the layout of the old yard must have hindered change: the old yard wall and old pier 'ordered to be taken down'. These have disappeared by the later plan of May 1774 (**152**). This plan includes the yard's measurements.

Why were only some of the proposals of the 1764 plan implemented? A further survey of the dockyards in 1774 (the American War of Independence started in 1775) intended to supplement the earlier survey of 1698 is most informative.[136] The original estimate for the 1764 plan amounted to £379,170 (although the total for map **128** was only £360,775 16s. 1d.), but by the end of 1773 only a third of this sum (£153,585) had

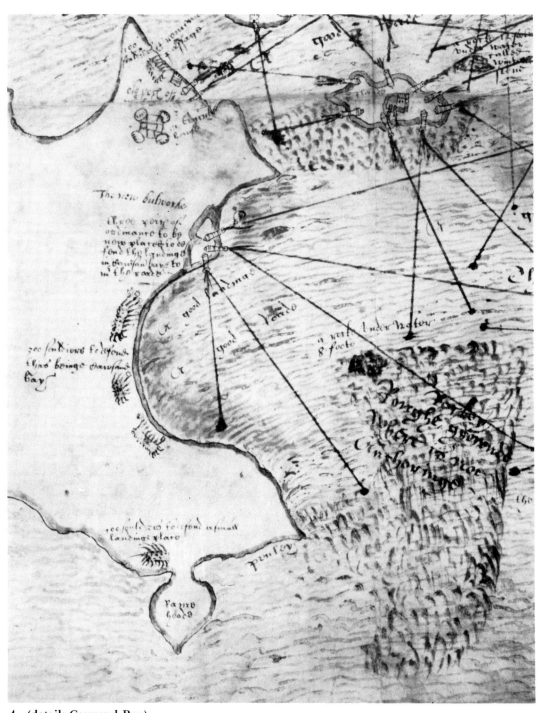

4 (detail: Cawsand Bay)

been spent. Although the plan was perceived as 'a Noble one', yet the Dockyard had some irremediable defects and as a result it was considered the Hamoaze 'can never be a proper place of Rendez-vous for great Fleets, therefore the execution of the whole Plan would be improper'.

What were these defects? It is interesting to compare them with the reservations of the 1698 survey. The crooked and narrow passage and rapid tide are again mentioned: it was feared that these might prove fatal if the ships at Plymouth were unable to join those at Portsmouth heading for a general rendezvous at Spithead. Moreover, the lack of a roadstead before the harbour was also considered serious and the Sound regarded as an unsafe place for ships to lie at anchor except in summer.

Nevertheless, the Plymouth yard was accepted as having some advantages to offset these defects. Its convenient layout, a better supply of timber than any other yard, and its westerly situation giving a ready outlet clear of the Channel meant that it was regarded as the best port in the country for cruising squadrons. Staffing of the yard on 14 January 1774 was 22 officers, 23 clerks, 790 shipwrights and 1,157 other workmen. The 1774 survey is complemented by an interesting model of the yard made in January of that year; this is now held at the National Maritime Museum.[137]

Other maps add to our knowledge of the relative advantages and disadvantages of the Plymouth yard. The haphazard nature in which Dock town had grown up around the embryo yard meant that it would have been difficult to expand north, south or west without pulling down buildings. On the other hand, de Béville was able to count thirty-five ships in the Hamoaze, the least of which were equipped to carry fifty guns (**135**). A squadron of six men-of-war was ready to put to sea at a moment's notice; the other ships were drawn up unmasted behind them; their armoury was kept in the Docks, but it was said that they could be armed and equipped in a very short space of time. The great advantage of the Hamoaze as a port was that, unlike Portsmouth, the ships did not ground every tide (in Portsmouth they were obliged to be moored head and stern). Furthermore, the extent of the Tamar and the depth of water meant they could be moored for nearly 4 miles in length, and swing round with the tide.

In considering Dockyard plans, we may be surprised at the amount of detail shown (for example, maps **114–15** and **133**). Likewise, the ease with which Paradès was able to infiltrate the Citadel suggests that attitudes towards national security were lax at times. On the other hand, the confiscation of Richard Cowl's map in 1783 shows that this type of map information was regarded as sensitive by that date.

Cawsand

Several of the maps refer to Cawsand's assets as a harbour. It is described as 'a good roode [harbour] and good landing' on the earliest map in this catalogue. Late seventeenth-century sailing instructions called it 'a fair sandy Bay . . . where you may anchor close under the Land in 9 or 10 fathoms'.[138]

In attempting to defend the Sound against invaders, it was regarded as a liability. Map **2** estimated that it would need 300 soldiers to defend it, and it is shown barricaded on map **5**. The survey of 1623, referred to earlier, remarked that it was often used by pirates to the annoyance of the inhabitants.

Yet despite all this, there is only one chart (**212**), and that little more than a sketch, devoted solely to Cawsand. One reason for this is probably that, since it was cut off from Plymouth, arrangements would need to be made to transport the invaders across the mouth of the Hamoaze in order to attack the main coastline. Moreover, the steep banks overlooking the good anchorage would be an additional problem for an invading army.

Maps such as **186** show that there were two batteries commanding these steep banks (besides the regiments encamped on Maker Heights during the War of American Independence). Lieutenant-Colonel Dixon's report of 1780 makes it clear that there was a very real fear that the enemy might land at Cawsand or Whitsand, transport their guns and erect batteries to destroy the Dockyard.[139]

Conclusion

Problems of Survival

The probability that many of the maps of Plymouth made during the period covered by the catalogue that follows have not survived is borne out by references among the Plymouth municipal records to maps which are no longer in the collection. What has happened, for instance, to the divers 'platts of the Towne and porte' recorded in the Old Audit Book for 1538/9? Could these have been the sources from which the chart of 1539 was compiled? Where is the 'platt' made by John Sprye in 1546/7 for 13s. 4d., or his haven 'platts'? What has happened to the 'plott of the Towne and parrishe with a Bourder' recorded in 1584/5, the 'plott of the Towne' in 1588/9, the 'plott of the Kayes' of 1591/2 and the 'plott of the forte and of the havre' of 1595/6? It would be nice if the basin and ewer of silver-gilt engraved with a map of the town of Plymouth by another Spry, 'Robert Spry the Paynter', had survived among the possessions of John Glanvyll, recorder of the borough, to whom it was given by the grateful townsfolk in 1621/2.[140] Finally, Jerome Roche the younger's map of the town made in 1678/9 does not appear to survive,[141] though this may well be the original of Edmund Dummer's 'The Plain or Plott of Plymouth Sound, Ham Oaze and Cattwater' (**43**).

Plymouth is particularly unfortunate in the accidents which have befallen its municipal records, worse than for most English towns. Thus in 1548/9 during the Western Rebellion, the rebels took over the castle, in one of the four towers of which the town records were kept: 'then was our stepell burnt with all the townes evydence in the same by Rebelles'.[142] In 1601/2, Nicholas Goodridge of Totnes burnt a chest in the council chamber 'wherein were Contayned divers evidences and writings Concerninge the Towne'; the town authorities did, however, fine him £100.[143] Later, when the Old Guildhall was pulled down in 1800, we have a vivid picture of what happened from the pen of John Harris:

> The Records were sent to the Mayoralty House, and before they cleared the Hall, there was a general examination, or perhaps more properly speaking a general rummage, of all old parchments and deeds. But who selected there those appointed for destruction I know not. But so great was the number of those given away: for one Tailor, who only had a part, had enough to last him for 8 or 10 years. . . . The Tailors came in one day and found him on the eve of destroying the original Magna Charta, with all its seals and appendages.[144]

The survival rate of maps of Plymouth now housed in national institutions is almost certainly higher than those held locally. But even here the fact that most of these institutions were not founded until the middle or end of the period covered by this catalogue should be borne in mind. Of those national institutions which house maps included here, the Bodleian Library was founded in 1602, the British Museum was established in 1753, the Public Record Office Act was passed in 1838, and the National Maritime Museum opened in 1937.[145] Small wonder, perhaps, if a proportion of the maps has gone missing.[146] A consequence of these missing maps may be that there is a distortion factor, in that those maps and charts which have survived are mainly those which were useful for self-defence, be it military or naval.

The relatively late foundation of our national institutions may be contrasted with the situation abroad, particularly the Iberian peninsula. The Casa da India, for example, was established in Lisbon around 1500. One of its functions was to keep corrected charts for the lucrative trade with Africa and India; another was the examination of coastal pilots.[147] The Casa de Contratacion was set up in Seville in 1504 with a similar purpose. In France the Dépôt des Cartes et Plans des Marines was not established until 1720. In addition to training pilots and surveyors, it was also responsible for looking after charts; hence the French pre-eminence in hydrography in the eighteenth century.[148]

By contrast, in this country official British chart production did not start until 1800 (the Hydrographic Department of the Admiralty was founded in 1795). Colonel Christian Lilly, sent to survey the coastline of the United Kingdom in 1714–17, commented to the king upon presenting his surveys that he had had to make new plans of nearly all the places because none were to be found in London.[149]

The lack of a hydrographic department until this relatively late date meant that knowledge gained was not built upon or corrected. We may be surprised by the longevity of some of the printed charts. Greenvile Collins's *Great Britain's Coasting Pilot,* published in 1693, included charts which continued to be reissued throughout the eighteenth century until 1792, far more often than any comparable chart. Yet it had been condemned by Pepys as that 'Ill Performance of the Book of Carts' and also by Trinity House.

The reason for this longevity was commercial. The publisher, Mount and Page, had a virtual monopoly of chart production in eighteenth-century England; the cost of surveying afresh would have been too high for a private company, and the government was not prepared to pay for this work.

Maps as a Social Tool

Maps are an image on paper or parchment of the mental maps which people carry in their heads. Therefore maps are tools, self-conscious or not, of the society which uses them. Furthermore, since maps develop largely because they are useful, both the information recorded on them and the way in which this is done is circumscribed by contemporary perceptions.

Maps are tools of communication, and to communicate effectively any society works from the familiar to the unfamiliar. A map using a totally fresh set of landmarks might fail in its purpose to communicate information. Yet, on the other hand, 'safe' copies of maps, recording information which has become stereotyped, are no more communicative. Sometimes foreign maps of an English town reveal features which native maps do not, reflecting an assumption by the latter that the knowledge is common and therefore not worth recording. Even if this type of information is not strictly correct, it can be useful to us two centuries later in revealing the nature of the landscapes that have been lost.

Maps are subject to other limitations of the society which produces them. As we have seen above (p. 48), scales are rare on the earliest maps because in the sixteenth century many people did not think in spatial terms.

Authority of Maps as Historical Documents

How authoritative are maps as historical documents? Can they be regarded as primary sources? One difficulty here is that many maps were drawn up for a particular purpose, and the evidence which they present is partial. As we have seen in the course of this introduction, many map-makers did not regard it as incumbent upon them to reproduce features which they would have considered irrelevant to the purpose of the map, if indeed they paused to consider these features at all. Hence it is extremely dangerous to argue either that because a feature is shown on a map it necessarily existed on the ground, or conversely that because a feature is not shown on a map, it did not exist on the ground. Maps are useful supplementary sources.

Maps as Sources for the History of Plymouth

The superb natural harbour of Plymouth Sound allied to its geographical position determined that the town should have a national, rather than a purely local, role at times, particularly when England was at war with France and Spain. One point which emerges clearly from a study of the maps in this catalogue is that in many respects the task of defending the realm from invasion was easier in the eighteenth than the sixteenth century, because the theatre of war became more clearly defined. This enabled the defenders to concentrate upon certain focal points, as is obvious from many of the late eighteenth-century maps.

If the Dockyard had been built elsewhere there is little doubt that the whole countryside around Plymouth Sound would have developed differently. There would have been no Dock town, hence it is unlikely that Stonehouse would have developed as it did in the late eighteenth century, and there would have been fewer fortifications. The town of Plymouth would have had an important role as a merchant port, but it is unlikely that that role would ever have been played out on a national stage.

Notes

1 See particularly 'The Barton of Mount Wise' (**65**), showing the newly-built Dockyard *c.* 1694 with fields around it. A barton was, strictly speaking, the demesne lands of a manor; now, the word is often used to mean a farm.

2 'In Consequence of the Concourse of People [at Dock] on such Occasions as the Fleet makes necessary, a Large Town is since that erected here, very much already to the Prejudice of the Town of Plymouth, and which may in Time rival it for Trade' (**93**, *Atlas Maritimus et Commercialis*).

3 John Leland *The Itinerary, in or about the Years 1535–43*, parts I–II, ed. L. Toulmin Smith, 1907, p. 212.

4 Helen M. Wallis and Arthur H. Robinson (eds.) *Cartographical Innovations*, Map Collector Publications in association with the International Cartographic Association, 1987, pp. 2, 51.

5 Ibid.

6 N. Pevsner *The Buildings of England: South Devon*, Penguin, 1952, p. 228.

7 D. Marshal 'Military Maps of the 18th Century and the Tower of London Drawing Room', *Imago Mundi* 32 (1980), pp. 21–44.

8 Maps **117–24** are based on map **116**.

9 Col Sir Charles Close *The Early Years of the Ordnance Survey*, ed. J.B. Harley, New York, 1969, p. 12.

10 M. Mollat du Jourdin *Sea Charts of the Early Explorers, 13th–17th Centuries*, Thames and Hudson, 1984, chart 6.

11 'Remembraunces of Thomas Cromwell', *Letters and Papers . . . of . . . Henry VIII* XIV (1) 400 BL Cotton Titus B 1 H 473–4. I owe this reference to Peter Barber.

12 BL King's 45. The gunners' ages, qualifications and length of service are given.

13 France's Secretary of Foreign Affairs, 1758–70.

14 PRO PRO 30/8/86 No. 3: '. . . *comme une Malheureuse expérience a appris que la politique de la Nation dont les Efforts sont les plus à craindre pour la France n'est pas dictée par des principes aussy Equitables, et aussy modérés [as those of France], il est de la prudence de ne pas attendre qu'elle ait donne de nouvelles preuves de son ambition démesurée pour Examiner s'il n'y a pas de moyen d'y mettre des Bornes et de l'en faire repentir . . .*'.

15 Very little is known concerning de Béville.

16 Very little is known concerning Paradès.

17 *Secret Memoirs of Robert, Count de Paradès, written by himself on coming out of the Bastille*, London, 1791.

18 Antoine Raimond Jean Gualbert Gabriel de Sartine (1729–1801); Secretary of State for Marine from 1774 until his disgrace in 1780.

19 Map **A3** includes an inset of the town, ports, harbour and Citadel of Plymouth, although they are not shown in great detail.

20 Louis Guillonet, Comte D'Orvilliers (*c.* 1708–92). French admiral, sent to attack England with the Spanish squadron in 1779.

21 John Harris *An Essay Toward the History of Plymouth . . . written for the use and amusement of my Children*, West Devon Record Office, 1806. The original and a typescript copy of this book are kept at West Devon Record Office; A. Temple Patterson *The Other Armada: the Franco-Spanish attempt to invade Britain in 1779*, Manchester University Press, 1960.

22 *The Annual Register*, p. 15.

23 Headed '1779 a 1783. *Guerra con Inglaterra*' with a note '*Sur différents points d'attaque et invasion en Angleterre. Fait en Mai de 1779 pour l'intelligence de tout ce qu'on démontrera, on a copié les Cartes ci-jointes, qui sont estimées Angloises qui ordinairement sont exactes.*'

24 AHN Leg 3000 num. 44 Sa 195. These have not been included in this catalogue because they show only part of the dock, and are in no sense maps.

25 Coolie Verner 'Captain Collins' Coasting Pilot: a Carto-Bibliographical Analysis', *Map Collector's Circle* 58 (1969), p. 42.

26 Tony Campbell has pointed out that the French interest in prisons was presumably in the hope of

freeing any French prisoners in the event of invasion. In 1779, some 1,300 French prisoners were moved from Plymouth to Exeter as noted in John Harris's account quoted above.

27 W. Ravenhill, 'Richard Cowl's Proposals for making a new County Map of Devon in 1787', *Devon and Cornwall Notes and Queries*, XXXV.ix (Spring 1986), pp. 338–44.

28 Quoted in A.H.W. Robinson *Marine Cartography in Great Britain*, OUP, 1962, Foreword.

29 There are some exceptions to this. Peter Barber has pointed out that John Rogers was as early as the sixteenth century distinguishing between high and low tide on his charts.

30 It is shown on maps **23, 86, 94, 117**.

31 'A Description of the Coast from Portland to the Lizard' in *The Coasting Pilot*, printed for J. Mount and T. Page, Tower Hill, London, 1769 (NMM Map 05).

32 Sir Cloudesly Shovel (1650–1707), was Admiral of the Fleet. He came to Plymouth in 1690 in command of a squadron during the war against France.

33 '*Il y a plusieurs baies de Sable qui en rendent l'entrée difficile, et il n'entre jamais de Batimt* [sic] *dans le port sans être conduites par les Pilotes Côtiers.*'

34 The earliest English chart to show soundings by numbers so far discovered is a manuscript chart of the River Humber *c.* 1569; Sarah Tyacke and John Huddy *Christopher Saxton and Tudor Mapmaking*, British Library, 1980.

35 Robinson *Marine Cartography*, p. 68.

36 See map **159**, for example.

37 'A contour depicting the location of the same vertical distances beneath a given surface datum, such as the mean sea-level.' *Cartographical Innovations*, p. 224.

38 *Cartographical Innovations*, p. 225.

39 WDRO W9.

40 Map **184** notes '*route des Vaisseaux pour entrer dans le port du Roi*'.

41 The wreck of a Portuguese ship off German Rock in 1540 is recorded (WDRO W46). A more famous shipwreck was that of *Die Fraumetta Catherina von Flemsburg*, sunk in the Sound in 1786.

42 John Allan's diary, held at Plymouth Athenaeum; a photocopy is available in Plymouth Central Library. *The Journal of James Yonge, Plymouth Surgeon, 1647–1721*, ed. F.N.L. Poynter, 1963; Daniel Defoe, *A Tour through the Whole Island of Great Britain*, vol. 1, 1927 edition, pp. 228–30.

43 BL King's MS 40, 1 August 1682.

44 F. de Dainville *La Cartographie Reflet de l'Histoire*, Editions-Slatkine, Geneva Paris, 1986, pp. 177–99.

45 Map **37** is endorsed: 'This Mappe was shewen to all the Jurors and Witnesses sworne and [examined] to the Commission.' A third map (**24**) by the same cartographer referring to the Lambhay as 'The ground in question' can be dated pre-1665 because it shows the castle. These maps are held among the papers of the Strode family, who owned the land, at West Devon Record Office.

46 WDRO W 359/23.

47 PRO T1 382/67: letter of 31 May 1758.

48 R.N. Worth *History of Plymouth from the Earliest Period to the Present Time*, Plymouth, 1890, p. 398.

49 Duchy of Cornwall DCO Maps and Charts 149.

50 Worth *History of Plymouth*, p. 431.

51 HMC *Calendar of the Manuscripts of the Most Hon. the Marquis of Salisbury . . . preserved at Hatfield House, Hertfordshire*, part XI, Dublin, 1906, p. 492.

52 Harris *An Essay toward the History of Plymouth*, vol. I, p. 88.

53 *The Illustrated Journeys of Celia Fiennes, 1685–c. 1712*, ed. Christopher Morris, Macdonald and Co., 1982, p. 201.

54 This distinction can be traced back at least to John Ogilby, who organized his road atlas of 1765 in two sections to distinguish these (Tony Campbell).

55 The activities of the combined fleet in 1779 have been discussed above (pp. 10–15).

56 Map **5** was engraved in 1740.

57 BL Royal MS 18 D III. The figure of 5,000 was provided for Lord Burghley and was as authoritative as possible.

58 Quoted in Worth *History of Plymouth*, pp. 409–10.

59 PRO SP 12/245 f. 30.

60 WDRO W132 f. 109.

61 The context of this plan lies among letters addressed to Burghley (PRO SP 12/262; the map was removed to a separate class in 1953).

62   BL Harleian 3324.
63   On a minor note, it is interesting to speculate how these plans got into Sir Robert Cotton's collection: were they, too, seized by Cotton in 1611/12 in the confusion following Salisbury's death?
64   NMM LAD/15.
65   BL King's MS 45.
66   'A True Narration . . . of the siege of Plymouth . . .'.
67   J. Barber, 'New Light on Old Plymouth', *Proceedings of the Plymouth Athenaeum* IV (1973–9), pp. 55–66.
68   WDRO W46 f. 112.
69   This view is also confirmed by a reference in the Siege pamphlet to 'the Towne walls, which then were not fully finished, and could not long have been defended'.
70   The Union of the Three Towns occurred in November 1914.
71   Maps **1** and **11** are much more accurate than map **6**, which gives a highly stylized view of the town. It shows St Andrew's Church with a steeple, although we know it had a tower, and the rows of houses look suspiciously tidy.
72   WDRO W132 f. 155v.
73   Worth *History of Plymouth*, p. 228.
74   Martin's Gate, Friary Gate and Gascoigne Gate.
75   The fish market was removed when George III visited the town in 1789; Worth *History of Plymouth*, p. 382.
76   Celia Fiennes, writing in 1698, tells us that 'Plymouth is 2 Parishes called the old town and the new', *Illustrated Journeys*, p. 201.
77   Map **2** refers to 'Stonehowse porte', occasionally it is called 'Limehouse' and on map **94** 'Stonhouse of steene huissen'. On Dutch maps, it is sometimes described as '*Vissersdorp*' (for example, **23**) and on a French map as '*bourg de pescheurs*' (**207**). Another reference to it is 'that Fishers Village (lying to the Northward a little within the land)' (**93**).
78   Referred to on a print of 1766 as 'New Baths'.
79   PRO SP 12/245 f. 30.
80   BL King's MS 43.
81   See, for example, map **43**.
82   '. . . on each syde the ground is falling sloping rise a 14 perches, the rest is very pleane and level ground'.
83   A prime example of this is map **51**.
84   Bracken (*A History of Plymouth*, 1931, p. 240) speaks of salt being made locally from Domesday times: 'So ancient was the business in Plymouth that it was allowed to continue in Queen Anne's reign when it had been made illegal to erect new refineries.' In 1814 Lower Street salt refinery closed, but Mr Ogg's works in Breton Side were so prosperous that he could contribute a payment of £12,000 in revenue. See also Worth *History of Plymouth*, pp. 350–1.
85   *Calendar of the Manuscripts of the Most Hon. the Marquis of Salisbury*, vol. XI, pp. 471–2.
86   Used for making cloth. The tuckers' racks are shown near Frankfurt Gate.
87   WDRO W496–8.
88   See especially maps **181** and **194**.
89   Fiennes *Illustrated Journeys*, p. 201.
90   BL Add MS 32556 f. 10.
91   Harris, *An Essay Towards the History of Plymouth*, vol. I, p. 52.
92   For example, maps **82** and **109**.
93   Map **30** has a note that a Mr Schoon of Cornwall had made an estimate of all the gardens adjoining this land 'taken in for His Majesties service'.
94   Ralph E. Ehrenberg *Archives & Manuscripts: Maps and Architectural Drawings*, Society of American Archivists, Basic Manual Series, Chicago, 1982, p. 33.
95   G. Terry.
96   Yet by the early nineteenth century there does appear to have been a handful of individuals living in Plymouth and Devonport who were described as surveyors. These included John Lambert, auctioneer, of Plymouth Dock, *c.* 1793; John Taperell, estate, road and tithe surveyor, as well as another auctioneer of Mill Street, Plymouth, *c.* 1830; Roger Hopkins, a railway surveyor, of Plymouth, 1832; David Robarts, estate surveyor, living at Torpoint in 1829 and later in Stonehouse; Francis Jenkyns, harbour surveyor who died on 4 November 1841 in Plymouth; Robert Hodge,

who became surveyor and engineer to Plymouth Corporation in the mid-nineteenth century; and John Rowe, a parish, mineral and tithe surveyor born in 1794 at Saltash, who died in 1866 at Plymouth. See *Dictionary of Land Surveyors of Great Britain and Ireland, 1550–1850*, ed. P. Eden, 1979. There is no evidence that a philomathic society existed in Plymouth such as the Exeter Philomathic Society instituted on 4 April 1793. *Devon and Cornwall Notes and Queries*, X.iii (July 1918).

97 Perhaps because of the very late development of local record offices in this country. See below, pp. 65–6.

98 WDRO W130 ff. 242, 249.

99 WDRO W132 f. 197v.

100 Harris, *An Essay Toward the History of Plymouth*, vol. II, p. 118.

101 WDRO W133 f. 63v.

102 Robinson *Marine Cartography*, p. 35. It is not necessary to look very far to detect indications that the English were jealous of Dutch pre-eminence in this field in the seventeenth century. John Seller's unsuccessful attempt to prohibit the import of Dutch wagoners for thirty years and Greenvile Collins's description of Dutch charts as 'very erroneous' suggest that Dutch activities were resented. Collins's comment is particularly interesting since his printed chart of Plymouth would appear to be a copy of Van Keulen's: both have insets for Salcombe, though the Dutch chart has many more bearings and soundings than Collins's . This may explain the large amount of blank space on Collins where Van Keulen has other material. For a comprehensive list of Dutch atlases and their coverage of Plymouth, see C. Koeman *Atlantes Neerlandici*, vol. V, p. 232. For practical reasons, it has not been possible to follow up all these references.

103 *Calendar of the Manuscripts of the Most Hon. the Marquis of Salisbury*, vol. VI, 1895, p. 517.

104 Robinson, *Marine Cartography*, p. 85.

105 E.G.R. Taylor *The Mathematical Practitioners of Tudor and Stuart England*, Cambridge, 1954, p. 259.

106 See **WM9**.

107 PRO WO 30/54 no 12. Quoted in Robinson *Marine Cartography*, p. 94.

108 **135**: '*Nr que l'on n'a pu placer sur cette carte qu'une echelle estimee, le plan n'etant figure que de Memoire*'.

109 Robinson *Marine Cartography*, p. 115. However, the correspondence of John Adams suggests that dedications may sometimes have had an ulterior motive: either direct financial support or increased sales, the dedication setting an example. See *Geographical Journal* 151.1 (March 1985), pp. 21–39. I owe this reference to Peter Barber.

110 **WM3** is reproduced from this volume.

111 Tony Campbell 'Understanding Engraved Maps', *The Map Collector* 46 (Spring 1989).

112 Quoted in Robinson *Marine Cartography*, p. 46.

113 See **WM13**

114 For instance, some sixteenth-century charts emphasize harbours disproportionately, because of the threat of invasion.

115 See above pp. 32–3. Here it is suggested that parts of the town were walled.

116 Perhaps because it was a port, Nonconformity appears to have flourished by the late eighteenth century. John Harris noted 'As toleration prevails, Plymouth may be distinguished by the variety of its places of worship . . . [which] . . . exceed by three times the churches of the Establishment'; Harris *An Essay Toward the History of Plymouth*, vol. I, p. 104.

117 Map **207** refers to a '*peuplade de Religionnaires francois*', a reference no doubt to the many Huguenots who left France after the revocation of the Edict of Nantes in 1685.

118 Harris refers to the Reverend James Deviot who left France in 1685 for religious reasons and was minister of the French Reformed Church in Plymouth for thirty-two years. There is also a note of French children baptized at St Andrew's Church from 1689 to 1728 in the parish register (WDRO 358/6/4).

119 R.N. Worth *Calendar of the Plymouth Municipal Records*, Plymouth, 1893, pp. 18, 22, 143 respectively.

120 Fiennes *Illustrated Journeys*, p. 201.

121 Pp. 7–8.

122 '*Pour la Surete du Havre en tems de Guerre l'on tend une Grosse Chaine*' (**208**).

123 *Calendar of the Manuscripts of the Most Hon. the Marquis of Salisbury*, vol. VIII, 1899, p. 230.

124 NMM LAD/15.

125 BL King's MS 45.

126 Map **42** is almost identical and it is interesting to speculate how it got into French hands, probably

during the eighteenth century since the plan itself is in English but has a label pasted on the back giving the key in an eighteenth-century French hand.

127   Map **170** and accompanying report.
128   BL King's MS 43.
129   Lansdowne 847.
130   BL Add MS 9329.
131   Bodleian Gough Maps 5 f. 16b; **61**.
132   BL Add MS 33061.
133   Lansdowne 847.
134   Henry Winstanley built a lighthouse on the Eddystone Rock, 14 miles south of Plymouth, in 1696; it was swept away, and Winstanley with it, in the storm of 1703.
135   BL King's MS 43.
136   BL King's MS 44.
137   It is reproduced here as **WM 8**.
138   '. . . a Description of the Coast of England from Portland to the Lizard', *The English Pilot: Part I Southern Navigation* NMM 423 SEL 03.
139   The report accompanies map **170**.
140   WDRO W 130 ff. 200, 242, 249; W 132 ff. 61d, 81, 92, 109.
141   WDRO W 133 f. 95.
142   WDRO W 46 f. 5v.
143   WDRO W 132 f. 136v.
144   Harris *An Essay Toward the History of Plymouth*, vol. I, pp. 19–20.
145   Although, as Peter Barber has pointed out, many of these institutions had their precursors. The Cotton Library within the British Museum (since 1973, British Library) had been a distinct library *cum* archive since the early seventeenth century. Likewise the Old Royal Library, incorporated into the British Museum in 1757, dates back to the reign of Edward IV. Similarly, in the case of the Public Record Office, a State Paper Room had been created as early as 1609. Maps were also stored in the Tower of London by the Board of Ordnance from 1683, though this became much more effective after the establishment of the Drawing Room in 1717.
146   Peter Barber has also drawn attention to the importance of the quality of guardianship in these libraries. Even if a library or archive existed, items could and did disappear if custodians were slack. For example, Robert Beale, clerk of the Privy Council and Walsingham's secretary in the late sixteenth century, complained that ministers often confused public records with their own material, removing the former to keep with the latter, to the detriment of future generations. See Conyers Read *Mr Secretary Walsingham and the policy of Queen Elizabeth*, vol. I, Oxford, 1925, p. 431.
147   D. Howse and M. Sanderson *The Sea Chart*, David and Charles, 1973, pp. 12, 93.
148   A.H.W. Robinson 'The Evolution of the English Nautical Chart', *International Hydrographic Review* XXX.1 (May 1953), pp. 123–30.
149   Robinson, *Marine Cartography*, p. 90. This again reflects slack custodianship. James II's charts disappeared by gift into the hands of the Earls of Dartmouth until much later (1948) when they were presented to the National Maritime Museum. I owe this example to Peter Barber.

Maps, Charts and Plans of Plymouth to 1800:
A CATALOGUE

Key

Catalogue entries follow a standardized format as follows:

Title

As written/printed/endorsed on the map. In some cases, the map is specified as an inset; in these cases, scales and sizes refer to the insets only unless otherwise stated.

Scale

As expressed by the map-maker and as a representative fraction, although the size of the map may have altered slightly in the course of time, affecting these calculations. When no scale has been expressed on the map, an approximate scale has been calculated wherever possible, but no representative fraction has been given in these cases. Representative fractions have also been omitted in some cases when the precise measurements for units which we would now regard as standard, for instance, a mile or a perch, have not been clarified. (See also above, p. 48.)

Creator/Statement of Responsibility

In some cases, persons cited here were engineers or draughtsmen of the Drawing Office of the Royal Engineers. (See Appendix III for notes on map-makers.)

Date

In the catalogue, *c.* denotes some evidence or good reason for assuming the date given, whereas ? is merely a suggested date. If a later copy of a map has been made, the map has been catalogued under the date of the original; where both dates are known, the date of copying has been given in square brackets. Likewise, printed maps have been catalogued under 'situation date' rather than date of publication. Unless there have been changes, only first editions are cited. In cases where there are both later printed editions and manuscript copies of a map, a strictly chronological approach has been adopted.

Orientation

This is only stated when the map is not oriented to north.

Extent

Square brackets denote that a place-name is not specified on the map. In the case of a few charts, the chart is so vague that it has not been possible to be specific; in these cases extent is expressed as 'Plymouth Sound'.

Materials

Unless otherwise stated, all maps are manuscript.

Size

Given in inches and millimetres; measurements are height by width. Where a map has been damaged, warped or repaired, size may not be regular from one border to another.

Repository and reference

Where a repository holds more than one copy of a printed map, only one reference is given. In the case of printed maps, the list of repositories holding copies of these maps (particularly very common maps) is obviously not exhaustive but is intended as a helpful guide.

Abbreviations used for repositories frequently cited

AHN	Archivo Histórico Nacional, Madrid
BL	British Library
BN	Bibliothèque Nationale. SH denotes Service Hydrographique in the Département des Cartes et Plans.
NMM	National Maritime Museum
PRO	Public Record Office
WDRO	West Devon Record Office

Repository catalogues cited

Blakiston, H.N. *Catalogue of Maps and Plans in the Public Record Office*, vol. I, HMSO, 1967

Skelton, R.A. and Summerson, J. *A Description of Maps and Architectural Drawings in the Collection made by William Cecil, first Baron Burghley now at Hatfield House*, printed for members of the Roxburghe Club, OUP, 1971

Tello, Pilar Leon *Mapas, Planos y Dibujos de la Seccion de Estado del Archivo Histórico Nacional*, Madrid, 1969

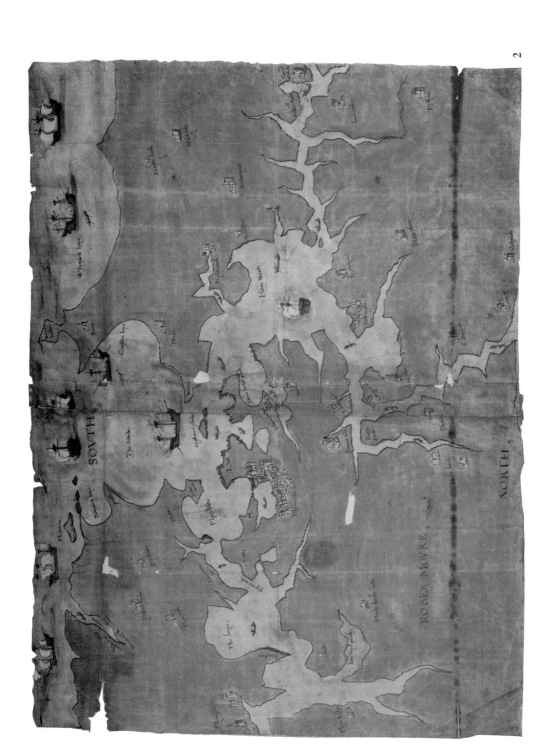

1

No title
No scale given, but approx. 1:18,750
No statement of responsibility
c. 1539
Scilly Isles(W)–Seaton(E)
Ink and watercolour on paper (red, green, blue,
    brown)
31.3″ × 120.7″ (795mm × 3068mm)
BL Cotton MS Augustus I i 35–36, 38–39

Harbour chart covering the south-west of England,
made in defence against invasion. Fortifications
include 'the fortresse of Plymouth' (fortification on
Fisher's Nose with defensive barricade along the
Hoe); 'the fortresse of stonehowse' (three towers).
Some fortifications, however, are marked in a later
hand 'not made'. Hoe Chapel. Friary. Market-
cross. Chain across Cawsey. Mount Edgcumbe is
shown as a deer-park only; in fact, licence to
impark was granted in 1539 and the house built
between 1549 and 1553. Prominence is given to
harbours: 'Cawsand baye a goode roode and good
landyng'; 'from Dudman [Dodman] to Rame
hedde a kenyng' (a kenning represents the range of
sight at sea). The configuration of the coastline is
not altogether accurate since the Avon and Erme
estuaries have been missed. The size of the ships in
harbour and of the boats up the estuaries indicates
navigability. It has been suggested that this map
was collated, possibly in London, from information provided by a variety of people and from
pre-existing plans and views which were miniatu-
rized. This would explain how so much detailed
knowledge was assembled in so short a time, and
may be borne out by an entry among the Plymouth
municipal records [W 130] that in 1538/9 divers
'platts of the Towne and porte' were made. Physically, the upper section of the map consists of long
strips of paper pasted together; the map has been
repaired later. According to a note now attached to
the verso of Cotton MS Augustus I i 55, signed by
William Watkins and dated 28 April 1707 (OS), this
map was then 'one sheet of Paper but making four
Leaves'.

2

'Plat of Plymo[uth]'
No scale given, but approx. 1:25,650
No statement of responsibility
? Pre-1549
Orientation: S
Rame Head(SW)–Calstock(NW)
    –Plymbridge(NE)–Mewstone(SE)
Ink and watercolour on paper (red, green, blue,
    grey, yellow)

22.8″ × 30″ (579mm × 762mm)
The Marquess of Salisbury. Hatfield CPM I 36
    (Skelton and Summerson Catalogue no. 20)

Harbour chart of the Sound. Fortifications along
the Hoe coastline and Stonehouse peninsula. Gallows upon the Hoe. Country parishes represented
by church towers, in many cases presumably also
visible from at sea. Many place-names: 'Hecke
bocke lande' (Eggbuckland), 'Howe stert' (Mount
Batten), 'Trystrams Ylonde' (Drake's Island),
'Stonehowse porte' (Stonehouse), 'Plym Rode'
(Plym estuary).

3

No title
No scale given
No statement of responsibility
Post-1553
Orientation: S
St Germans(SW)–Calstock(NW)–Plympton(NE)
    –Newton Ferrers(SE)
Ink and watercolour on paper (green, grey, pale
    brown, red)
16″ × 21.10″ (410mm × 560mm)
The Marquess of Bath. Longleat House,
    Warminster

Harbour chart of the Sound. Navigability is shown
by the size of ships and boats in the Sound and up
the various creeks and estuaries. The towns of
Plymouth and Tavistock are the only built-up areas
in a landscape of hamlets and minor settlements,
which are named. At Plymouth, 'the key' projects
out into Sutton Pool; this quay is also shown on
map **1**; it may be the precursor of Southside Quay,
built in 1572 in a different place. Tower fortifications along the Hoe coastline. Road from Plymouth to Tavistock shown with men, women,
pack-animals and dogs. Mount Edgcumbe house.
Mills including one at 'Shesewick' [Sheviock].
Grey border. Physically, the map has been torn
around two of its borders and stuck on to a piece of
paper.

4

'Sr Ric Grenvyle for the fortifying of Plymm'
No scale given, but approx. 1:21,688
c. 1586–8
Seaton(SW)–Saltash(N)–Yealm estuary(SE)
Ink and watercolour on parchment (red, pale
    brown, light and dark blue)
19″ × 23″ (variable) (483mm × 585mm)
PRO MPF 6 (SP 46/36/4) (PRO Catalogue no.
    2028)

A defensive map giving details of potential landing places and the men and armaments necessary to repel them. Little groups of armed men have been drawn and guns are shown with firing ranges across the Sound from the Hoe, Stonehouse, Mount Edgcumbe, Drake's Island, Whitsand, How Start (Mount Batten) and Staddon. Writing in red ink (the second hand) indicates work to be done. 'The towne of plymothe': 'Fysher noase' (Fisher's Nose); '300 souldiers to keepe this place called the Hawe' [Hoe]; 'the passage spoken offe [of] in the advise defended bie 200 men' (Cattedown–Oreston passage). 'Stonehowse': '100 souldiers to defende this place' (Western King's); (second hand: '3 new peac[es] to be plasid';) '100 souldiers to defende this place' (Eastern King's). 'Cromewell [Cremyll] passage': '100 souldiers' (second hand: 'old pec[es] of'). Mount Edgcumbe house. Kingsand: (second hand: 'the new bulworke [bulwark]'); 'three peic[es] of ordinance to be new placed to defend the landinge in Cawsan baye to mr [master] the roade'.

Cawsand: '300 souldiers to defend this beinge Cawsand bay'. Rame Head: '100 souldiers to defend a small landinge place'. Seaton: 'a good landinge place defended by 200 men'. Oreston: 'Wosen the landing, of the passage towards Plimpton'. Mount Batten: 'howe stearte' (second hand: 'A new bulworke'); '3 new pec[es] to be placed'. Jennycliff Bay: '400 souldiers to keepe & defende this place beinge nowe easie for the enemye to take and bie nature beinge stronge and dothe com[m]ande the towne of Plymothe and all this p[ar]te of the harber'. 'Stodden downe' [Staddon Heights] (second hand 'A new bulworke'); 'three peic[es] to be placed to impeche the roade & the landinge in Bovesande'; 'an easie place of landinge called bovesand bay'; '300 souldiers to defende the landinge here'. Large houses shown: Antony 'Easte Anthonie Mr Ric Carewe his howse'; Mount Edgcumbe house; 'Radforde Mr [Christo]pher Harrys his howse and he a sufficient gentillman to take charge to defend this quarter w[i]th thinhabitants of

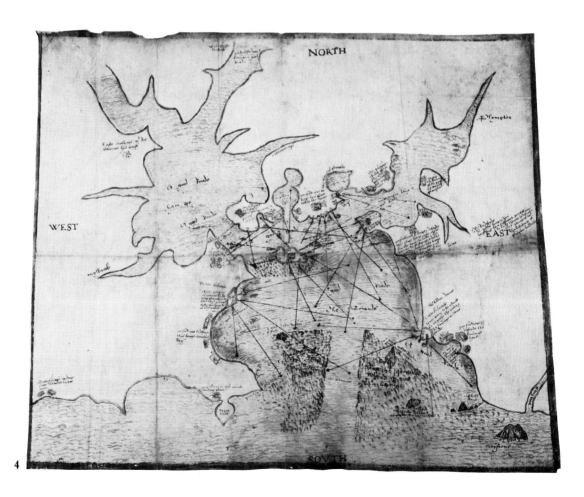

Plimpton hundred'. In the centre of Plymouth Sound is a stretch of water marked 'the Channell'; on either side (i.e. off Penlee and off Bovisand) is noted 'Rockey Roughe grownde where is noe Anchoringe'. Whitsand 'a good Roade', 'a good landinge'. Hamoaze 'a good Roade'. 'Saltash Wat[er] beinge a good Roade'. 'Cattwater being a good Roade'. Rocks: off Penlee 'a rocke under water 8 foote'; 'a rock 12 foote under water called winters stone'; 'a rock called Rowden 9 foote under Water'; 'A Rocke called Chittells Bottome 9 foote under water'; 'Sheete stone'; 'Maystone' (Mewstone).

5

'A Plott of all the Coast of Cornwall and
    Devonshire as they were to bee fortyfied in
    1588 against the landing of any Enemy'
No scale given
No statement of responsibility
? Post-1588
Land's End(SW)–Whitsand Bay(NW)–Coombe
    Martin(NE)–Dartmouth(SE)
Ink and watercolour on paper (red, blue, grey,
    yellow)
23.7″ × 60.4″ (variable) (602mm × 1535mm)
BL Cotton MS Augustus I i 6

Map showing harbours throughout the south-west peninsula of England, which has been compressed. The map has little detail apart from place-names and, at harbours considered potentially vulnerable, barricades along the coastline, guns and men.
    A printed version of this map was published by J. Pine in 1740.

6

'discriptio[n] of a Tow[n]'
No scale given, but approx. 1:9,009
No statement of responsibility
c. 1590/1
Cawsand(SW)–Landulph(NW)–Plympton(NE)
    –Bovisand(SE)
Ink and watercolour on paper (red, green,
    yellow, blue, grey)
20.9″ × 28.9″ (531mm × 734mm)
Hatfield CPM I 41 (Skelton and Summerson
    Catalogue no. 21)

Out-of-scale map of the landscape around Plymouth Sound. The town of Plymouth is shown extending further east round Sutton Pool than it did. Identifiable landmarks such as the castle, St Andrew's Church (shown with a spire, though in fact it had a tower) and the market-cross are given,

but no attempt has been made to show street patterns accurately. The area marked out for the late sixteenth century fort is out of proportion to the rest of the map, and may explain its *raison d'être*. Gun emplacements on the Hoe coastline.

7

No title
No scale given
No statement of responsibility
? 1590/1
Plymouth Sound (extremely rough sketch)
Ink on paper
16.5″ × 12″ (419mm × 305mm)
Hatfield CPM Supp. 10 (Skelton and Summerson
    Catalogue no. 22)

An extremely rough sketch of the Sound, identifiable by the place-names 'Plommowth', 'Stonhouse'.

8

No title
No scale given, but approx. 1:17,100
No statement of responsibility
c. 1591
St John's(SW)–Tavistock(NW)–Sheepstor(NE)
    –Staddon(SE)
Ink and watercolour on paper (red, green, blue,
    brown)
32.2″ × 26.4″ (818mm × 671mm)
Hatfield CPM I 60 (Skelton and Summerson
    Catalogue no. 23)

Map of the landscape north of the Sound, above Plymouth and up the Hamoaze estuary. Plymouth: chapel and beacon marked on the Hoe. South Gate. Old Mills ('Plymouth myll'); mills at Millbridge ('Stonehouse myls'); Lipson Mill. North of the town: 'The Maudlen'. Roads: 'the way from Stonehouse to Plymouth', and other ways from Saltash to Plymouth, Plymouth to Tavistock, Plymouth to Plympton, Plymouth to Plymstock; 'There are many wayes more which are not made in this platt'. Passages: Cremyll, Saltash, Antony, Oreston. Bridges: Denham, 'New bridg' (Gunnislake), 'Stickle path bridg', 'Hore bridge' (Horrabridge), 'Plymme bridge'. Rivers are much more significant than roads on this map. A primary purpose of the map was to show the leat running from Walkhampton into Plymouth; the length of the leat is measured in miles from 1 to 27 beginning from the diversion of the leat at 'the head weare' (near Sheepstor). On the right-hand side of the map is a rectangular box with the legend: 'From the

Fyrst taking in of the river, that is now brought into Plimmouth (as it is caried everie waie to geat the vantage of the hilles) is by measure 27 miles after 1000 paces to a mile and fyve foot a pace.' Rock formations are shown at the start of the leat 'the huge rockes'; a note explains 'Here the river is taken out of the old river and carried 448 paces through mightie rockes which was thought impossible to carrie water through'. Other rock formations at 'leathe torre' near Walkhampton, and at Shaugh both north and south of the confluence of the Plym and the Meavy (Dewerstone Rock). Also 'Uddell torre'. Tinworks shown on Roborough Down. Beacons shown on Roborough Down ('Rouber beaken') and Pennycross, besides the Hoe. Crosses: 'Broken crosse', and 'Great crosse', both situated near the leat. Large houses and their owners: Cotehele ('Cuttell'), Halton Barton ('Halton Rouse'), 'Clifton Arundell', 'Sir F Drake' (for Buckland Abbey), 'Warle Coplestone' (War-leigh), 'Bodugulfasyde Gorge' (Gorges of Butshead), 'Warwick Lay Heale', 'Efford Halse', 'Boraton Parker' (Boringdon), 'Nuna Strood' (Strodes of Newnham), 'Radford Harres' (Harris of Radford), 'Mount Edgcombe Edgcombe' (Edg-cumbes of Mount Edgcumbe), Trematon Castle. Many place-names, including: 'Plymton marsh', 'Dee Mill poole', 'Beggers forte' (Cornwall), 'Beg-gers Ylande' (Beggar's Island); note in another hand: 'lypso hyll' (Lipson).

The whole map is surrounded on all four sides by a thick black border; cardinal points of compass are shown.

See E.M. Tenison *Elizabethan England: Being the History of this Country . . . from original manuscripts . . .* , vol. VIII, Leamington Spa, 1947, plate 33.

9

As **8** except:
Anthony(SW)–Tavistock(NW)–Newnham(NE)
Ink and watercolour on paper (red, green, blue, brown, yellow)
15.7" × 12.2" (399mm × 310mm)
BL Cotton MS Augustus I i 41

The title of the map may have been contained in the rectangular box to the right of the map which has now been cut out. The whole map is surrounded on three sides by a frame enclosed in a solid pink wash, punctuated as appropriate by the cardinal points of the compass.

10

'Sa[in]t Nicholas Ilande by Plimmouthe'
'The Scale of yardes' 200 [= 7.2"] 1:1,000
Robert Adams
1592
St Nicholas Island
Ink and watercolour on parchment (pale pink, pale green, brown, yellow)
Orientation: S
12.4" × 23.5" (315mm × 597mm)
Hatfield CPM II 31 (Skelton and Summerson Catalogue no. 25)

Neat survey of the island, made by Adams on one of his visits to Plymouth at the request of the government. 'ye Freshe Water' (NE of island). Fort in centre of island flying St George's flag. Road following edge of the island and leading up to fort. Guns firing at various points out into the Sound from wall surrounding southern edge of island. Boathouse and small boat at landing place to NW of island.

See Tenison *Elizabethan England*, vol. IX, 1950, p. 26.

11

'Plat of Plymoth' (endorsed)
No scale given, but approx. 1:5,555
No statement of responsibility
? 1592
Cawsand Bay(SW)–Stoke Damerel(NW) –Efford(NE)–Shagstone(SE)
Ink and watercolour on parchment (red, green, blue, black, yellow)
28.5" × 36.5" (variable) (725mm × 928mm)
Hatfield CPM I 35 (Skelton and Summerson Catalogue no. 24)

Town plan of Plymouth illustrating its geographical position at the north of the Sound. The contrast between the built-up area around Sutton Pool and the landscape outside the town is heightened by the existence of a wall surrounding Plymouth. The wall has ten bastions, of which five include guns; it extends from Barbican Gate as far as Coxside Gate. Old Town Gate. 'The circuit or compas of the [w]hole fortification of the towne amountes unto a 500 perches at 18 foot the perche'. Throughout the Middle Ages, the town had suffered from being vulnerable to attack; this map represents part of an attempt to defend it using accurate measurements. The fort: 'The circuit of the forteficatio[ns] of the fort conteans 112 [crossed through, with '75' written across it] perches at 18 foot the perche and note that fro[m] the hethermost and farthermost boulwork of the fort towardes the sea – on each syde the ground is falling slopeing rise a 14 perches, the rest is very pleane and level ground'. This is probably the most accurate depiction of the town at this date, with the exception of the wall whose existence as shown is questionable. Besides identifiable landmarks such as the castle, St Andrew's Church, the market cross, the town gates and the Fish Cage, the streets are accurately set down and their names given: 's. andrew's stret, the heigh street [High Street], the market street, loders lane, the olde towne'. Roads leading out of the town have been clearly identified: 'myll lane' (from Plymouth to Millbay), 'the way from stonehouse to plymmouth' and other ways from Plymouth to Tavistock, Stonehouse to Tavistock, Saltash to Plymouth, Plymouth to Plympton and Plymouth to Oreston. Annotations are in more than one hand. A later hand has made note of the pool behind Millbay 'This was plimmouth milpoole before the River was brought there by Sir Fraunses Drake and ye milles builded by him, and this poole was made drie for a medow.' 'The Hoo cleves' (Hoe cliffs), 'Lipson Woose' (Cattewater estuary), 'Ham Woose' (Hamoaze) are noted. Intertidal area: 'Note alway that where it is full of

prickes, theire it is drie at lowe water, when the springe is at hiest.' Cardinal points of compass.

See Tenison, *Elizabethan England*, vol. IX, plate 3.

12
'The platte of ye forte upon ye hoo of Plimouthe'
'The Scale of Perches, every perche conteyninge
  18 foote'; 10 perches = [3.1″] 1:696
'Rob[erto] Adamo *authore*'
'Anno D 1593 Maii ulti' (31 May 1593)
Plymouth Fort
Pen and ink on paper
8.6″ × 13″ (218mm × 330mm)
PRO SP 12/245 f. 31 (PRO Catalogue no. 2027)

Plan of the fort built overlooking the sea between the Hoe and Fisher's Nose from 1593 to 1596 to defend the town from attack by sea. 'This forte upon ye hoo of Plimouthe conteyneth in compasse 99 perches.' Fort to be built as a triangle: 'this syde standeth to ye beacon' (NW); 'this syde standeth to ye towne' (NE); at W and E points of these sides, 'this syde steepe rocke and therfore unflancked'; 'this syde standeth to ye sea' (S). The NW and NE

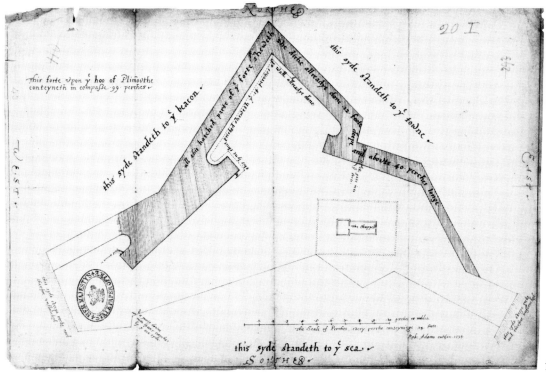

12

sides are hatched: 'all this hatched parte of ye forte sheweth the diche allreadye done 12 foote deepe and about 40 perches longe'. Within the NW hatched section is a pricked line: 'this lyne thus pricked sheweth ye 14 perches of wall allreadye done'. On NW side, 'a secrett posterne'; on NE side, 'the gate into ye forte'; on S side 'a porte downe into lower trenches by ye seasyde'. Within the fort, the chapel is marked. Cardinal points of the compass.

13

As **12** except:
'S.B. *authore*' [? Simon Basil]
8.5″ × 13.5″ (216mm × 343mm)
PRO SP 12/245 f. 32

Plan does not have the secret postern. 'This platt was made for ye woorcke this tyme twelfmoneth, since which tyme both ye wall and the trenche are brought unto ye marcke A from which marcke eastwarde unto B the firste beginninge of ye woorcke with the gate, posterne drawebridge and plattformes will amounte unto 900 li.'

14

'Platt of Plimowth by [Si]r Ferd[inando] Gorges' (endorsed)
No scale given
Sir Ferdinando Gorges
March 1596
Plymouth fort
Ink on paper
16.6″ × 21.8″ (422mm × 554mm)
PRO MPF 262 (SP 12/262) (PRO Catalogue no. 2030)

Outline plan of the fort as built showing ditch, perimeter wall, main gate, guns and sea wall on south side, which also has guns. Gorges was confirmed as governor of the fort in 1596.

15

'Il novo recinto della fortification de la ville de Pleymouth'
Scale: 'Passi geometrii 1000' [= 5.5″] 1:10,909
Federico Genibelli
1601/2

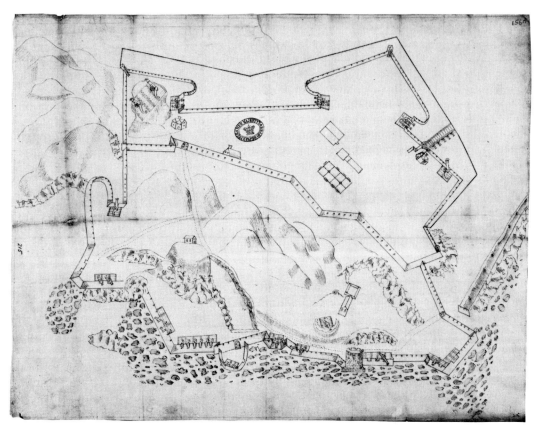

14

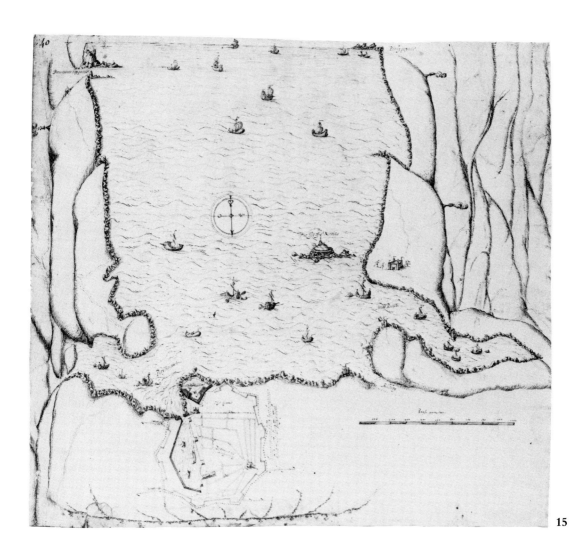

15

Orientation: S
Penlee Point(SW)–Bovisand Bay(SE)
Ink on paper
15″ × 18.2″ (381mm × 462mm)
BL Cotton MS Augustus I i 40

Map showing the landscape around Plymouth
Sound by the Italian engineer, Federico Genibelli.
Genibelli had been sent by the Privy Council in
response to requests by the governor of the fort, Sir
John Gilbert, that defects in the fortifications be
repaired. The plan illustrates the position occupied
by the fort in relation both to the town and to the
surrounding countryside, although the latter is
inaccurately portrayed and out of scale. The town
of Plymouth is surrounded by a perimeter wall:
'The Milbay bolevard' (? Frankfurt Gate), '[?]Bend

bolevard' (Old Town Gate), 'The fryers bolevard'
'Bulwork' (Friary Gate), 'The Cassey bolevard'
'Bolward' (Coxside). Beacons at Staddon, Maker
and Penlee. Compass.

16
'Plimouth Forte'
Scale: 'Passi Geometrici 50' [= 3.9″] .Scale in
    margin: 100 = 7.8″ 1:769
[Federico Genibelli]
c. 1601/2
Plymouth fort and town near Fisher's Nose
Ink on paper
14″ × 19.1″ (356mm × 485mm)
BL Cotton MS Augustus I i 42

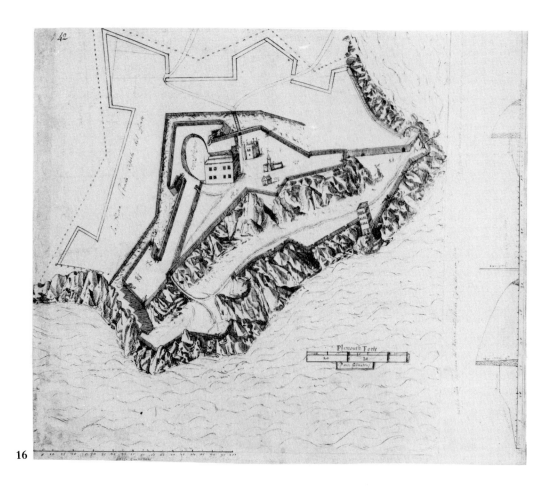

16

Genibelli's detailed plan of the fort. As **14** but buildings further developed. Chapel. Behind fort itself: 'Empty of the forte'. Beyond ditch on NW and NE sides are drawn further fortifications: '*La Nova strada coperta del forte*' (possibly the purpose of this plan?). Right-hand margin has section drawings: '*Perfilo della Trinecera del Recinto dell strade Cosi la del sudta forte*' and '*Perfilo del parapetto della defere del forte e de lisola de sante Hicot* [St Nicholas Island]' marked off in feet.

17

No title
'This Scale is made after 16½ foote to a Pearch, Statute Measure etc.'
5 + 25 [= 9.8″] 1:1,212
No statement of responsibility
Early seventeenth century
North-west edge of town of Plymouth

Ink and watercolour on parchment (red, green, yellow, blue, brown)
23.11″ × 31.9″ (variable) (612mm × 811mm)
WDRO W489

This is an unusual, thematic map showing the water system to the north of the town, also the mills and streams. An entry in the Plymouth municipal records [WDRO W132 f. 148] for 1603/4 records that Robert Sprie was paid 40s. for 'makinge the water-course in the olde towne'; it is possible that the entry may refer to this map. Mills: the malt mill (including 'ye well in question'), the tucking mill (used for finishing cloth) and the higher, middle and lower mills. Mill account books in West Devon Record Office (W496–99) show that between 1627 and 1631 the three last were used to grind wheat and barley. Streams: 'All the yellow Lines in this Mapp, are the Streames of water'; a network of streams running across the town is shown. 'Horse poole' by Frankfurt Gate 'ffrom the west side of the streame to ye eastside of the land 22 foote wich is ye bredth of ye land'. Floodhatches shown and marked along streams. Roads: 'Stonhouse Lane', 'Horsenpool Lane', 'The Lane leading towards Penicom Quick', 'The way leading towards Saltash', 'The Way leading towards Tavistouke'. 'The bredth of ye Lane and mountt is 18 foote'. Fields. Ownership: 'townes land', 'Mr Fowens land' (? Humphrey Fownes, mayor 1588/9, 1596/7), 'This Close belongs to Mr Harris and Capt Pollard' (? Anthony Pollerd, *fl.* 1592). 'The distance of the 2 Closes Right against the one the other is 27 foote.' Gates shown leading from some of the fields to the lane. Tuckers' racks shown near Frankfurt Gate (2 sets). Conduit near Old Town Gate. Barn near Saltash road shown. Part of this property was included in a lease for 70 years by the mayor and commonalty to Sir Francis Drake on 10 August 1593; in 1653, they ran out of money and let the property again. See Charity Commissioners' Report, pp. 627–33.

18

'A TRUE MAPP AND DESCRIPTION OF
  THE TOWNE of Plymouth and the
  Fortifications thereof, with the workes and
  approaches of the Enemy, at the last Seige [sic]
  Ao 1643'
in *A True NARRATION of the most Observable
  Passages, in and at the late Seige of
  PLYMOUTH, from the fifteenth day of September
  1643, untill the twenty fist [sic] of December
  following . . .*, 'printed by L[uke]N[orton] for
  Francis Eglesfeild . . . to be sold at the signe of
  the Marygold in Paul's Churchyard', London,
  1644
'A Scale of Miles' 3 [= 5.6″] 1:22,628
Engraved by Wenceslas Hollar
Rame Head(SW)–Saltash(NW)–Plympton(NE)
  –Wembury(SE)
Printed
10.5″ × 14″ (267mm × 356mm)
Ashmolean Museum, Oxford C II 304; BL E 31
  (15); Plymouth Proprietary Library

Engraving by Wenceslas Hollar intended to illustrate a Parliamentarian pamphlet. The map shows the landscape around Plymouth Sound including the fortifications erected by the Parliamentarians and the (Royalist) enemy's advances. The town of Plymouth, in which the Parliamentarians were besieged, is shown surrounded by a wall running from the Barbican to Coxside (Frankfurt Gate, Charles Fort, Resolution Fort, Maidenhead, East-

gate marked, besides spurs and drawbridges). North of the town runs a defensive line of Parliamentarian fortifications: New Work, Pennycomequick, Maudlyn, Holywell, Lipson and Lipson Mill work. There are also forts at Devil's Point, Stonehouse, Cattedown, Prince Rock, Laira Weir and St Nicholas Island. The enemy camps lie beyond the defensive line north of the town, also at Mount Batten (where there is just one Parliamentarian camp at Stanford), at Cremyll, St Stephens and Torpoint. Pomphlett Mill. Weston Mill. Churches. Large houses. Saltram. Ships and boats to indicate navigability. Compass with directional fleur-de-lys.

See R. Pennington *A Descriptive Catalogue of the
Etched Work of Wenceslas Hollar, 1607–77,* CUP,
1982, p. 88.

I owe the identification of Luke Norton to Francis Herbert.

19

As **18** except:
'A True Mapp and Description of ye Towne of
  Plymouth and the Fortification thereof, with
  the Workes and Approaches of ye Enemy at
  the Last Seige Ano 1643'
1643 [eighteenth century]
Ink on paper (note beneath the border states that
  red denotes 'the Oliverians or Anti-Royalists'
  and blue 'the Enemy or Royalists')
Bodleian Library Gough Maps 5 f. 9B

Manuscript copy of **18**. Minor differences: Pennycross, Ham, Millbridge Mills, Lipson Mill, Pomphlett Mill, Plympton St Mary omitted. Staddon Point, Whitsand Bay marked. Note the boundary line marking Mount Edgcumbe peninsula as part of Devon.

20

As **18** except:
'A TRUE MAP AND DESCRIPTION OF THE
  TOWN OF PLYMOUTH and the
  Fortifications thereof, with the works and
  approaches of the Enemy at the last Seige Ao
  1643'
'A Scale of miles' 3 [= 5.9″] 1:32,216
1643 [post-1828]
Ink and watercolour on paper (light grey, brown,
  green)
10.5″ × 14.2″ (267mm × 361mm)
NMM LAD 11/f. 71

A TRUE MAP AND DESCRIPTION OF THE TOWN OF PLYMOUTH and the Fortifications thereof, with the works and approaches of the Enemy at the last Seige An° 1643.

Plymouth Sound

A Scale of miles

20

21

As **18** except:
'A Map and Description of the Town of
  Plymouth and the Fortifications thereof with
  works and approaches of the Enemy at the last
  Seige AD 1643'
1643 [nineteenth century]
Hydrographic Department L1290 Shelf Od

Content the same as **18** apart from minor differences (style of drawing, place-name spellings). 'Old
Church' and 'New Church' marked.

22
'Plimouth'
No scale given, but approx. 1:29,280
? Charles Wilde
c. 1646
Cawsand(SW)–Mount Batten(SE)
Ink and watercolour on paper (yellow border
  wash around parts of coastline)
17.9″ × 12.1″ (455mm × 307mm)
BL Add MS 15737 f. 24v

Rough harbour chart of the Sound, drawn from on
board ship. The place-names of Stonehouse and
Mount Wise have been transposed. Soundings.
Compass. The chart occurs half-way through a sea
journal begun *c.* 1646 in the East Indies which
includes several Mediterranean ports. The charts
are beautifully drawn, and those in the first half of
the volume coloured. The journal was presented by
the Lords of the Admiralty to the British Museum
in January 1844.

See W. Foster 'A Seventeenth Century Cartographer' in *Geographical Journal*, July 1914, p. 78.

23
Plymouth inset
on 'Pascaerte van ENGELAND tusschen
  Poortlant en I Lou. t'Amsterdam By Theunis
  Iacobsz op't water inde Lootsman'
in *'T nieuwe en vergroote Zee-Boeck Dat is des
  Piloots ofte Loots-Mans Zee Spiegel*
'Duytsche mylen 15 in een Graet' 2 [= 2.3″]
  1:125,596

[1654]
Plymouth Sound
Printed
3.2″ × 4.3″ (81mm × 109mm)
NMM 101/59 JAC 01 PB D8258

Inset of Plymouth Sound on chart showing south coast from Talland Point to Portland. The inset gives an unconvincing survey of Plymouth Sound, showing 'Kattewater', 'Pleimuyen' (Plymouth), '*Visschersdorp* [Fisher's Town]' (Stonehouse), 'West Comber' and 'West Colyford' (Saltash), 'Ramshooft' (Rame Head). Soundings. Anchorages. 'Kocxbroot Meusteen' (the Mewstone). Compass rose.

See C. Koeman *Atlantes Neerlandici*, vol. IV, Amsterdam, 1970, p. 263.

24
No title
No scale given
No statement of responsibility
Pre-1665
Orientation: S
Lambhay, castle and part of town
Ink and watercolour on paper (red, blue, yellow, brown)
approx. 10.5″ × 14″ (incomplete) (267mm x 355mm)
WDRO 72/1204/Ai

Rough plan of the land beneath the castle between the Lambhay and the Barbican, described as 'The ground in question'. Barbican and Gate drawn, also houses along Castle Street. The plan relates to buildings belonging to Sir William Strode which were intended to be docks and cellars until demolished by an order in council on the grounds that they were not consistent with the honour and security of the Citadel and harbour. The ground was then taken into government service (part used for the Citadel and part for the Victualling Office of the Navy). Strode appealed to Charles II in 1671 (**36**), a jury of twenty-four men found in his favour, but despite efforts by other members of his family to get compensation, nothing was done until a petition of *c.* 1720.

25
'Plymouth Harbour Containing the Sounde, Causen Bay CatWater, Hamause, Mill Bay Extending from Staddon Pointe to Penlet point, more then 10 myles Circuit'
'Scala perticarum' 100 + 200 [= 5.4″]

Sir Bernard de Gomme
Pre-1665
Orientation: S [NB: Compass rose says E, but this is wrong]
Penlee Point(SW)–[Wembury Point(SE)]
Ink and watercolour on paper (red, green, blue, brown, yellow)
19.8″ × 27.6″ (503mm × 702mm)
BL Add MS 16370 f. 41

Map of the landscape around Plymouth Sound. Out of scale but with identifiable landmarks shown from a bird's eye view: Plymouth ?Guild Hall, St Andrew's Church, the castle; in the countryside beyond, Mount Wise Chapel, Mount Edgcumbe house. The purpose of the map is probably explained by the reference to the Citadel and to 'the kinge's land fitting for a docke' at Hooe (in fact, the Dockyard was not to be built for over twenty years and on another site). Note also 'sterne Chapell' at Devil's Point, Stonehouse. Compass rose. Bernard de Gomme was a Dutch engineer who had been appointed Chief Engineer of England and Wales in 1661. In 1665, he and six other commissioners received a warrant 'to strengthen and fortify our fortt upon the Hoe of Plymouth' which led to the building of the Citadel. This is one of three plans by him in a volume entitled *PLANS OF FORTIFIED TOWNS IN ENGLAND*. Book-plate of Francis Gwyn of Lansanor, Glamorgan, and Ford Abbey, Devon, who apparently took it home when working at the War Office. Later purchased from Thomas Rodd, 14 November 1846.

26
'Plan van de Harbour of Pleymouth with the niewe Cittadeell upon the How 1665' (endorsed)
Scale: '500 ffeete' [= 5″] 1:1,200
'Sr Ber de Gomme fecit 1665'
Citadel and part of the town of Plymouth
Ink on paper
21″ × 23″ (533mm × 585mm)
BL Add MS 16370 f. 43

De Gomme's detailed plan of the projected Citadel and the existing late sixteenth-century fort. The Citadel plan gives measurements in feet of space along the bastion walls. Individual buildings within the Citadel plotted. Windmill. Covered way running around edge of Citadel. Below Citadel, the fort showing chapel, sally port, gate. Below fort, the lower fort. Lime-kiln. Sally port at Fisher's Nose. Along Lambhay, deep valley and Sir George Cartaret's houses. Hoe Gate. Note the crane leaning over from the Barbican into Sutton Pool. Direction pointer.

27

No title

'This Scale Containes 1800 Jaerds, or an English
  Mile'; 1,800 [= 4″] 1:16,200
[Sir Bernard de Gomme]
c. 1665
Orientation: E [NB: Before this item was bound,
  orientation could have been N]
Rame Head(SW)–Saltash(NW)–Plympton St
  Mary(NE)–Mewstone(SE)
Ink on paper
20.6″ × 31.5″ (523mm × 800mm)
BL Add MS 16370 f. 45

Map by de Gomme of the landscape around the
Sound, showing the location of the Citadel. 'Hoggs
peck point' (Pigg's Point, Coxside). New Bridge at
Plympton drawn, Saltram quay. 'Froward poynt'
(site of the future Dockyard) mentioned for the first
time. Direction pointer.

On the back of this map is an account for
building the sentry-house of the Citadel. This
includes bringing timber and Portland stone from
Portland by sea to Plymouth at a cost of £21 5s.
The whole account amounted to £44 15s. for 'The
stoone Geate of Pleymouth' besides £22 for work-
manship and a further £3 for the king's arms.

28

No title

'Scale of 500 foot' [= 5″] 1:1,200
Sir Bernard de Gomme
1666/7

Citadel and part of Plymouth
Ink and watercolour on paper (red, green, blue,
  yellow, brown)
20″ × 28.6″ (508mm × 727mm)
NMM P/45

Later plan of the Citadel, drawing attention to its
defensive capabilities. Chapel within Citadel
shown, and other buildings in outline with a note
of their intended occupants: sergeants, corporals,
ensigns, captain. Governor's house, lieutenant
governor's house and garden, the great magazine.
'Bath bastion' (later named as Clifford Bastion,
contained powder house); 'Albemarle bastion'
(Bath bastion; sally port adjoining); 'Rupert's bastion' (Albemarle bastion). Above, on escarpment,
'a great defend'. Site of castle noted. Little Hoe
Gate . New Street. Breadth and depth of Barbican
noted, length of old causeway. New Quay. Smart's
Quay. South Quay. Extent of Sutton Pool
recorded as 31 acres, 146 perches. The map was
presented to the National Maritime Museum by Sir
James Caird in 1948.

29

'Plane of the Royal Cittadel of Pleymouth'
  (endorsement)
'Scale of 500 English foot' [= 5″] 1:1,200
Sir Bernard de Gomme (endorsed)
1668 (endorsed)
Citadel with part of the town of Plymouth and
  Mount Batten

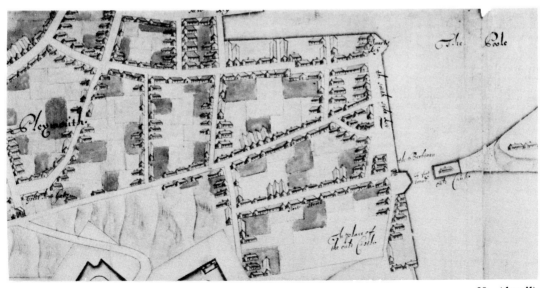

29 (detail)

Ink and watercolour on paper (red, green, blue, brown, yellow, black)
26.7″ × 38″ (variable) (679mm × 966mm)
BL Add MS 16371 D

Another plan of the Citadel by de Gomme, with some alterations to **28**, but again drawing attention to its defences. Guardhouse at main entrance. Suttler's house (the suttler was responsible for providing food and drink to the soldiers). Main guard. Position of chapel changed since **28**. '*Corps de guarde*'. Note the dotted line for alterations in Citadel wall above Lower Fort. Also, faint designs in pencil near Rupert's bastion suggesting alternative design. Old castle near Fisher's Nose. The Lambhay noted (Sir George Cartaret's storehouses on **28**). Battery at Pigg's Point, and another in front of the fort at Mount Batten (valley and high ground behind Mount Batten promontory noted). Section drawing of Charles bastion with measurements in feet. Heights of stone wall around the Citadel at Charles bastion (28 ft), Katherine bastion (34 ft), James bastion (37 ft), Rupert's bastion (42 ft), Bath bastion (30 ft) and near the powder tower (40 ft). Circumference of wall: 1,100 yds (1,760 yds to a mile).

30
No title
No scale given, but approx. 1:1,177
[Sir Bernard de Gomme]
[1671]
West Hoe–East Hoe–part of town of Plymouth
Ink and watercolour on paper (red, green, blue, brown, yellow)
19.3″ × 27.7″ (variable) (490mm × 705mm)
PRO MPE 436 (LRRO 1/199) (PRO Catalogue no. 2031)

Map to show ownership of land on the Citadel site (the handwriting is that of de Gomme). The land has been divided up into plots. Both the East Hoe ('A') where the Citadel was built and the West Hoe ('B') are shown as belonging to Sir Edward Hungerford (18 and 16 acres respectively) and also some fields ('C') beyond. Behind the East Hoe, much of the land is shown as individual garden plots. Sir Edward Hungerford's house and garden ('D') are adjoining Little Hoe Gate (shown on **28**). 'B' has been marked 'bought', 'C' and the adjoining fields 'not bought'. The lands were apparently conveyed by a royal warrant issued in June 1671. Boundary stones are shown between the East Hoe and the Lambhay, which is noted as the property of Sir George Cartaret and Sir William Strode. A landing place has been marked on Cartaret's

property. A note in the left-hand corner of the map records that a Mr Schoon of Cornwall has made an estimate of all the gardens 'taken in for His Majesties service' at Plymouth, as also of the Lambhay. Points of compass.

31
As **30** except:
R. Searle
[1671] [June 1814]
PRO MPH 374 (PRO Catalogue no. 2032)

The Crown's assumption of the land on the Hoe in the seventeenth century had become a matter for dispute between Plymouth Corporation and the Board of Ordnance. Searle's copy of de Gomme's plan was certified by William Test as Chief Royal Military Surveyor and Draughtsman in 1814.

32
As **31** except:
PRO MPHH 223/4

33
No title
'This scale of Equall partes is after 16½ foote to the perch stattut Measure' 5 + 35 [= 8.9″] 1:889
Jonathan Sparkes and John Ward
Post-1671
East and West Hoe with part of town of Plymouth
Ink and watercolour on parchment (red, green, yellow, pink, grey, turquoise)
25.8″ × 34.8″ (variable) (656mm × 884mm)
PRO MPE 363 (LRRO 1/200) (PRO Catalogue no. 2033)

Map showing ownership and tenancy of the Citadel site (cf. **30**). Although both maps cover the same ground, this map is a much less accurate survey; on the other hand, however, it supplements our knowledge by giving tenancies. The drawing of the Citadel (not shown on **30**) is crude. There are slight discrepancies between the two maps as to the acreages of the East and West Hoe. A beacon and hill are drawn on the West Hoe ('West Beacon Field'). The reference to Mr Gloynes Field being the 'beanes and Charters Land' is intriguing. Footpaths drawn on this map to the Citadel, 'The new way leading to the Cittydell' and 'This was the old way to the Hooe', suggest that this map is later than **30**, although neither are dated. Direction pointer.

34

As **33** except:

PRO MPH 539 (WO 78/1777) (PRO Catalogue
  no. 2035)

A note of 25 June 1814 by William Test certifies
that this is a copy of the original plan deposited in
the Land Revenue Office. See **31** for the circumstances in which the copies were made.

35

As **34** except:

PRO MPHH 223/5 (WO 78/1728) (PRO
  Catalogue no. 2034)

Also note: 'Copied by JW Anderson RMS & D to
accompany Lt Genl Mann's letter to Mr Crew
dated 25 June 1814.'

36

No title
No scale given, but approx. 1:12,720
No statement of responsibility
? 10 July 1672 [1758]
Orientation: W
The Lambhay
Ink on paper
9.2″ × 14.6″ (232mm × 371mm)
PRO T1 382/70

Diagram to show ownership of the Lambhay,
distinguishing between land belonging to Sir
George Cartaret and Sir William Strode; and the
Old Castle (King's ground) and land on which the
Citadel was built (Sir Edward Hungerford's).
Boundary stones between Lambhay and Citadel.
The legend on the plan is similar to **30**, although
this map has an additional note: 'The length of the
ground towards Catwater according to Sir William
Strode's petition in 1671 was about 600 feet but
there is no dimensions nor scale to the plan.' This
plan is part of Sir William Strode's case for compensation for his land at the Lambhay, which had
been acquired by the Crown to build the Victualling Offices and storehouses upon. The plan was
dug out again in a dispute of 1758 between the
Victualling Office and Plymouth Corporation over
the same piece of land. A letter in this eighteenth-
century dispute refers to Edgcumbe and Skelton's
enquiry and how 'they had caused a Land Meater to
take an Exact measure of the said Lambhay and had
transmitted a draught thereof with their said letter'.

37

No title
'Scale of 20 perches' [= 7.4″]
No statement of responsibility
4 September 1672 (endorsed)
Orientation: W
The Lambhay from Fisher's Nose (S) to Castle
  wall (N)
Ink and watercolour on parchment (red, green,
  brown, blue, yellow)
13″ × 22″ (variable) (560mm × 330mm)
PRO E 178/6198

Sketch map of the Lambhay showing the landing
place and houses (called 'palaces') adjacent. Land
from the Castle to Fisher's Nose surveyed (3 acres,
31 perches), also the beach (1 acre, 40 perches). Six
tenements in the Lambhay, three adjoining the
castle wall. Map endorsed: '4to die Septembris 1672
This Mappe was shewen to all the Jurors and
Witnesses sworne and exa[m]i[n]ed to the . . . to
the Com[m]ission hereunto likewyse annexed
R Edgcumbe Jo Skelton.' On 4 September an
enquiry was held in Plymouth before Sir Richard
Edgcumbe and Sir John Skelton as to the ownership and worth of this land. The purpose of the
enquiry was to investigate the development of this
waterside area beneath the Citadel for the Crown's
use: quays, landing-places, cellars, lofts etc.
Among the witnesses, Alexander Roch of Plymouth, gentleman, and Henry Cloake of Bere
Ferrers, carpenter, are referred to as having recently
measured this area of ground. This may be their
plan, although the figures given in their evidence
do not correspond exactly with those on the map,
and it is equally likely that this was just another of
the 'mapps and descripcions' generated by the
enquiry.

38

No title
'Scale of 600 English feete, or 200 Yards [= 6″]
  1:1,200
Sir Bernard de Gomme
1672
Orientation: S
Citadel and part of town from West Hoe to
  Cattewater
Ink and watercolour on paper (red, blue, green,
  yellow, pale brown, turquoise and grey)
35.7″ × 39.2″ (907mm × 996mm)
NMM P/45

Decorative plan of the Citadel illustrating its commanding position between the town and the sea.
The upper portion of the plan shows a bird's eye

view of the same area, emphasizing the hills surrounding the town. Citadel: the following buildings have different sites from the preceding plans: Deputy governor's house, suttler's house, storekeeper's house, great storehouse. Lodgings for Earl of Bath's company and Sir John Skelton's company. 'Necessaire house' within James bastion. New Harbour below Citadel. Highway from Plymouth to Millbay intersected by footpaths from the town to the West Hoe. 'St Nicolas Island' (Drake's Island).

39
No title
'The Scale of Perches' 20 [= 7.5″]
No statement of responsibility
c. 1672
Orientation: W
Fisher's Nose at southern end of Sutton Pool running north along water's edge towards town
Ink and watercolour on paper (brown, blue, green, pink, turquoise)
14.6″ × 21.6″ (385mm × 551mm)
WDRO 72/1204/Aii

A preliminary version of **37**, by the same cartographer. Note the intended street running along the edge of Sutton Pool from the Castle wall to Fisher's Nose.

40
'Plymouth'
Scale: '800 pieds' [= 8.1″] 1:1,185
No statement of responsibility
Post-1672
Citadel(SW)–town of Plymouth(N)–Queen Ann's Battery(SE)
Ink and watercolour on paper (red, green, yellow)
28.9″ × 29.5″ (735mm × 750mm)
BL K. Top. 11 81

An unfinished plan of the Citadel showing a projected extension on to the West Hoe. Key and notes in French. Street plan of the town. Hills. Canteen within Citadel noted for first time. Teat's Hill (Coxside) called Slade Hill. Memoranda that from the Citadel to Mount Batten tower is a quarter-mile; from the Citadel to St Nicholas Island three-quarters of a mile. Part of key to Citadel missing, including the key to the proposed extension. Fleur-de-lys pointer.

41
No title
'A Scale of Geometrical Paces or of 5 foot to a Pace' 1 + 5 [= 4.1″] 1:87
'JR'
1677
Citadel and part of town
Ink and watercolour on parchment (red, green, blue, brown, yellow, mauve, orange, pink)
25.6″ × 29.1″ (651mm × 740mm)
BL Add MS 5415 E art 2

Plan of the Citadel with detailed key to the buildings. Alterations since the 1672 plan include renaming of the following bastions: Albemarle, Bath, Clifford; and resiting of the chapel. The Grotto or Giant's Cave is noted for the first time, as is the Little Powder Tower. The design alterations suggested by the dotted line in the Citadel wall above the Lower Fort on the 1668 plan have now been carried out: the terrace walk. A water-gate and a water-tower are also shown for the first time.

42
'The Royall Cittadell, Plymouth' (endorsed 'citadelle de Plimout')
'A Scale of Geometricall Paces' 60 [= 5.3″] 1:679
No statement of responsibility
c. 1677
Orientation: S (despite direction pointer)
The Citadel
Ink and watercolour on parchment (red, yellow, blue, green, beige, orange, brown)
26.7″ × 29.5″ (678mm × 750mm)
Service Historique de la Marine, Vincennes, Recueil no. 32 (62)

Another plan of the Citadel, almost identical to **41** apart from the way in which some of the buildings are drawn. A label pasted on the back of the map has the key in a French eighteenth-century hand. The plan is in a volume entitled *Iles Britanniques Villes Rivières et Canaux d'Angleterre*.

43
'The Plain or Plott of Plymouth Sound Ham Oaze and Catt water'
No scale given, but approx 1:38,475
? Copy by Edmund Dummer of original by Jerome Roch. Original missing.
August 1682
Orientation: E
Rame peninsula(SW)–Hamoaze estuary(NW) –Plym Bridge(NE)–Mewstone(SE)

Pencil, ink and watercolour on paper (yellowish-
  green, blue, grey, brown)
27.5″ × 11″ (699mm × 280mm)
BL King's MS 40 f. 8

Simple chart showing Hamoaze and Cattewater
estuaries. Plym Bridge marked. Compass.
Edmund Dummer was appointed midshipman
extraordinary on board HM *Woolwich* which sailed
from Deal round the south coast past Plymouth
and on to the Mediterranean beginning in 1682. He
began the journal to give a sense of direction to 'A
Voyage into the Mediterranean Seas . . . Finished
in the Yeare 1685'. An interesting insight into life
on board ship occurred on Monday 7 August 1682:

> This Evening wee Anchored in Plymouth
> Sound, a Matter (it appear'd) the Moors expected
> not, or wanted Occasion to quarrell amongst
> themselves. The Aggressor was Cuddum
> Hamett animated by Lucas against the Ambassa-
> dour. The Matter of fact was this: Cuddum sends
> to Capt Holding (then upon the quarter Deck)
> for Irons for a Man, but not understanding well
> the Moorish messenger, desired the Renegado to
> be called, meaning by him to have understood
> more fully the Message of Cuddum. But
> Cuddum comes himself to the Capt: and at that
> same Instant the Renegado also, whom Cuddum
> seeing, in a very violent transport takes by the
> Throat saying (in Moorish) Secure the Christian
> Dog, and therewith Laboured to push him
> downe into the great Cabbin; The Ambassadour
> and his Men (being upon the Poope) seeing the
> passage, some of them leapt downe and with us
> that were Christians present, endeavoured to
> stop his fury, so that Instantly the rest of the
> Moors from above and those from below were
> gott together, some with Knives, some with
> stilletto's, striking one at another over, and
> under our Arms, that were Christians prom-
> iscuously mixt among them.
>   A Symiter was handed to the Ambassadour,
> he came from the Poope to the Gangway the
> whole Ships Company was in an Uproar, the
> Anchor just fallen from the Catt, but the Capt
> (the Surprize a little past) ordered in a Moment, a
> few Lusty fellows upon the Quarter Deck with
> Cuttlaces Drawne laid hold of Cuddum, bidding
> One of his owne Moors (who spoke a little
> English) advise him to retire immediatly or he
> should be Cut in peices, the Moor apprehensive
> desired the Captaines Care of the Renegado
> (whome he pretended would escape) and went
> with great quickness, and Rage to the great
> Cabbin, where two sentinells were placed upon
> him.

> The Ambassadour by this time was gotten
> within the Cuddy Door his appartment (for
> Lucas and Cuddum had dismist him of the great
> Cabbin in the Downes, or he willingly left it for
> his personall Security which in this Action
> greatly appeared) and there disputed with Lucas
> very hotly without attempting violence, at
> length they drew into the Cuddy; and there
> argued themselves in some better agreement (but
> the animosity not to be removed) all became
> againe outwardly quiet, and that it might con-
> tinue soe, the Captaine (an Eye Witness to the
> violence) resolves to keep Cuddum Strictly con-
> fined till wee should arrive at Tanger.

Dummer's journal also records weather, wind
directions and latitudes.

44

'The Mannour of Stonehouse Surveyed & Plotted
  March 1682/3 By Jerom Roch Jr'
'A Scale of Chains, each Chain containing 4 Poles
  of 16 foot & halfe the Pole or 66 foot Divided
  into 100 parts or Links' 1 + 10 = 4.5″ 1:1,936
Orientation: S
Stonehouse peninsula from Millbridge to
  Firestone Bay
Ink and watercolour on parchment (red, blue,
  green, yellow, gold, purple, brown)
34″ × 26″ (variable) (863mm × 660mm)
DRO Exeter 1120Z/F247

The only map within this catalogue which relates
purely to Stonehouse. A typical estate map giving
acreages for the plots (which are numbered within
the borough, but allotted letters beyond). Note that
the area tinted with red belongs to the king
(Charles II). Chapel and burgage tenements drawn.
Chapel Street. Stonehouse Quay. Almshouse.
Freedom stone. Passage house for Cremyll Ferry.
Limestone kiln and quarry. Gates. Ship and boat.
Points of compass.

45

'Thus sheweth Plimouth sound when you are at
  an Anker ye Sitadell bearing NNE . . .'
No scale given, but approx. 1:15,500
? Jacob Ward
23 June 1689
Plymouth Sound from Penlee Point(SW)–
  Renney Rocks(SE)
Pencil, ink and grey wash on paper
11.3″ × 14.1″ (287mm × 358mm)
BL Add MS 18989 f. 5

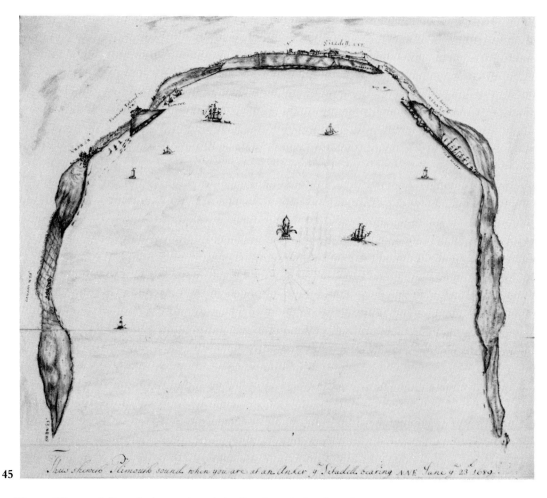

45

Chart of Plymouth Sound taken on board the Good Ship *Benjamin* the commander of which was Leonard Browne of the East India Company. The *Benjamin* sailed from Gravesend to Surat, India (11 April 1689–19 November 1690), and returned from Surat to Plymouth (14 October–31 October 1693). On stylistic grounds, the chart is attributable to Jacob Ward (chart of St Iago made by him on 22 August 1689 in this volume). The chart gives compass bearings to the Citadel, 'Francis Island' (Drake's Island), Cawsand, Penlee Point and Mount Batten. The journal records that when the ship set sail from Plymouth on 26 June it did so in company with the Dutch fleet. Journal purchased at Messrs Putticks on 3 July 1852.

46

'THE ORIGINAL PLAT OF GROUND on
   which Plymouth Yard now stands with its
   Elevations and Buildings as at first Designed'

'Scale of Feet' 100 + 400 [= 3.5″] 1:1,714
No statement of responsibility
? 1689/90
Orientation: E
Point Froward (site of Dockyard)
Ink and grey wash on paper
13.3″ × 15.3″ (338mm × 390mm)
NMM LAD/11 f. 70

Retrospective plan of Point Froward showing the original shore-line and the remodelled version for the Dock and basin. Section drawings in the margin show the rise and fall of the tide. Cf. Lansdowne 847 f. 79.

47

'The Plan of Point Froward with ye Yard
   Designed therein in 89'
'A Scale of Feet to Measure all ye Generall Plans
   of ye Dock Yard' 1,900 + 100 [= 9.2″] 1:2,608

No statement of responsibility
1689 [1698]
Orientation: E
Dockyard
Ink and watercolour on paper (red, green, blue,
   brown, pink, grey)
10.2″ × 24.6″ (259mm × 625mm)
BL King's MS 43 f. 130 (see **69** for the context of
   this plan)

As **46** but in addition the plan for the officers'
houses, offices, gardens and stables has been lightly
drawn in.

48
'Plan of Point Froward with the Yard first
   Designed there in 1689'
NMM LAD/11 f. 72

49
'The Plan of Point Froward with the Yard first
   Design'd there in 1689'
'Scale of Feet to all these plans 1200 + 200'
   [= 6.4″] 1:2,625
1689 [1774]
8.3″ × 11.3″ (211mm × 287mm)
BL King's MS 44 ff. 13–14

50
'Plymouth Harbour with all the Rivers, Creeks,
   Bayes, Lakes & Places Adjacent
   Hydrographically describ'd by Jerom Roch'
'A Scale of Geometrical Miles' 8 [= 4.7″]
   1:102,127
Jerom Roch
c. 1690
Rame Head(SW)–Tideford(NW)–Lopwell
   Dam(NE)–Newton Ferrers(SE)
Ink and wash on paper (brown, red, green,
   yellow, blue)
34.8″ × 21″ (882mm × 534mm)
The Duke of Buccleuch. Boughton House,
   Kettering

Map of the landscape around the Sound
(compressed) and river estuaries inland, particularly the Tamar. Plym estuary shown as far as New
Bridge; River Tavy shown to beyond Lopwell;
Tamar to beyond Calstock; Lynher to Notter
Bridge and Tideford. The map concentrates upon
the settlements on either side of the river bank
(many place-names); houses of the gentry, quarries, mills (including salt-mills above Saltash and
Cargreen), and a silver mine near Calstock. Bridges

marked. A few anchorages. Soundings. Compasses.

51
No title
No scale given, but see **52**
No statement of responsibility
? 1692–4
Thancks(SW)–St Germans(NW)–Weir Quay(NE)
   –Weston Mills(SE)
Ink and watercolour on paper (red, green,
   yellow)
20″ × 27.1″ (508mm × 689mm)
BL K. Top. 11 74 1

A map showing settlements around the Tamar,
Tavy, Lynher and Notter Rivers. The countryside
is drawn as a mass of hills punctuated by hamlets
and villages along the water's edge. Mills. Many
place-names.

52
'Plymouth'
Scale: '800 pieds' [= 7.5″] 1:1,280; '1 Mille'
   [= 3.8″]
No statement of responsibility
? 1692–4
Penlee Point(SW)–St John's(NW)–Crabtree(NE)
   –Yealm estuary(SE)
Ink and watercolour on paper (red, green,
   yellow)
18.9″ × 26.8″ (480mm × 681mm)
BL K. Top. 11 74 2

A map of the landscape around Plymouth Sound,
by the same hand that drew **51**. Mills. In the
left-hand margin of the map is an inset showing St
Nicholas Island with its perimeter wall, gun platforms and buildings in detail. Compass of twelve
points with fleur-de-lys pointer.

53
'PLYMOUTH to the Rt Honble ARTHUR Earle
   of TORRINGTON, Baron HERBERT of
   Torbay, first Lt of the Admirality [sic]
   ADMIRAIL of their Maties Navy & Capt
   Genll of the Narrow Seas Humbly Dedicated
   by Ct G Collins Hydrogr[apher] to the KING'
in *Great Britain's Coasting Pilot* by Captain
   Greenvile Collins, 'Hydrographer in Ordinary
   to the King and Queens most Excellent
   Majesties'. 'Printed by Freeman Collins . . . to
   be Sold by Richard Mount Bookseller, at the
   Postern on Tower Hill', London, 1693

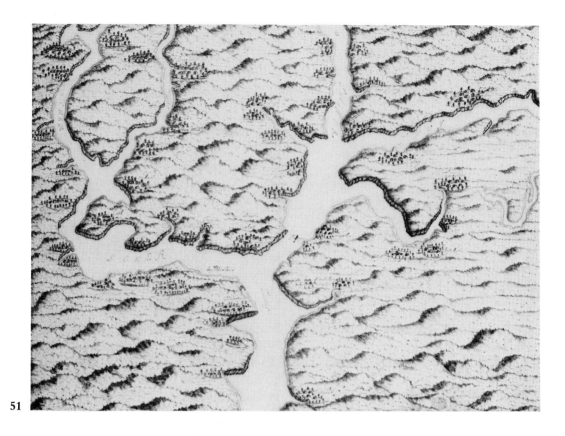

51

'Scale of 1 mile' [= 2.5″] 1;25,344
Greenvile Collins
Rame Head(SW)–Saltash(NW)–Yealm
    estuary(SE)
Printed
17.4″ × 21.8″ (442mm × 554mm)
BL Maps C.8 d.7; BN Ge DD 1172 (23);
    Bodleian Gough Maps 86; Naval Historical
    Library Ve 44; NMM 335/8 (GRC 01) PB
    D8205; Plymouth City Museum (two copies)

Chart of Plymouth Sound from Rame Head to the
Yealm estuary. 'Cittadell'. 'King's Dock' at Froward Point. Saltram Quay. Mills at Weston Mills,
Old Mills, Pomphlett. Beacons at Rame Head and
on Staddon Heights. Many place-names. Withy
hedge on Staddon Heights; stone hedge on the Hoe
and at Stonehouse. Tamar described as 'Pline
River'. Lower Lary 'All owse and dry at low
water'. Major rocks in Sound noted with depths:
German; Winter Rock (15 ft); Shovel (16 ft);
Tinker; Swiftsure (17 ft); Shagstone; Mewstone.
Soundings. A few anchorages. Bearings. Two
compasses. Salcombe inset.

See C. Le Gear *Geographical Atlases*, Library of
Congress, 1963, c. 7, 7995; C. Verner 'Captain
Collins' Coasting Pilot: a Carto-Bibliographical
Analysis' in *The Map Collector's Circle*, 58 (1969).

54

'Port de Plymouth' (endorsed)
Scale: 'one Mile' [= 2.6″] 1:24,370
No statement of responsibility
1693 [*c.* 1779]
Ink and watercolour on paper (red, orange,
    brown, turquoise, green, grey)
17.4″ × 22.1″ (442 mm × 562mm)
Archivo Histórico Nacional, Madrid Leg. 4218 Sa
    193

Manuscript copy of **53**. Minor variations (no trees
at Plymouth, Cawsand, Millbrook) and spelling
differences ('Swist sure', 'Showell').

See Tello *Mapas, Planos y Dibujos*, catalogue no.
143.

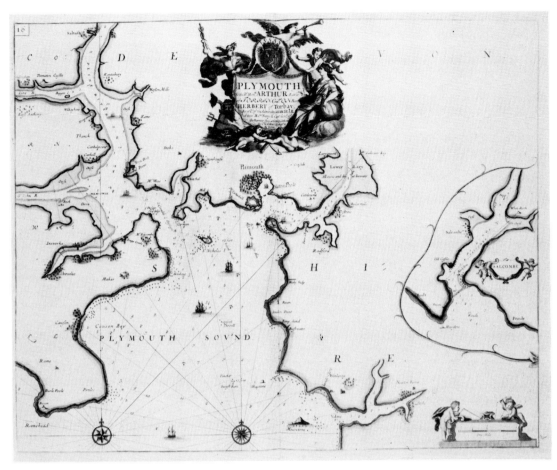

53

55
As **53** except:
1693 [1792]
NMM 340/54 (GRC 09) PB D8198

Later printed state. Additional rocks: Cobbler, Panther, Knap. Tower at Penlee Point.

56
'PLAN DE LA RADE DE PLYMOUTH Et des Ports de CattWater Hamowse et Salcombe copie sur celui du Pilote Costier de la Grande Bretagne de Greenvile Collins'
BN SH Portefeuille 23 Division 5 Pièce 5 (two copies)

'*Les Sondes sont des brasses* [fathoms]. *La brasse vaut 6 pieds Anglois. Le pied Anglois* [foot] *vaut 11 pouces 3 lignes du pied Francois.*'

See C. Verner 'Captain Collins' Coasting Pilot', p. 44, for the printed edition of this map, from which this copy was made.

57
'Carte de Plimouth'
Scale: 'one mil' [= 2.5″] 1:25,344
No statement of responsibility
1693 [eighteenth century]
Ink on paper
16.8″ × 23.4″ (427mm × 595mm)
BN SH Portefeuille 23 Division 5 Pièce 4/1

Poor copy of **53**.

58
'A CHART OF THE HARBOUR OF PLYMOUTH From Capt Collins's Survey'
'A Scale of one Mile' [= 1.95″] 1:32,492

1693 [eighteenth century]
Ink and watercolour on paper (brown and red
    ink; green, brown, grey)
13.7″ × 13.2″ (348mm × 335mm)
BN SH Portefeuille 23 Division 5 Pièce 6

59
'The First Draught'
No scale given, but approx. 1:2,117
Edmund Dummer
1694
Orientation: E
Mount Wise
Ink and watercolour on paper (red, green,
    brown)
11.6″ × 14.5″ (296mm × 376mm)
BL Lansdowne 847 f. 80

Edmund Dummer drew up these eight early
draughts of the Dockyard in an account which he
presented to the Navy Commissioners in
December 1694. This one shows the original track
of the sea shore before work on building the Dock
began, the cove out of which basins were to be
built; dotted lines show the subsequent works,
including the limits of the level ground. Section
drawings. This site was particularly favourable for
building the Dock, because of its deep water, the
course of the tide, and the oozy ground. Nevertheless, it was uneven, and made of slate rock. Nearly
4 acres of uneven ground had to be made up. This
volume later belonged to Robert Harley of
Brampton Castle, Hereford.

60
'First Draught. The Plot of the Ground about
    Point Froward'
Printed
BL Add MSS 9329 f. 171

Printed version of **59** though with a few minor
variations and a key.

61
'Plan des ouvrages du Port de Plymouth 10 pieces
    1745'
'1st Draught The Plot of the Ground about Point
    Froward'
'Scale of Feet' 300 [= 2.7″] 1:1,333
Ink and watercolour on paper (green, brown,
    grey)
12″ × 11.8″ (305mm × 300mm)
BN SH Portefeuille 23 Division 5 Pièce 13

Manuscript copy of **60**.

62
'Second Draught Representing the Yard
    Compleate'
No scale given
Edmund Dummer
1694
Orientation: E
Dockyard
Ink and watercolour on paper (red, green,
    brown)
11.2″ × 14.5″ (285mm × 376mm)
BL Lansdowne 847 f. 82

Plan for early Dock buildings including hemphouse, white yarn house, ropehouse, slips, timber
wharf, sawpits, pitch kettles, shipwrights' sheds,
anchor forge, crane, officers' dwelling houses,
clerks' offices.

63
'Second Draught The Yard and Docks Compleat'
Scale: 100 + 300 Feet [= 2.6″] 1:1,846
Printed
BL Add MSS 9329 ff. 172–73 (two copies)

Printed version of **62** though with a few minor
variations and a key.

64
'2nd Draught The Yard and Dock Compleat'
11.5″ × 14″ (292mm × 356mm)
BN SH Portefeuille 23 Division 5 Pièce 13

Manuscript copy of **63**.

65
'The Barton of Mount Wise'
No scale given
No statement of responsibility
Orientation: E
Mount Wise
Ink on paper
9.4″ × 11.1″ (variable) (240mm × 283mm)
BL Add MSS 9329 f. 170

Plan of Mount Wise showing the newly built
Dockyard and its perimeter wall. Around it are
fields, whose names and acreages are given in a
key.

66
'9th [Draught] The Barton of Mount Wise'
9.5″ × 11.5″ (244mm × 292mm)
BN Portefeuille 23 Division 5 Pièce 13

67

'PLYMOUTH SOUND Catwater & Ham Ouse' (inset)

on 'To the Right Honble my Lord Berkley Admiral of the Blew Commander in Chief in the Present Exped. etc This Map of the Channel is Dedicated by your Lordships Most Humble Servant P. Lea at the Atlas and Hercules in Cheapside 1695'

'Sold by Philip Lea Globemaker at the Atlas and Hercules in Cheapside near Fryday Street end London'

'A League' [= 2.5″] 1:87,552 (inset)

Rame Head(SW)–Saltash(NW)–Plympton(NE) –Wembury(SE)

Printed

5″ × 6.2″ (127mm × 157mm)

Bodleian Gough Maps 83; BL K. MAR III 74: NMM 382/18 (LEA 01) PB E7505

Chart of Plymouth Sound. '[Sutton] Harbour or Poole 20 foot'. Fish-House at entrance to Sutton Pool. Coxside: 'Kingstore H[ouse], Mastyard Forge'. Teat's Hill: 'King's Ship Buildings'. Intertidal area. Soundings. Bearings. Compass.

NMM 382/18 is in *Hydrographia Universalis.*

68

'A VIEW of Plymouth Sound & ye River HAMOUZE & CATWATER taken from ye Riseing Land above Mount Edgecomb opposite Mount Wise wch shews yt St Nicholas Island is ye Principal gaurd [sic] to ye New Dock and ye SHIPS In this Harbour D[E]LINEATED 1697'

'A Scale of English Miles to Measure the Harbours' 12 + 1 [= 9.3″] 1:88,567

67

No statement of responsibility
Mount Edgcumbe(SW)–Hingston Down(NW)
  –Plymstock(SE)
Ink and watercolour on paper (red, yellow,
  green, blue, grey)
18.6″ × 49″ (473mm × 1245mm)
BL King's MS 43 f. 127

Bird's-eye view of Plymouth Sound. Although
very attractive, the *raison d'être* of the view appears
to have been defensive. Brent Tor shown in the
distance. However, 'hills towards Dartmouth'
betrays the cartographer's limited geographical
knowledge. The cartographer was possibly
Edmund Dummer, who had been sent to Dartmouth to examine it as an alternative site for the
Dockyard before Plymouth was finally chosen.
Hills. Fields. Wooded areas.

69
'A Plan of PLYMOUTH Sound ye Rivers of
  Hamouze & Catwater together WITH ye Coast
of Devon to Dartmouth and TORBAY,
Shewing ye Rocks Soundings Buoys and
Anchor ground & The late Erected Navy-yard
Scituate on ye River of Hamouze
DELINEATED 1698'
'A Scale of English Miles to Measure the
  Harbours' 12 + 1 [= 9.3″] 1:88,567
No statement of responsibility
Rame(SW)–Cargreen(NW)–Bob's Nose [? Hope's
  Nose](NE)–Berry Rock(SE)
Ink and watercolour on paper (red, yellow,
  green, blue, pink, grey)
20.5″ × 24.5″ (521mm × 623mm)
BL King's MS 43 ff. 125–26

Map of the coastline from Rame Head to Torquay.
Most of the detail shown relates to Plymouth
Sound (left-hand side of the map), although the
Dart estuary has been carefully described. Saltram
Quay. Whitehall Mill at Stonehouse. 'Pline River'
(Tamar). Buoy, island reef (St Nicholas Island),
Winter 15 ft, Shovell 16 ft, Tinker Swiftsure 17 ft.

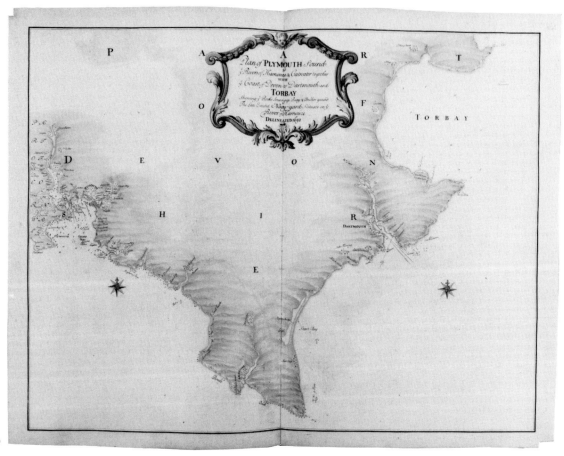

Inter-tidal area. Soundings. A few anchorages. Bearings. Compass.

BL King's MS 43 is a volume entitled 'A SURVEY and Description of the Principal HARBOURS with their ACCOMODATIONS & CONVE-NIENCES for Erecting Moaring Secureing and Refitting the NAVY ROYALL of England . . .'. It covers Chatham, Sheerness, Woolwich, Deptford, Portsmouth, and Plymouth. It gives an account of the improvements at each yard since the 1688 revolution, besides an account of all the buildings and an estimate of their worth. See **47**.

70

'A VIEW of his Maties DOCK Yard at PLYMOUTH taken from On Board a Vessell Riding opposite ye North Crane'

'A Scale of Feet to Measure all ye Generall Plans of ye Dock Yard'

1900 + 100 [= 9.2″] 1:2,608

No statement of responsibility

1698

Orientation: E

Dockyard

Ink and watercolour on paper (red, green, blue, brown, pink, grey)

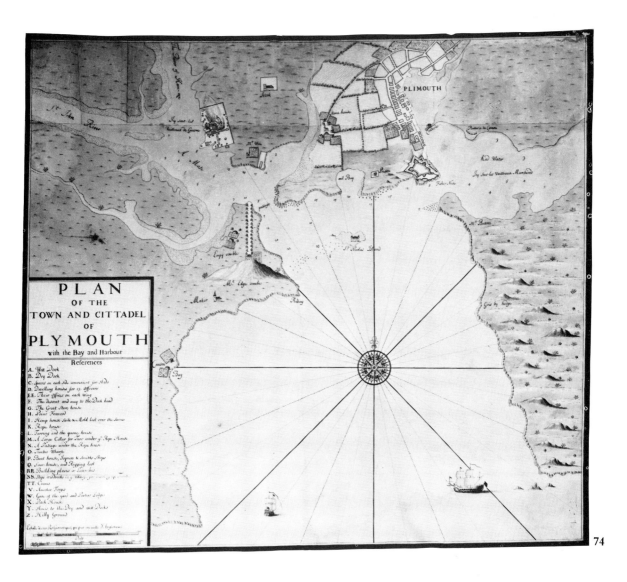

74

10.2″ × 24.6″ (259mm × 625mm)
BL King's MS 43 f. 130

View of the upper reaches of Plymouth Sound with major landmarks noted. Brent Tor.

71
As **70** except:
'The same Plan as it Appears with the Buildings
    performed & Designed but part not finished
    Delineated 1698'
8.4″ × 10.1″ (213mm × 257mm)
BL King's MS 43 f. 130

Plan of the early Dockyard, showing Dock, basin, sail loft and rope walk, mast-houses, boat houses, horse pond, plank house and brick shed.

72
As **71** except:
'Plan of the same Yard with the improvements in
    1698'
NMM LAD/11 f. 72

73
As **71** except:
'The Plan of the same Yard with the
    Improvements in 1698'
'Scale of Feet to all these Plans 1200 + 200'
    [=6.4″] 1:2,625
8.3″ × 11.3″ (211mm × 287mm)
1698 [1774]
BL King's MS 44 ff. 13–14

74
'PLAN OF THE TOWN AND CITTADEL OF
    PLYMOUTH with the Bay and Harbour'
'Echelle de 1250 Pas Géometriques, qui font un mille
    d'Angleterre' 1,000 + 250 [= 5″] 1:12,672; 'Pieds'
    6,500 [= 5.3″]
? G. Delahaye
Between 1698–1712
Penlee Point(SW)–[Torpoint](NW)
    –[Cattedown](NE)–[Heybrook Bay](SE)
Ink and watercolour on paper (red, green, blue,
    yellow, brown and grey)
23.8″ × 27″ (605mm × 685mm)
The Duke of Buccleuch. Boughton House,
    Kettering

Map of the landscape around Plymouth Sound

made for military reasons. Draws distinction between the Cattewater and Sutton Pool as a merchant shipping area ('Icy sont les Vaisseaux Marchands') and the Hamoaze where battleships lay ('Icy sont les Vaisseaux de Guerre'). Key to Dockyard buildings. Fish-Cage described as 'Corderie' (rope-factory); the cartographer has presumably confused this with the rope-walk nearby. Land use indicated. Inter-tidal area. Soundings. Compass. The cartographer is a Frenchman, possibly G. Delahaye, who was responsible for a plan of Alicante in the same folder.

75
'PLYMOUTH HARBOUR' (inset)
on 'A large chart of the Channell'
'To the Rt Honble the Master, Wardens and
    Assistants of ye TRINITY HOUSE of
    Deptford Strond This Chart is Humbly
    Dedicated and Presented by Thier [sic] most
    humble and Obedient Servant Richard Mount'
in THE ENGLISH PILOT PART I . . . ,
    'printed for Richard Mount and Thomas Page,
    at the Postern on Tower Hill, MDCCI [1701]'
3 miles [= 2.9″] 1: 65,544
? Joel Gascoyne
Rame Head(SW)–Dock(NW)–Oreston(NE)
    –Wembury(SE)
Printed
4.5″ × 5.4″ (114mm × 137mm)
NMM 423/69–71 SEL 03 PB E6863

Chart of Plymouth Sound. Soundings. A few anchorages. Bearings. Sailing directions.

76
'Plan Particulier du Port et Rade De Plemme [sic]
    où les Sondes sont En Brasses' (fathoms)
'3 milles' [= 5.8″] 1:32,772
No statement of responsibility
? Early eighteenth century
Rame Head(SW)–[Saltash](NW)–[Saltram](NE)
    –Wembury(SE)
Ink on paper (grey wash)
9.1″ × 12.6″ (231mm × 320mm)
BN SH Portefeuille 23 Division 5 Pièce 9

Manuscript chart of Plymouth Sound after Green-vile Collins, but not a copy (for instance, the road leading from Stonehouse to Plymouth). Inter-tidal area. Soundings. A few anchorages. Compass pointer with bearings. Note on map: 'Provenant de Mr le Marechal de Cortlogon'.

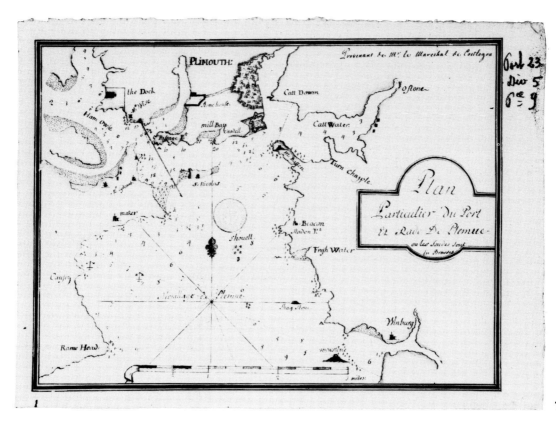

76

77

'PLYMOUTH HARBOUR laid down from a
 Survey' (inset)
on 'A NEW CHART of the BRITISH
 CHANNEL Extending from North Foreland;
 to Scilly Islands &c on the English Shore; and
 from Dunkirk to Ushant on the French.
 Collected from Accurate Surveys. Where unto
 are added the Flowing of the Tydes and Setting
 of the Currents, as they were observed by Capt
 Edmd Halley.'
'Sold by Willm Mount and Thos Page on Tower
 Hill, London'
Royal Geographical Society England and Wales
 S. 107

Minor variations from **75**.

78

'A NEW CHART of the PLYMOUTH
 SOUND observed by Capt Edmd Halley'
BN SH Portefeuille 23 Division 5 Pièce 16

79

'Navy Office. The Ground Platt of Her Majesty's
 Dock Yard at Hamose; with the Roads
 designed to and from it so far as they relate to
 the land of Mr Morris Shewing where they end
 into the common Way's'
'A Scale of Feet' 100 + 400 [4.5″] 1:1,333
No statement of responsibility
c. 1712
Dockyard
Ink and watercolour on paper (red, green, blue,
 brown, yellow)
18.6″ × 38″ (473mm × 966mm)
NMM ADM/Y/PD 1

A detailed plan, with key, of the Dockyard, showing several additions to the yard since the 1698
plan, notably a chapel, porter's house, boatswain of
the yard cabin, house for small mast, saw houses,
brewhouses within the courtyards behind the
officers' dwelling-houses. Also, planned additional
plankhouses and junk and deal yard. The plan also
shows buildings outside the yard where the Clerk
of the Cheque and other individuals were to live.

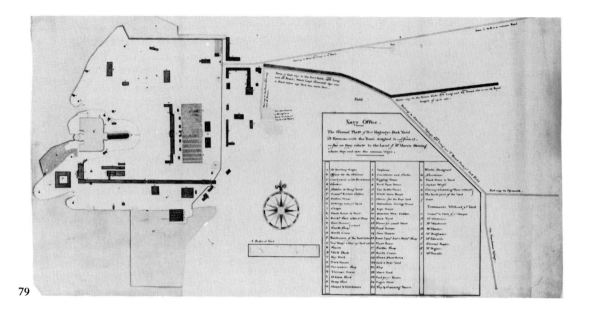

79

Besides this is a plan for a pond to serve the yard with water. The main features of this plan, however, are the roads, footpaths and bridlepaths leading to the Dockyard together with their measurements. This suggests that the date of this plan is *c.* 1712, when there was discussion between the Navy and Sir Nicholas Morice as to the land proposed to be bought from the latter (a diagram of the footways at Dock of 8 April 1712 survives in the Public Record Office: T1/161 f. 125). Here, attention is drawn to roads in existence before the building of the Dockyard. The land on which the Dockyard was built formed part of the manor of Stoke Damerel, and was in private hands throughout this period. The Morice family was extremely reluctant to sell land to the government, who were forced to rent it from them.

80

'The EAST PROSPECT of PLYMOUTH'
In a volume entitled 'REPORTS of the present
   STATE and condition of his MAIESTIES
   FORTIFICATIONS, BUILDINGS and
   ARTILLERY in the SOUTH WESTERN
   Department of ENGLAND otherwise call'd
   PLYMOUTH DIVISION . . .
   CONTAINING Severall Surveys and exact
   Plans . . . BEGUN in the first YEAR of the
   REIGN of our SOVEREIGN LORD
   GEORGE KING etc . . . By Coll Christian
   Lilly one of his Majesties Ingeniers'
'A Scale of 2 Miles' [= 4.4″] 1:28,800

'Col Chr[istian] Lilly'
1714–17
Orientation: W
Hamoaze(W)–Sutton Pool–Mount Batten(E)
Ink and watercolour on paper (green, blue, pink, grey)
7.9″ × 28.1″ (201mm × 714mm)
BL King's MS 45 f. 34

A view of the town of Plymouth including both churches. Citadel.

81

As **80** except:
'A Generall PLAN of PLYMOUTH HARBOUR with its Fortifications and Avenues'
Rame Head(SW)–Saltash(NW)–Mouthstone Point(SE)
11.7″ × 15.4″ (297mm × 391mm)
BL King's MS 45 f. 34

Sparse map of the landscape around Plymouth Sound. Identifies Ordnance storehouses at Coxside and Naval Powder House at Oreston. Roads out of Plymouth. Old Mills slightly out of position. Hamoaze marked as 'Pline River'. Inter-tidal area. Soundings. A few anchorages. Compass.

82

No title
No scale given, but approx. 1:2,400
No statement of responsibility

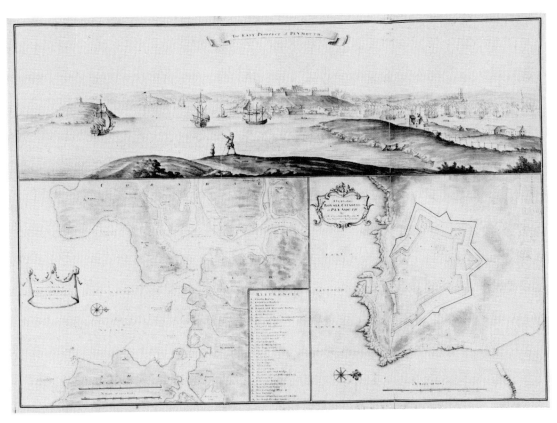

80

Mount Wise(S)–Bull Point(NW)–Weston
  Mill(NE)
Ink and watercolour on paper (red, green)
21.10″ × 44.7″ (555mm × 1143mm)
Bodleian Gough Maps 5 f. 25B

Survey of Dockyard and town and the fields lying
to north, south and east. Roads. Gates. State of
cultivation noted in some cases (furze, bush).
Wooded areas. This map, though unfinished, is
extremely similar in style to **81** and could possibly
be a rough for this detail.

83
As **81** except:
'A PLAN of the ROYALL CITADELL of
  PLYMOUTH By Col: Christian Lilly one of
  his Majesties Ingeniers, 1715'
'A Scale of Feet' 100 + 1,000 [= 5.6″] 1:2,357
Citadel and southern edge of town
11.2″ × 12.6″ (284mm × 320mm)
BL King's MS 45 f. 34

Lilly's plan of the Citadel. Victualling Office. New
Harbour Tower. Old Castle has been renamed
'Queen Elizabeth's Tower'. Note the reference to
'the Ditch cutt out of the Solid Rock' around the
edge of the Citadel. Compass.

84
'A GENERAL PLAN of PLYMOUTH
  HARBOURS with the several Waters, Rocks,
  Shoals, Soundings and Sea coast adjacent by
  C. Lilly 1718'
'A Scale of one English Statute Mile' [= 5″]
  1:12,672
1718
Millbrook(SW)–[Saltash](NW)–Saltram(NE)
  –Staddon Point(SE)
Pencil, ink and watercolour on paper (black and
  red ink, green, grey, yellow)
19.4″ × 27.8″ (variable) (493mm × 706mm)
Bodleian Gough Maps 5 f. 21B

Harbour chart of Plymouth Sound indicating shal-
low water though only Winter Rock, German and
a passage ledge near Cremyll passage are marked.

On land, major fortifications belonging to the Crown are shown (with key) and their situation in relation to each other. Shown for the first time are the French prison, Naval Brewhouse at Southdown and Mount Wise Gun Wharf (later referred to as 'Old Gun Wharf'), the place where a new gun wharf was proposed to be built near Stonehouse and the place where it actually was built near the Dockyard. St Nicholas Island is referred to as the chief defence to the entrance into Hamoaze. 'Empy Combe'. Accurate survey of the landscape with finely drawn street plans of Plymouth, the growing Dock town and Stonehouse. Roads leading out of Plymouth to Exeter, London and Tiverton marked; Saltash road. Many place-names. 'No Place H' shown for first time. Fields. Rivers. Inter-tidal areas ('owse'). Soundings. A few anchorages. Compass rose.

85

'A GENERAL PLAN of the PORTS of HAMOUSE and PLYMOUTH with the Waters, Rocks, Shoals Soundings and Seacoast adjacent'
'Scale of one Mile' [= 3.9"] 1:16,246
No statement of responsibility
Post-1719
Maker(SW)–[Saltash](NW)–[Plympton](NE) –[Staddiscombe](SE)
Ink and watercolour on paper (red, green, grey, brown)
18.8" × 27.4" (478mm × 696mm)
BL K. Top. 11 76

A chart of the Sound showing similar detail to **84**, but much cruder and without the fortifications. Gun wharf above the Dockyard shown for the first time. Mount Wise redoubt. Soundings. A few anchorages. Direction pointer.

86

'A Correct Draught of PLYMOUTH SOUND CATT WATER and HAM OWSE' (inset)
on 'A NEW and CORRECT CHART of the CHANNEL between ENGLAND & FRANCE with considerable Improvements not extant in any Draughts hitherto Publish'd; shewing the Sands, Shoals, depths of Water and Anchorage, with ye flowing of the Tydes, and setting of the Current; as observ'd by the learned Dr Halley'
Sold by Mount and Page on Tower Hill, London
'2 English Miles' [2.6] 1:48,738
Greenvile Collins
1723

Rame head(SW)–[Torpoint](NW)–Lipson(NE) –Mewstone(SE)
8.3" × 9.6" (211mm × 244mm)
Printed
BL Maps C. 26 f. 22(7); NMM 336/49 (GRC 03); Royal Geographical Society England and Wales S. 178

Chart of Plymouth Sound. French prison. Queen's Dock. Sir Francis Drake's or St Nicholas Island. Soundings. A few anchorages. Compass.

See C. Verner 'Captain Collins' Coasting Pilot', p. 38.

87

1723 [1779]
Ink and watercolour on paper (red, orange, brown, turquoise, green, grey)
Archivo Histórico Nacional, Madrid Leg 4218 Sa 194

Manuscript copy of **86**. Minor variations of detail and in copyist's own style, for example, five houses at Rame instead of four, and two trees. Note 'Cidatell' for Citadel.

See Tello *Mapas, Planos y Dibujos*, catalogue no. 144.

88

As **86** except:
'A New & Correct Large Draught of PLYMOUTH SOUND CATTWATER and HAMOAZE'
in *GREAT BRITAIN'S COASTING PILOT: Being a NEW and EXACT SURVEY of the SEA COAST of ENGLAND and SCOTLAND . . .*, printed for Mount and Davidson, on Tower Hill, London, 1792
'A Scale of Two English Miles' [= 6.3"] 1:20,114
17.6" × 21.7" (448mm × 551mm)
BN SH Portefeuille 23 Division 5 Pièce 12 (two copies); NMM 340/54 (GRC 09) PB D8198

See C. Verner 'Captain Collins' Coasting Pilot', p. 41.

89

'A PLAN of the TOWN, CITADEL and HARBOUR of PLYMOUTH, and also of St NICHOLAS ISLAND, the DOCKYARD, NEW GUNN WHARF and parts Adjacent 1724'

'Scale of 400 Feet to an Inch' 50 + 2,000 [5.2"]
  1:4,800
No statement of responsibility
1724
Millbrook(SW)–Torpoint(NW)–[Plympton](NE)
  –[Staddiscombe](SE)
Ink and watercolour on paper (red, yellow, sepia
  and grey wash)
28.1" × 60.4" (714mm × 1535mm)
BL K. Top. 11 75

Map of the landscape around Plymouth Sound.
Saltmarsh shown but not marked. Morice Yard
Gun Wharf. 'Stonehouse Bridge' (Millbridge) with
Mill Pond marked behind. 'Horse Ferry' and 'Pas-
sage House' for Cremyll ferry on Stonehouse pen-
insula. Fields, gardens, orchards shown. Compass.
Map has been repaired.

90
'A PLAN of the TOWN, CITADEL and
  HARBOUR of PLYMOUTH together with
  that of St NICHOLAS's ISLAND, the New
  GUNN WHARF, the DOCK YARD and
  Places Adjacent'
'A Scale of 400 Feet to an Inch' 2,000 [= 5"]
  1:4,800
Drawing Office
1725
Maker peninsula(SW)–Stoke Church(N)
  –Plympton(NE)–Oreston(SE)
Ink and watercolour on paper (red, blue, grey)
53.7" × 27.7" (1365mm × 704mm)
PRO MR 902 (2) (WO 78/1648) (PRO Catalogue
  no. 2039)

Accurate survey of the landscape around the
Sound with inter-tidal areas at Millbay and Sutton
Pool shown in detail. Guildhall. Old Gun Wharf
(Mount Wise). Roads. Fields (land use). Gardens.
Four graving basins at Dockyard.
'STONEHOUSE RIVER'. 'HAMOUSE [Tamar]
RIV . . .'. 'ANCHORING PLACE' off Empy-
combe. Compass rose. Map badly torn on left-
hand side.

91
'An Exact PLAN of the ROYAL CITADEL and
  TOWN of PLYMOUTH 1725'
'Scale 200 Feet to an Inch' 100 + 800 [= 4.5"]
  1:2,400
No statement of responsibility
Orientation: W
The Hoe–Coxside

Ink and watercolour on paper (red, yellow, grey
  wash)
19.5" × 27.8" (495mm × 707mm)
BL K. Top. 11 82

Detailed plan of the Citadel (key) and the town
showing street layout and identifying particular
buildings and features (key). Citadel: houses of
the Fort Major and Chaplain identified. Flag
Staff. New Harbour Tower now renamed Wilhen's Tower. This is the first eighteenth-century
plan to show the town in detail. The town gates
(Martin's Gate and Gascoigne Gate are shown for
the first time) and streets are identified, also civic
buildings (the town hall, workhouse) and markets
(fish market, shambles). The siting of water conduits is also shown and 'the great Tree'. Note
references to the town wall north of the town.
Ropewalk.

92
'St Nicholas Island in Plymouth Sound, 1725'
'Scale 50 Feet to an Inch' 50 + 300 [= 7"] 1:600
? Drawing Office
Orientation: S
St Nicholas Island
Ink and watercolour on paper (red, green, grey)
19.8" × 42.2" (503mm × 1,081mm)
BL K. Top. 11 91

Plan of St Nicholas Island showing perimeter wall
with ten gun-platforms (named), gatehouse,
guardhouse, powderhouses, carriage house and
barracks including suttling house. Bogg houses.
Shot piles. Bottom right-hand corner has section
drawings.

93
'PLIMOUTH SOUND To the Right
  Honourable George Lord Viscount Torrington,
  John Cokburne Esq, Sir John Norris Knt, Sir
  Charles Wager Knt, Sir Thomas Littleton Bart,
  The Lord Viscount Malpas AND Samuel
  Molyneux Esq, COMMISSIONERS For
  Executing the OFFICE of Lord High Admiral
  of GREAT BRITAIN and IRELAND, AND
  OF ALL His Majesty's Plantation Etc THIS
  WORK is most Humbly Inscribed'
in *Atlas Maritimus et Commercialis* . . . , printed
  for James and John Knapton, London, 1728
'A Scale of one Mile' [= 2.4"] 1:26,400
No statement of responsibility
Penlee Point(SW)–Torpoint(NW)–Catdown(NE)
  –Mewstone(SE)
Printed

11″ × 10.4″ (280mm × 265mm)
BL Maps C.11.a.5; NMM 341/9 (DDC 01/9) PB
  D8196

Chart of Plymouth Sound showing White Hall
('White Leale') at Stonehouse. Stone hedges
described as 'Stone henge' and 'Stone hemp'. 'Mt
Batter'. 'Sladen Point' (Staddon). Soundings. A
few anchorages. Compass. Sailing directions
include reference to 'the Cloudesly . . . or . . .
Shovel Rock, call'd so from Sir Cloudesly Shovel,
who order'd a Buoy to be put upon it . . . it lies
sunk in 16 Foot Water'. 'Tinker 16 foot'. Plymouth
is one of several charts on this sheet: the others are
of: Sheerness and Shoeburyness; the Isle of Wight
and Portsmouth; Portland; Dartmouth; Falmouth.

94
'Nieuwe Afteekening van het Inkoomen van
  PLYMOUTH en Salcombe Rivier geleegen int'
  Canaal aan de Zuijdkust van Engeland tot
  Amsterdam bij Gerard van Keulen aan de
  Nieuwen brugh met Previlegie'
'*een halve Duytse Myl van 15 in een Graad of 2 Mile
  Engels*' [6.6″] 1:43,768
Gerard van Keulen
[1734]
Rame Head(SW)–Trematon Castle(NW)
  –Plympton(NE)–Stoke(SE)
Printed
20.2″ × 23.5″ (513mm × 597mm)
NMM VKE 19/38 40 PB D8039; Plymouth
  Central Library

A chart of the Sound with inset of the estuary at
Salcombe. Place-names are given, and some
important features drawn in, but in general houses,
trees and hills are representational and the coastline
is not precise. Maker Church shown twice!
'Stonehedg' drawn in on the Hoe and on
Stonehouse peninsula. 'Stonhouse of steene
huissen'. Blockhouse at Mount Edgcombe. 'Freshwater of Vars Water' at Bovisand. Rocks: 'Winter
Rok 14 Voet', 'Shovell 15 Voet', 'Tinker Swiftsure
16 Voet'. Inter-tidal area. Soundings. Anchorages
('Anchor Grond'). Compass bearings.

See C. Koeman *Atlantes Neerlandici*, Amsterdam,
vol. IV, 1970, p. 375.

95
'Plymouth Sound' (inset)
on 'To the Hon Charles Churchill Esq Major
  General of his Majesty's Forces Colonel of a
  Regt of Dragoons Groom of the Bedchamber
  to his Majesty Governour of Plymouth and
  Member of Parliament for Castle Rising in
  Norfolk This View of the Royal Citadel of
  Plymouth is humbly Presented by His most
  obliged Grateful & most Obedient servt
  Sandford Mace'
'Scale of half a Mile' [= 2″] 1:15,840
'S. Mace *Del*[*ineavit*]'; 'Cha[rles] Mosley *sculp*[*sit*]'
Published 25 July 1737
Plymouth Sound
Printed
5.6″ × 9.2″ (142mm × 234mm)
BL 2140 (25); Bodleian Gough Maps 5 f. 10B;
  BN SH Portefeuille 23 Division 5 Pièce 19;
  Archives du Génie ART 14: PLYMOUTH /2

Inset of Plymouth Sound on a plan of the Citadel
showing its buildings in detail. The inset is a simple
map to illustrate the Citadel's geographical position. It has a few landmarks, roads leading out of
Plymouth to Dock and to London. Inter-tidal area.
Soundings. 'The King's Moarings' below Millbay.

96
No title
Scale: 400 [= 4″] 1:1,200
'Robertus Madgett *Delineavit*'
? 1741
Citadel
Ink and watercolour on paper (red, green,
  yellow, grey, brown)
17.3″ × 22.6″ (440mm × 574mm)
PRO MPH 728 (WO 78/863) (PRO Catalogue
  no. 2064)

Coloured plan of the Citadel. A more finished
version than its nineteenth-century copy, though it
lacks the key and does not include so much of the
East Hoe. Note gardens shown in Governor's
meadow north of Citadel adjoining site of the Old
Castle, and at the Lambhay.

97
'Plan of the Royal Citadel at Plymouth, 1741'
'Scale of 100 + 300 Feet' [= 4″] 1:1,200

B. O

'Copied by R[ober]t Hoddle'
[15 October 1812]
Citadel
Ink and watercolour on paper (red, green,
    yellow, grey, brown)
28″ × 19.2″ (712mm × 498mm)
PRO MPHH 223/2

Early nineteenth-century copy of **96** prepared for the
Ordnance Board during its dispute over the fields
adjoining the Hoe claimed by Plymouth Corporation. Key to Citadel buildings. Note bowling-
green on the Hoe set out by the Governor; also
encroachments made by the inhabitants of Plymouth. A pencilled note on the Hoe reads: 'This
Bowling Green is no more it having been added to
Hooe [sic] and is the Property of a private Individual
by what right is not known– it appears to have been
in 1741 the property of the Ordnance . . .'.

98
'PLYMOUTH SOUND' (inset)
on 'A correct CHART of the ENGLISH
    CHANNEL From the No. Foreland to the
    Land's End on the Coast of ENGLAND and
    from Calais to Brest on the Coast of
    FRANCE: From the latest & best Observations
    For Mr Tindal's Continuation of Mr Rapin's
    History'
No scale given
'R.W. Seale del[ineavit] et sculp[sit]'
1744–7
Rame Head(SW)–Hamoaze estuary(NW)
    –Oreston(NE)–Mewstone(SE)
3.8″ × 4″ (97mm × 102mm)
Printed
Plymouth Central Library

Small printed chart of Plymouth Sound.

99
No title
'A Scale of one Mile' [= 2.8″] 1:22,628
[B. Slade]
[27 November 1747]
Maker(SW)–[Wilcove](NW)–? Weston Mill
    Lake(NE)–Mount Batten(SE)
Ink and watercolour on paper (red, grey and
    brown washes)
7.5″ × 12″ (191mm × 305mm)
PRO MPI 253 (Adm 106/3545) (PRO Catalogue
    no. 2044)

Harbour chart of the Hamoaze intended to show
suitable sites for the proposed moorings. The chart
was made to accompany a letter of 27 November
1747 from B. Slade at the Plymouth Yard to Sir
Jacob Acworth at the Navy Office (PRO Adm
106/3545). The sketch gives the names of the coves
and pools on either side of the Hamoaze estuary. It
notes the moorings already laid (below the *Berwick*
hulk) and the places where chain moorings and
transporting anchors are proposed to be laid for
conducting ships out of and into Hamoaze, and in
and out of the south channel. These would be
especially useful for ships detained for lack of wind.
Soundings. Compass.

100
'A PLAN OF HIS MAJESTY'S DOCK YARD
    NEAR PLYMOUTH 1748'
'A Scale of Eighty Feet to an Inch' 480 [= 6″]
    1:960
No statement of responsibility
Orientation: E
Dockyard
Ink and watercolour on paper (red, green, grey,
    yellow, pale brown wash)
19.9″ × 28.3″ (506mm × 719mm)
NMM ADM/Y/PD 2

A plan of the Dockyard. The following buildings
(shown on a key) have been added since the last
plan of the Dockyard *temp.* Queen Anne (**79**):
armourer's shop, plumber's shop, houses for top-
pings of hemp, powderhouses, pumphouses,
houses of ease, pounds for slabb quarters, sailmakers' tarring house, stoving kilns. Other additions (shown in red and marked on the plan):
plankhouses, working sheds, engine house, oar
house, taphouse, sail loft, mould loft, joiners and
house carpenters' shops, line spinners' shed, top
house. Other additions (shown in grey and marked
on the plan): slips, graving slip, docks, mud dock.
(Graving was a means of cleaning a ship's bottom
by scraping or burning and coating with tar). The
date of this plan coincides with the end of the War
of the Austrian Succession.

101
'PLAN of the CITTADEL of PLYMOUTH'
Scale: 200 + 1,000 ft [= 3″] 1:4,800
'AD' [? Augustus Durnford]
Between 1750 and 1752
Citadel and the Lambhay
Ink and watercolour on paper (red, blue, brown,
    yellow)
4.5″ × 7.1″ (115mm × 180mm)
BL Add MS 22875 f. 20

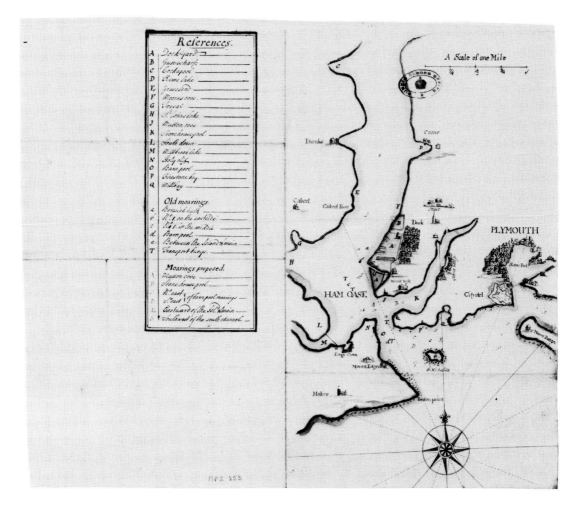

References.

A Dockyard
B Gunwharf
C Cockapool
D Lime lake
E graveland
F Weeped cove
G Areval
H St. Nicholas lake
J Mutter cove
K Stonehousepool
L Sulk dorve
M Millbrook lake
N Holy cliff
O Barn pool
P Friestons bay
Q Millbay

Old moarings.
a Barwich hulk
b No 1. on the eastside
c No 1. in the middle
d Barnpool
e Between the Sand & main
T Transport hups

Moarings proposed.
Mutton cove
Stone-housepool
No east   } of them pool moarings
No west
x Eastward of the St. Nicholas
y Southward of the south channel

A Scale of one Mile
¼ ½ ¾

Thanks
Caine
Cabool
Cabool Point
Dock
PLYMOUTH
Citadel
HAM OAZE
Mount Edgcombe
St. Nicholas
Maker
Beson point

99

Batteries noted (Royal, Ligonier's, Frederick's).
Victualling Office buildings depicted in detail.
   This map is included in the volume, 'PLANS OF
FORTIFICATIONS', as are **102** and **103**.

Key gives details of guns on the platforms around
the perimeter wall (eleven posts). Also capacity of
barrels that can be held by powder magazine and
gunners' magazine.

102
'PLAN of ST NICHOLAS ISLAND'
Scale: '400 Feet' [= 2″] 1:2,400
'A.D.' [? Augustus Durnford]
Between 1750 and 1752
Orientation: W
St Nicholas Island
Ink and watercolour on paper (red, blue, brown,
   yellow)
4.5″ × 7.1″ (114mm × 180mm)
BL Add MS 22875 f. 21

103
'PLAN of the GUN WHARF and the KING'S
   DOCK YARD near PLYMOUTH'
'Scale 400 Feet to an Inch' 200 + 600 [= 2″]
   1:4,800
'J.H.' [? Joseph Heath]
Between 1750 and 1752
Orientation: E
Dockyard
Ink and watercolour on paper (red, blue, brown)
4.5″ × 7.1″ (114mm × 180mm)
BL Add MS 22875 f. 22

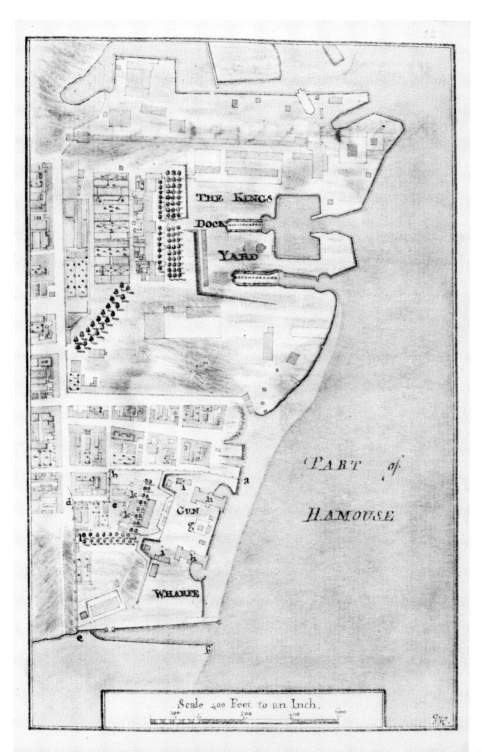

THE KINGS
DOCK
YARD

PART of

HAMOUSE

GUN

WHARFE

Scale 400 Feet to an Inch.

103

Key notes that the Gun Wharf has the capacity to equip thirty-six ships; also gives details of small arms, number of barrels held by powder magazines and civil staffing.

104

'A PLAN of the TOWN and CITADEL of PLYMOUTH' (inset)

on 'An ACCURATE MAP OF DEVON SHIRE Divided into its HUNDREDS. Drawn from the best Authorities, assisted by the most approved Modern Maps with various Improvements. Illustrated with HISTORICAL EXTRACTS relative to its Natural produce, Mines, Minerals, Trade, Manufactures and present State of the City of Exeter and the principal Towns, with a Plan of Plymouth'

'To the Most Noble John Duke of Bedford Lord Lieutenant and *Custos Rotulorum* for the COUNTY of DEVON'

Sold by I. Tinney at the Golden Lion in Fleet Street, London

'A Scale of Furlongs 8 to a Mile' 2 [= 2″] 1:7,920

'Eman: Bowen Geogr[apher] to His Majesty' April 1754

Town and Citadel; small inset of Mount Batten

Printed

8.5″ × 7.4″ (216mm × 189mm)

BL Maps C.10 d.18; Bodleian (E) C17:25 (8); Service Historique de l'Armée de Terre KII B 2 3. Frequent editions.

Plan showing blocks of streets with their names, and also roads leading out of the town. The plan also identifies churches, civic buildings, town gates, water-conduits etc. References to buildings and features within the Citadel. Fish-House. Victualling Office also shown in detail. Orchards, gardens on edge of town shown. 'PLYMOUTH from a poor fishing Village originally is become a rich fair well-inhabited and frequented Town of Trade; the Haven is so large and safe as to admit of Ships of the greatest Size and Burden. . . .'

This map was also published in Bowen and Kitchin's *ATLAS OF ENGLAND & WALES* and in *The Large English Atlas*.

I owe the date given for this plan to Francis Bennett *A Cartobibliography of the Printed Maps of Devon* (forthcoming, 1993).

See Le Gear *Geographical Atlases*, vol. 6, Library of Congress, 1963, chart 11 8120

105

[*c.* 1779]

Ink and watercolour on paper (red, orange, brown, blue, green, grey)

Archivo Histórico Nacional, Madrid Leg 4218 Sa 182

Manuscript copy of **104** prepared for the proposed invasion of England by France and Spain in 1779. Minor variations from the original: e.g. buildings in street to right of Pig Market. Place-names suggest a French copyist: 'Officiers Houses', and 'St Budix . . . Rattre . . . Dardington' on main map. Endorsed '*le Devonshire*'. Margin contains scales of latitude and longitude.

See Tello *Mapas, Planos y Dibujos*, catalogue no. 132.

106

As **105**

Archivo Histórico Nacional Leg 4218 Sa 183

Minor variations from **105** include the depiction of the Citadel's outer ramparts.

107

As **105** except:

7.7″ × 7.4″ (195mm × 188mm)

Archivo Histórico Nacional Leg 4218 Sa 184

Minor variations in spelling, again suggesting that the copyist was French. Endorsed: '*Plan de Plymouth et ports de Darmouth a Plymouth avec leurs distance intermediare. La Baye de Torbaye aussi.*'

108

'A PLAN of the TOWN & CITADEL of PLYMOUTH in the COUNTY of DEVON'

in *London Magazine*, 1755 (facing p. 32)

Printed for R. Baldwin in Paternoster Row, London

'A Scale of 1320 feet or quarter of a Mile' 1320 [= 1.3″] 1:12,184

No statement of responsibility

Citadel and Town

Printed

6.7″ × 4.4″ (170mm × 112mm)

Bodleian Hope Adds 410

Plan of the Citadel and town. Key. In both style and layout, this plan closely resembles **131**, though they are not the same. For example, on this plan the

Citadel has a key (whose references are exactly the same as those on **104**). Also, the Fish–House at the entrance to Sutton Pool is marked here.

109
'PLAN of the LINES round PLYMOUTH
    DOCK Shewing in yellow where the proposed
    barracks A are plac'd without ye Bastions'
'Scale 400 Feet to an Inch' 1,600 ft [= 4″] 1:4,800
'D. Slack *Delin[eavit]*'
Pre-1756
Torpoint(W)–Stoke Church(N)–Firestone Bay(S)
Ink and watercolour on paper (red, green,
    brown, yellow, turquoise and grey washes)
14.3″ × 20.9″ (373mm × 531mm)
BL K. Top. 11 86

Plan of Plymouth Dock and town designed to show the new barracks. Limestone quarry opposite White Hall across Stonehouse Creek. Roads. Hills. Fields. Direction pointer.

110
'A Geometrical PLAN and West Prospect of
    STOKE TOWN in the County of Devon with
    His Majesty's Dock Yard and Ordnance
    Wharfe Humbly Inscrib'd to Sr John St Aubyn
    Baronet'
'A Scale of half a quarter of a Mile' 660 ft
    [= 5.4″] 1:1,466
'Bro Milton *inv[eni]t*'
? Pre-1756
Orientation: E
Dockyard and town of Dock
Printed
26.1″ × 23.7″ (663mm × 602mm)
BL K. Top. 11 85; BN SH Portefeuille 23
    Division 5 Pièce 18

Dockyard and Ordnance Wharf as **112** except this map lacks the new mast house adjacent to the timber ground. Chapel drawn. Plan of Dock town showing tenements with gardens. Gives street names. Parish church. Roads to Plymouth and 'Whitehouse' marked. 'Path way to Stonehouse'. Fields on edge of town shown. View of Dockyard in perspective along top border of map.

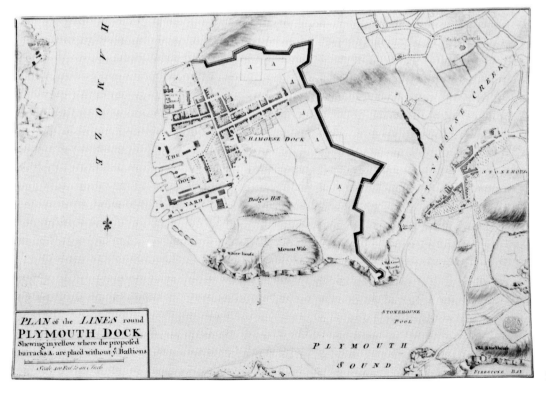

109

111

As **110** except:

'P. Fourdrinier *Sculp*[*sit*]'; 'T. Milton *Surv*[*?*] *et delin*[*eavit*]'

BL 2123 (53); Bodleian Gough Maps Devonshire 8

112

'A Geometrical Plan and West Elevation of His Majesty's Dock Yard near PLYMOUTH with the Ordnance Wharfe etc To the Rt Honble George Parker, Earl of Macclesfield Viscount Parker and President of the Royal Society etc This Plate is inscribed by his Lordship's most obedt Servant Thos Milton'

'A Scale of half quarter of a Mile' 660 ft [= 4.4″] 1:1,800

'T. Milton *Surv*[*?*] *et delin*[*eavit*]. Shipping by I. [John] Cleveley. P.C. Canot *Sculp*[*sit*].'

'According to Act of Parliament February 2d 1756'

Orientation: E

Dockyard

Printed

10.2″ × 19.7″ (excluding borders); (259mm x 501mm)

BL K. Top. 11 87; BN SH Portefeuille 23 Division 5 Pièce 17 (two copies); Bodleian Gough Maps Devonshire 7

Plan of the Dockyard and Ordnance Wharf adjacent, published in the year in which the Seven Years' War broke out. Key. Only slight changes since the 1748 plan (**100**): a new mast house adjacent to the timber ground and sawpits nearby. Officer's garden beyond the pond. The Ordnance Wharf (begun 1719) shows magazines, storehouses, workshops, Officers' houses and gardens. The plan has a richly decorated border around the edge including cartouches with ships inside, of which one is 'Burnt to the Water's Edge' and another 'Blown up'.

See A.W. Skempton *British civil engineering 1640–1840: a bibiliography of contemporary printed reports, plans and books*, Mansell, 1987, no. 938.

113

'A PLAN of the Great and Cross Roads about PLYMOUTH and DOCK taken in February 1756'

'A Scale of One Mile and a Half or Twelve Furlongs' 1½ Miles [= 5″] 1:19,008

No statement of responsibility

Southdown(SW)–Saltash(NW)–[Crownhill](NE) –Mount Batten(SE)

Ink and grey wash on paper

18″ × 16.8″ (457mm × 427mm)

Devon Record Office, Exeter L1258/Maps: Road 3

An early road-widening scheme! Map of the towns of Plymouth, Stonehouse and Dock and their hinterland to show existing and proposed roads. It is proposed to widen the roads to Plympton, Oreston, Dock, Saltash, Stonehouse (A, B, C, D, E on the map) and to construct a new road leading northwards out of the town. The road widening and repairing arose out of the Turnpike Act. Roads leading from North Devon and Cornwall to Plymouth are coloured red to distinguish them from the cross roads (minor roads) which are described as mostly very narrow and deep. Many place-names. Pound at Dock and old pound at Milehouse. St Budeaux Common. New Inn (Whitleigh). Hospital (Lipson). The large houses of the gentry are again used as landmarks (Mr Were's at Weston Mills, Docton Esq at Whitleigh, Manadon, Mr Moreshead at Widey, Mr Culme at Tothill, Parker Esq at Saltram, John Harris Esq at Radford). Ships and boats. Direction pointer.

114

'PLAN OF THE TOWN CITADEL DOCK AND COUNTRY round PLYMOUTH'

'Scale 800 Feet to an Inch' 800 + 4,000 ft [= 6″] 1:9,600

'Drawn by John Manson Ens[ign] 1756'

Maker(SW)–Torpoint(NW)–Lipson(NE)– [Staddon Point](SE)

Ink and watercolour on paper (red, green, turquoise, yellow and grey washes)

19.7″ × 24″ (501mm × 610mm)

BL K. Top. 11 77

Map of the landscape around the Sound designed to show gun entrenchments, the recently built barracks and lines at Dock. The barracks consisted of two large squares (39a, 39f) of barracks for four companies each, and four lesser (39b–e) for three companies each. Thirty guns could be mounted round the lines. Main and small *barrières* at Dock lines shown. Place of arms. Dock horsemill and windmill. At the Citadel, batteries which can mount five, nine and nineteen guns respectively to 'scour the Channel to Hamoze' and another of fifteen guns to defend the Cattewater. St Nicholas Island can mount 100 guns. Salt-marsh behind Old Mills marked for first time (though shown on **89**), also Stonehouse–Dock passage (bridge built in 1767). 'Stonehouse Lane' (from Plymouth)

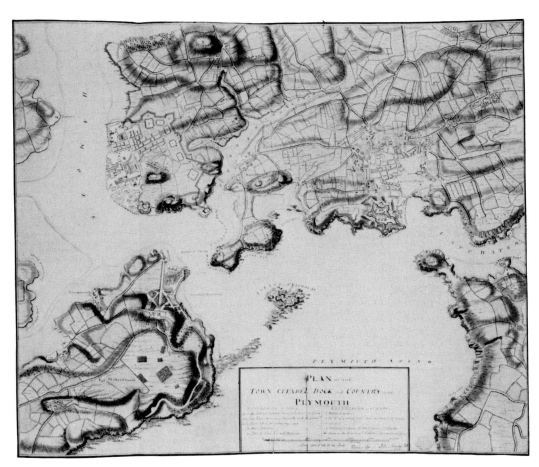

114

marked, also footway from Dock near Millbridge. 'Quint' (probably a quintain, a form of tilting board) and parson's house at Stoke shown. Mount Pleasant blockhouse. Stonehouse blockhouse. Barn Pool moorings. Roads. Hills. Fields (land use). Inter-tidal area.

115

As **114** except:
'PLAN OF THE TOWN, CITADEL, DOCK and COUNTRY round PLYMOUTH 1756'
'Abr[aha]m D'Aubant *delin[eavi]t*'
19.4″ × 24.1″ (493mm × 612mm)
BL K. Top. 11 78 1

Same content as **114** except that Maker Town and landing place on St Nicholas Island are not marked.

116

'Plymouth Sound'
'Scale 800 Feet to an Inch' 1,000 + 5,000 [= 7.5″]
    1:9,600
'Col[onel] Desmaretz'
Between 1756 and 1767
Rame peninsula(SW)–Mutley(N)–Down Thomas(SE)
Ink and watercolour on paper (red, green, brown, grey wash)
25.5″ × 37.6″ (648mm × 956mm)
PRO MPHH 129 (WO 78/1474) (PRO Catalogue no. 2041)

Map of the landscape around Plymouth Sound showing limestone quarries and kilns (Mount Wise, Millbay, Crabtree), also a quarry at Foss (Millbrook) and a claypit (Wilcove). Many place-names. Under Hill Farm, Burrough House (Stoke Damerel). Turnchapel Rock. Radford Mill. Rivers.

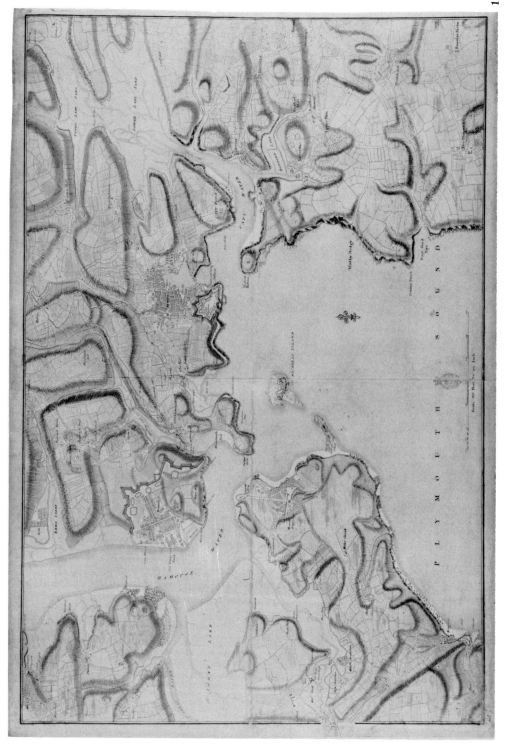

Roads. Hills (relief). Fields (land use). Wooded areas. Some inter-tidal areas. Fleur-de-lys direction pointer.

117
As **116** except:
'Office of Ordnance Copy'd by Thomas Smart May ye 30 1765'
BL K. Top. 11 78 2

Hills around Plymouth are given more emphasis than in **116**.

118
As **116** except:
'Copy'd by F. Gould 20 Sepr 1775'
PRO MPHH 129/1

St Nicholas fort marked 'B'.

119
As **116** except:
'Copy'd by Wm Test'
PRO MPHH 129/3

Closer in style to original than the other copies of **116**.

120
As **116**
PRO MPHH 129/2

121
As **116**
PRO MPHH 129/4 (five copies)

122
As **116**
PRO MPHH 129/5

123
As **116**
PRO MPHH 129/6

Hills shaded in grey wash

124
As **116**
BL Add MSS 57638 6

125
'The PLAN or Particular to which the Annexed Certificate of Edward Bayntun Esq His Majesty's Surveyer [sic] General of the Dutchy [sic] of Cornwall doth refer 1757'
'Scale of Feet' 100 + 500 [= 4.3"] 1: 1,674
Sutton Pool
Ink and watercolour on parchment (red, green, yellow, grey, blue)
26.5" × 25" (675mm × 635mm)
WDRO W 467

Plan of Sutton Pool drawn by Bayntun to show the duchy's ownership. He had been asked to make an official viewing and survey in the presence both of a committee of the mayor and commonalty and of Thomas Veale, lessee of the Pool from the duchy. Veale had complained to the Surveyor General about the mayor and commonalty's encroachments. The plan draws a distinction between the area coloured green (Sutton Pool to high-water mark, which belonged to the duchy) and that coloured red (erections made by the mayor and commonalty, or their lessees). The key tells us that in several cases these erections have been recovered by law from the lessees. The key gives the names of several small quays around the Pool. The Salt House is also noted and what was previously Coxside storehouses is now a hospital for sick and hurt seamen.

R.N. Worth (*History of Plymouth*, 1890) discusses this dispute.

126
'An EXACT PLAN of the GROUND humbly proposed to be PURCHASED at the DOCK of PLYMOUTH'
'Scale of 250 Feet to an Inch' 500 [= 2"] 1:3,000
'Engraved by Thos Jefferys'
? 1759
Dockyard and town
Printed
20.7" × 17.7" (526mm × 450mm)
BL 2147 (6); NMM MS 80/046

Plan of land surrounding Dockyard and town which the Ordnance Board proposed to buy. Most of this land is coloured green, apart from a section at the eastern edge extending nearly to Stoke parsonage which is coloured brown denoting that it was church land. Of the land to be bought, 150 acres 2 roods 14 poles are described as good ground; 44 acres 2 roods 35 poles as coarse rocky ground. A barrier beyond the Ordnance Wharf is described as the 'barrier thro which the Townspeople fetch their best drinking Water'. Features not noticed elsewhere are a public house and timber merchant's yard at Mutton Cove; shipbuilders near the Old Gun Wharf, and the passage house on the Dock side of Stonehouse–Dock passage.

127

'A PLAN of His Majesty's Yard PLYMOUTH
  as in the Year 1761 with the Additions &
  Alterations propos'd to be made thereto as
  describ'd in Yellow'
'Scale of Feet 510' [= 6.7"] 1:913
Navy Office
November 1764
Orientation: E
Dockyard
Ink and watercolour on paper (yellow, green)
23.1" × 35.5" (588mm × 901mm)
NMM LAD/11 f. 39

Plan of the Dockyard. Only the areas shaded yellow are marked and all have measurements in feet. 'Working Shed', 'Blockmakers Shop', 'House Carpenters and Wheelwright's Shop and Mould Loft', 'Working Shed and Store Cabbins', 'Joiners Shop and Houses for Plank and Deal', 'New Dock

Propos'd', 'New Dock lately finish'd and part of the propos'd design', 'Slopes', 'Hemp Houses', 'Laying House', 'Spinning House', 'White Yarn House', 'Tarring House', 'Black Yarn House', 'Working Boat House', 'Locks for stowing Rough Masts over then Houses for Masts and Yards of Ship Laying Up', 'Locks for stowing Rough Masts over then Houses for Planks and Deals', 'Smiths' Shop', 'Crane', 'Saw Pitts' (twice), 'Rigging House', 'Store House Buildings', 'Sail Loft', 'Store Houses' (three times)', 'Graving Place', 'Anchor Wharf', 'Slips', 'Working Mast House', 'Pound for the Security of Mast & Yards of Ships Refitting or Laying on shore, & Surveying Rough Masts', 'Jetty head for Furze'.

128

'Plan of Plymouth Yard with the Estimat for the
  several Buildings'
Scale: 10 + 500 [= 6.7"] 1:913
No statement of responsibility
c. 1764
Orientation: E
Dockyard
Ink on paper (red, black)

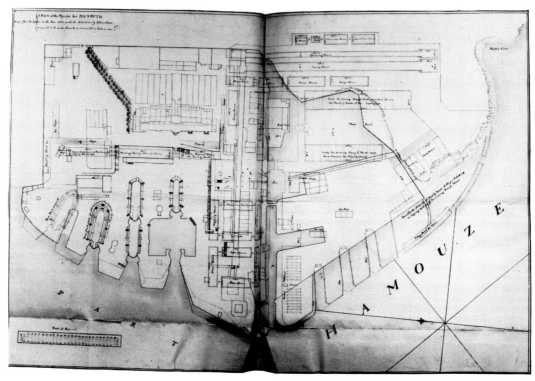

21.3″ × 44.5″ (541mm × 1127mm)
NMM ADM/Y/PD 3

Plan of the Dockyard showing the buildings for which estimates have been prepared. Key:

		£	s.	d.
A	Estimate of the Charge for Erecting a New Jetty head	2,747	5	0
B	Charge for Building a New Dock	51,131	19	6
	Works that are detach'd from the New Dock though in their uses connected with it	22,695	5	0
C	Charge for the North Building Under the Rock [blockmaker's house, carpenter's and wheelwright shop and mould loft on **127**]	4,576	18	3
D	Do. for the Middle Building Under the Rock [working shed and store cabins]	4,576	18	3
E	Do. for the South Building Under the Rock [joiner's shop and houses for plank and deal]	3,602	14	2
F	Do. for Building the Stairs under the Rock	1,772	12	2
G	Do. for Building the Brest Walls	622	2	0
	No. 1 For finishing the two houses	4,040	0	0
	2			
H	Charge for Building the New Storehouses South Side the Yard			
	3	8,355	0	0
	4	8,355	0	0
	5	6,266	0	0
	6	6,200	0	0
	7	6,266	0	0
	8	6,266	0	0
I	Wharf Walls in the South Channel	44,353	0	0
K	Smith's Shop	2,857	0	0
L	Charge for Building Eighteen Saw Pitts	1,735	1	6
M	Do. for Ten Bays of Boathouses	5,612	3	4
N	Do. for Building five Hemp houses	9,777	7	9
O	Do. for a Spinning House	12,158	12	4
P	Do. for a Laying House with Celler's for Tarr	17,024	6	4
	[NB. O and P have been transposed since **127**]			
Q	Do. for a White Yarn House	500	15	0
R	Do. for a Wheel House, and Kettle House for tarring of Yarn	407	7	0
S	Do. for two Black Yarn Houses	1,841	7	8
T	Do. for Piling and planking for a Foundation for Building the Walls of the Boat	46,982	7	10
	And mast pond, With a Pair of gates, and Apron and Locks for Confining the Masts			
V	Do. for Building Eight Bays for Mast Houses with two Slips	6,111	9	6
W	Do. for Building the Yard Wall	1,800	0	0
X	Do. for Piers fronting the New Mast Houses and New Ground	13,304	0	10
Y	Do. for Anchor Racks	1,243	0	0
Z	Levelling the Ground for a Foundation to the Rope and Hemp Houses &c &c	13,019	0	0
&	To a Drain under the North end of the Rope House to the Boat Pond	1,175	5	0
a	For Building and Compleating one Pier and Finnishing the third Slip	15,744	16	0
b	Wharf Wall between the third Slip and Mast House to be built with Stone the Same as the Slips and to Return by the North Side of the New Mast houses	5,765	1	8
	For Digging and Making Level the Rock for the South end of the Mast Pond	16,111	0	0
	For Making Level the Rock at the North part of the Yard and Rigging House Hill where the Rope House now stands	5,506	0	0
	Charge for Building the house Crane in the Room of that on the New Ground or at the upper part of the Channel that May be first wanted	265	0	0

Total   360,775 16 1

129
'CARTE DE LA BAYE ET PORT DE PLIMOUTH'
in *LE PETIT ATLAS MARITIME Vol IV Contenant L'EUROPE ET LES DIVERS ETATS QU'ELLE RENFERME Excepté La France*, plate 10

'Echelle d'une demie Lieue $\frac{1}{2}$' [= 1.6″] 1: 59,400
No statement of responsibility
? 1764
Rame Head(SW)–Saltash(NW)–Plymouth(NE)–
    Yealm estuary(SE)
Printed
8.3″ × 6.7″ (211mm × 170mm)
BL K. MAR 1 12; BN Ge FF 4696; NMM
    211/483 PB D8194

Chart of Plymouth Sound. Soundings. A few
anchorages. Bearings.

130
As **129** except:
'PLAN DES VILLE ET CITADELLE DE
    PLYMOUTH'
in *LE PETIT ATLAS MARITIME*, vol. IV,
    plate 11
'Echelle de Trois Cent vingt Toises' 320 [= 2″]
    1:12,480

Town and Citadel
7.2″ × 6.6″ (183mm × 167mm)
BL K. MAR 1 12; BN Ge FF 4696; NMM
    211/484: PB D8194

Plan of Plymouth town and Citadel. Very similar
to Bowen (**104**) but in French, also key has one
transposition of order 'm *La Douane*' and 'n *Porte du
Sud*'. Mount Batten marked 'Patton'. Soundings
given (not in Bowen).

131
'A PLAN of the TOWN and CITADEL of
    PLYMOUTH' (inset)
on 'A MAP OF THE COUNTY of DEVON
    . . . Delineated from an ACTUAL SURVEY
    . . . By BENJAMIN DONN'
'LONDON, Printed for the AUTHOR, And
    Sold by the Booksellers of Devon; by Mr
    JOHNSTON, in Ludgate Street; Mr LAW, in
    Ave Mary Lane; Mr JOHNSON, opposite the

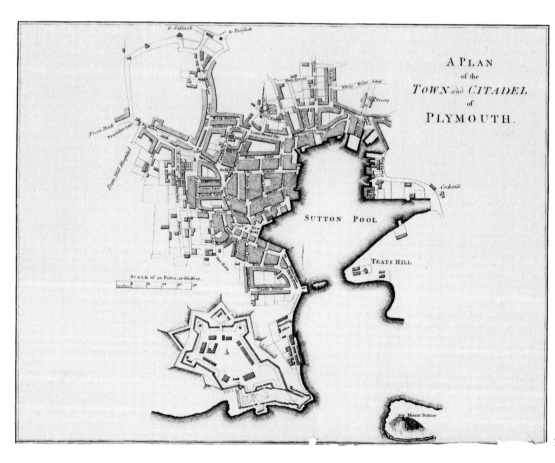

Monument; Mr BALDWIN, in Pater noster
Row; and the Print-Sellers of London
MDCCLXV [1765]'
'To John Baring of Mount Radford, & to
Matthew Lee of Ebford near Exeter Esqrs This
Map, as a grateful Acknowledgment of the
great and generous Assistance which they have
given thereto, is humbly Inscribed . . .'
'SCALE of 40 Poles or 660 Feet' 40 [= 1.7″]
1:4,658
'B. Donn, Teacher of the Mathematics etc late of
Bideford, now of the City of Bristol'
Citadel and town
Printed
11.3″ × 14.7″ (287mm × 373mm)
BL C.11 c.7; BN Ge DD 1488; Bodleian Gough
Maps Devonshire 3; Plymouth City Museum;
Royal Geographical Society England and Wales
D. 15

Plan of Plymouth town and Citadel showing street
plan including names and roads leading out of the
town to Dock, Saltash and Tavistock. Churches,
Guildhall, town gates, water-conduits identified.
Buildings within Citadel shown but no key. Victualling Office shown. Friary.

Benjamin Donn *A Map of the County of Devon 1765*,
reprinted in facsimile with an introduction by
W.L.D. Ravenhill, Devon and Cornwall Record
Society NS 9 and the University of Exeter, 1965.

132
'Carte de la Citadelle de Plymouth pris Sur la
Carte du Devon par Dunn'
Ink on paper (red and black ink; blue and grey
wash)
19″ × 27.1″ (483mm × 689mm)
Archives du Génie ART 14: PLYMOUTH/6

Manuscript copy of **131**.

NB: The Service Historique de l'Armée de Terre
holds another manuscript copy of **131** but
excluding the inset plans of Plymouth and Dock
(KII B N 20).

133
As **131** except:
'A PLAN of STOKE TOWN and PLYMOUTH
DOCK'
Orientation: E
Dockyard and town
11.6″ × 14.7″ (298mm × 421mm)

BL C.11 c.7; BN Ge DD 1488; Bodleian Gough
Maps Devonshire 3; Plymouth City Museum;
Royal Geographical Society England and Wales
D. 15

Plan of Dockyard and town showing street plan
including names, market, 'Passage House' to
Stonehouse–Dock passage, 'Whitehouse' adjoining
Dockyard boundary. Main features in Dockyard
and Gun Wharf shown. Land adjoining Dock town
and beyond the lines shown as uncultivated.
Dodge's Hill hatched.

134
'A PLAN of CATWATER with the Soundings
taken in Feet at Low Water, on a Spring Tide'
'A Scale of ¼ Mile' [= 3.2″] 660 ft [= 1.6″] 1:4,950
'A Copy . . . by I.S. Smith'
March 1767
Stonehouse(W)–Oreston–Staddon Point(E)
Ink on paper
15.7″ × 20.5″ (400mm × 520mm)
NMM LAD/11 f. 67

Coastal survey of the Cattewater estuary with
soundings recorded in parallel lines across the
mouth of the estuary and up the river. A dotted red
line picks out the deepest channel among the
soundings. Rocks. Shore distinguished as 'beach',
'ouse' and 'hard sand'. On land, 'King's Old Yard'
at Coxside facing the Victualling Office across the
entrance to Sutton Pool. Direction pointer.

135
'Plan de la Ville, des Ports, de la Citadelle et des
Chantiers de Plymouth'
No scale given, but approx 1:15,014
? 'M de Béville *Lieuten[an]t Colonel de Dragonees*'
'*Figuré de mémoire les 24 et 25 Septembre 1768*'
Orientation: S
Maker(SW)–Tamar estuary(NW)–Stoke–[Staddon
Heights](SE)
Ink and watercolour on paper (red, green,
brown, turquoise)
21.5″ × 16″ (546mm × 407mm)
PRO MR 1111 (PRO 30/8/86/9) (PRO Catalogue
no. 2045)

Chart of Plymouth Sound from an invader's point
of view. Shows passage taken by warships (east of
St Nicholas Island) and by frigates and small boats
(west of St Nicholas Island). Text notes the need
for special pilotage to reach the port. Lines of
unmasted warships have been ranged up the port

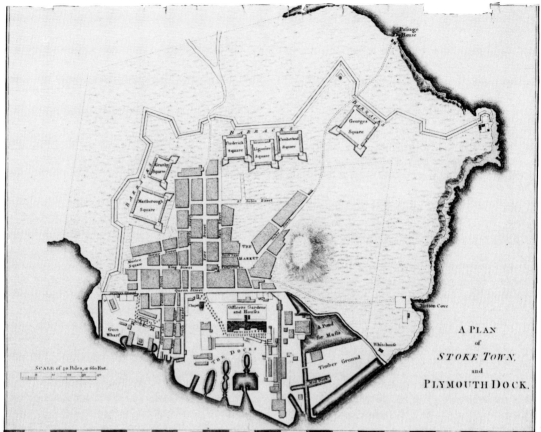

133

entrance to Dock (Millbrook, St John's Lake, Hamoaze). On land, references to several features of recent date, for example, Stonehouse Bridge (built 1767) described as '*pont de pierre nouvellement fait*', also Stonehouse Baths (where sea baths can be taken) and the Royal Naval Hospital for sick soldiers and seamen, which, when finished, could hold up to 1,500 patients according to the key on this chart. Mount Edgcumbe obelisk.

Two batteries noted at Cremyll, one of which, it is reckoned, could block off this side of the port. Proposal to build four batteries (two on either side of the mouth of the Hamoaze) in order to attack the Docks. Proposal to erect further batteries at Mount Batten, which could close the entrance of the port and bombard the Citadel and Island.

The highest and lowest points along the Dock lines have been noted; the lines are described thus: '*ces retranchemens consistent en un parapet en terre peu élevé et peu épais précédé d'un fossé sec non revêtu sans fraise ni palissade*'. The highest point of the Citadel wall whence it could be attacked from the Victualling Office.

Some roads. Some fields (land use). Hills. Intertidal area.

The chart occurs in the journal of the Seigneur de Béville, Lieutenant Colonel in the Dragoons, who made a reconnaissance visit to England in September–October 1768. In all, the journal has twenty-three maps and plans for the whole of the south coast of England, as well as Windsor and London. There are detailed notes for Plymouth: its harbour, Citadel and Dockyard and the most successful way to attack them. The Duc de Choiseul was a prime instigator of these invasion attempts, France criticizing England's unbridled ambition ('*ambition démesurée*').

136

As **135** except:

'PLAN de la Ville, des Ports, de la Citadelle, et des Chantiers de Plymouth'

'*Echelle d'environ un Mille*' [= 4.4″] 1:14,400

'*Nr que l'on n'a pu placer sur cette carte qu'une échelle estimée, le plan n'étant figuré que de Mémoire . . .*'

12.2″ × 21.1″ (310mm × 536mm)
Archives du Génie ART 14: PLYMOUTH/3

137

As **135** except:
'Plan de la Ville, des Ports, de la Citadelle et des
  Chantiers de Plymouth Figuré de mémoire les
  24 au 25 7bre [Septembre] 1768'
Scale as **136**
21.8″ × 26.8″ (variable) (554mm × 681mm)
Service Historique de l'Armée de Terre, Château
  de Vincennes L1 C 61

138

'PLYMOUTH SOUND SURVEYD BY
  JOSEPH GILBERT MASTER OF HIS
  MAJESTY'S SHIP *THE PEARL*'
'A Scale of one Mile' [= 4″] 1:15,840
Joseph Gilbert
1769
Orientation: NNW
Penlee Point(SW)–Plym estuary(N)
  –Mewstone(SE)
Ink and watercolour on paper (grey wash)
17″ × 21.6″ (432mm × 549mm)
BL Maps MT 11 h.1 (8)

Chart of Plymouth Sound. Features on land (leading marks) drawn in perspective: Staddon Farm,
Mount Batten, Round Tower, Citadel, Mount
Wise Gun Wharf, Dock windmill, Maker Church,
Cawsand. Hatching for hills. Rocks: Knapp 19 ft,
Shovel 18 ft, Tinker 17 ft. Inter-tidal area. Soundings. 3½-fathom line. Bearings. Compass. Two
views of the land as it appears from at sea: 1) 'when
in the fair way for sailing over the Bridg'; 2) 'at the
bottom of the sound when abreast the shagg rock
in midd channel between it and the red buoy'. Map
stamped: 'Howe Collection 1725–99'.

139

'PLYMOUTH SOUND, HAM OAZE and
  CAT WATER'
'Scale of one Thousand Fathoms' 100 + 1,000
  [= 4.5″] 1:17,600
J. Gilbert
? 1769/70
Rame Head(SW)–Saltash(NW)–[Plympton](NE)
  –Yealm estuary(SE)
Ink and watercolour on paper (yellow wash)
37″ × 24.8″ (940mm × 630mm)
NMM LAD/11 f. 40

Chart of the Sound giving many anchorages and
soundings. Saltash Passage (ferry). Several features

shown but not marked: Old Sugar House, Long
Room, Admiral Pritchard's house at Stoke. Penlee
Tower. Roads. Hills. Inter-tidal area. 3-fathom
line. Compass bearings. Instructions read as
follows:

To sail into the Sound, bring the Old Church [St
Andrew's] in a Line with the White Patch on the
Hoa, sail in that direction till Mount Edgecumbe
House appears in sight, then steer over to the
East Side, and Anchor with Block House Point
in a Line with Drake's Island. To sail into Ham
Oaze, keep Kingsand open with Reding Point till
the Large House at Stoke touches the East Side of
Mill Bay, steer in till the Obelisk (Mount Edgecumbe) comes on with Block house point, keep
in that direction till the Easternmost Summer-
house on Mount Edgecumbe Side, comes open
of the Point within which it stands, then steer
into Barn Pool till the East Side of Mount Wise
comes open of Blockhouse Point, then steer up
in Mid Channel for Stonehouse Pool till Drakes
Island is shut in with Blockhouse Point, do not
open it till South Down comes open of Obelisk
Point, then steer up into the Harbour. NB: The
South Side of Drakes island touching Passage
Point will lead you to the southward of the
Harbour Shoal on the outer part of which lies a
Rock with only 16 feet at Low Water Spring
Tides, but on the other parts are 3½ fathoms. The
Tide here flows five hours and a Quarter, the
greatest flow of Water is 20 feet & the least on a
Neap Tide 4 feet.

140

As **139** except:
'Survey'd in 1770'
37.5″ × 25″ (953mm × 635mm)
BL MT 11 h.1 (9)

Minor variations, such as Citadel marked, Dockyard marked 'Yard'. Roads to Exeter and Tavistock marked. Minor variations in sailing directions.
Stamped: 'Map Department Howe Collection
1720–1799 [sic] British Museum'.

141

Printed version of **140**
'Plymouth Sound, Hamoaze and Catwater
  Survey'd in 1770'
'Printed for Robert Sayer and John Bennett,
  Chart and Mapsellers No 53 Fleet Street, as the
  Act directs 10 June 1779'
'Scale of Fathoms 1200' [= 4.8″] 1:18,000
27.5″ × 20.4″ (690mm × 520mm)

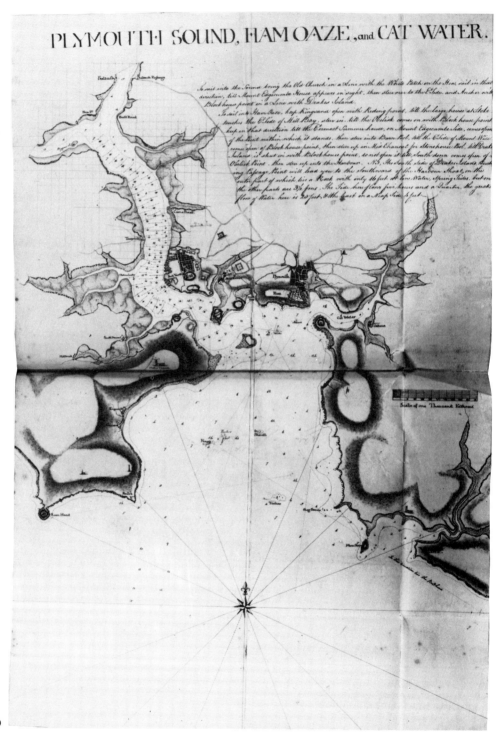

BL Maps C. 11 b. 7; BN SH Portefeuille 23 Division 5 Pièce 20 (two copies); Bodleian Gough Maps Devonshire 10; Hydrographic Department k93 Shelf Dk; Naval Historical Library Ve 33; Plymouth Central Library

Some variations: St Andrew's and Charles Churches not shown; Old Sugar House, Long Room and Admiral Pritchard's House now marked, as are Wembury Church ('Wembury Yealme Church'), Rame Church, Penlee Tower, Mount Edgcumbe House and the Obelisk. Old Gun Wharf at Dock marked, also lime-kiln at Cattewater. 'Tan chapel' (Turnchapel). 'White Patch' on the Hoe marked, also Spike Point at Cattedown. Panther Rock. Soundings do not agree exactly with **139**.

See Le Gear *Geographical Atlases*, c. 6, 9486.

142
As **141** except:
in *A COMPLETE CHANNEL PILOT: COMPREHENDING THE ENGLISH AND FRENCH COASTS, FROM The Thames Mouth to the Bay of Biscay: INCLUDING THE NORTH SEA: WITH SAILING DIRECTIONS . . . ,* 'PRINTED FOR ROBERT SAYER AND JOHN BENNETT, MAP, CHART AND PRINT SELLERS, NO 53 FLEET STREET', London, 1779–81
51.3″ × 20.1″ (1303mm × 511mm)
NMM 416/12 PB D8506

143
As **141** except:
'Plymouth Sound hamoaze et Catwater mesuré en 1770'
'Scale of Fathoms 1600' [= 5″] 1:23,040
c. 1779
Ink and watercolour on paper (red and black ink, blue, brown, grey)
28.2″ × 20.8″ (717mm × 528mm)
Archives du Génie ART 14: PLYMOUTH/4

144
'PLYMOUTH SOUND HAMOAZE and CATWATER SURVEYED in 1770'
'Scale of Fathoms 1200' [= 4.8″] 1:18,000
No statement of responsibility
c. 1779
Ink and watercolour on paper (red and black ink, brown and green wash)

27.7″ × 20.3″ (704mm × 516mm)
Archives Nationales Marine 6 JJ 32 Pièce 54 (two copies)

145
As **144** except:
No title
c. 1779
Ink and watercolour on paper (red and black ink, green, brown, orange, grey)
28″ × 20.7″ (712mm × 526mm)
Archives du Génie ART 14: PLYMOUTH/4

146
As **141** except:
'PLYMOUTH SOUND, HAMOAZE and CATWATER SURVEYED in 1786.'
'LONDON. Printed for Robert Sayer, No. 53 Fleet Street as the Act directs 10 Novr 1786'
'Scale of Fathoms 1200' [= 4.10″] 1:18,000
51.3″ × 20″ (1303mm × 508mm)
NMM 419/111 PB D8407

147
As **141** except:
'Scale of One Mile' [= 3.5″]
'Scale of Fathoms 1200' [= 4.8″] 1:18,000
'Surveyed in 1786. Published 12 May 1794 by LAURIE & WHITTLE 53 Fleet Street, London'
27.4″ × 20.1″ (696mm × 511mm)
Naval Historical Library Ve 34

148
As **147** except:
'Surveyed in 1797. Published 6th April 1797 by LAURIE & WHITTLE 53 Fleet Street, London'
27.8″ × 20.5″ (707mm × 520mm)
BL Maps 151 f. 1 (3)

Three stone beacons on the Hoe, black, red, and white respectively. Guns marked on Drake's Island (twenty-three 32-pounders), Mount Wise (eight 32-pounders), Dock ('the Lines and other Parts of the Garrison are mounted with 132 pieces of Canon'), Redding Point, Kingsand ('Amherst Battery 12 Eighteen-Pounders'). German Rock 'mostly Dry at Low Water Spring Tides', Vanguard, White Floating Beacon in the Sound besides details of beacons on the major rocks and position of buoys in the Sound noted. Additional sailing directions, including reference to 'Plymouth New Church which has a Spire Steeple'.

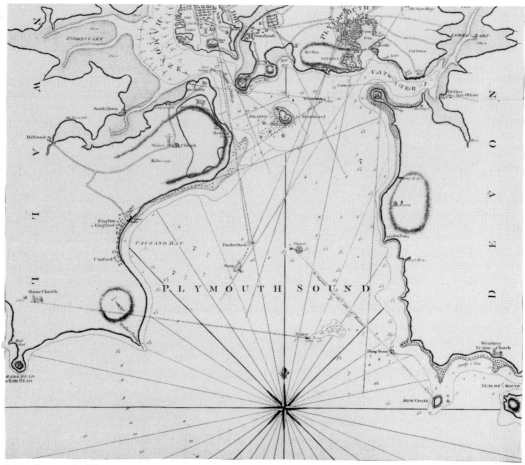

146   (lower half)

149

As **148** except:
'Surveyed in 1797. Published 1st Jany 1798 by
  LAURIE & WHITTLE 53 Fleet Street,
  London'
BL Maps C.10 d.7; Hydrographic Dept B315
  Shelf Dk; Naval Historical Library Vf 11/9 &
  10; NMM 379/72 LAW 03; Plymouth Central
  Library; Plymouth City Museum

White stone beacon on the Hoe appears to have
been moved. Tinker 14 ft, Shovel 17 ft below
water. Yellow globe and white globe marked near
Panther and Knap Rocks respectively. Detailed
notes on the beacons placed on the major rocks in
the Sound. 'The Tower of Plymouth Old Church
. . . is square, and has four Pinnacles on it.'

BL Maps C.10 d.7 occurs in: *THE COMPLETE*

*EAST   INDIA   PILOT,   OR   ORIENTAL
NAVIGATOR . . . chiefly composed from actual
surveys and draughts communicated by experienced
officers of the Honourable EIC and from the French
Neptune Oriental*, Laurie & Whittle, 1800

Additional annotations on the Naval Historical
Library copy (Vf 11/9 & 10): blue line around the
coastline 'shows the Water within the bounds of the
Tamar at high Water'; yellow line just beyond the
blue 'shows the Beaches or Strands at Low Water';
red line bridging the Hamoaze at various points
'shows the encroachments'; red bar across the
entrance to St John's Lake 'shows what has been
sold to Mr Carew, as part of the Manor of West
Antony'. Docks and moorings belonging to Lord
Boringdon noted.

See Le Gear *Geographical Atlases*, c. 16 9488.

150

'PLAN of His Majesty's Yard at Plymouth the 20th December 1771 the lines in Black is the Yard in its present State and those in Yellow are agreeable to the General Plan of Improvement'

'A Scale of Feet' 20 + 300 [= 8″] 1: 480

No statement of responsibility

Orientation: E

Dockyard

Ink and watercolour on paper (yellow, brown, grey)

48.5″ × 76.8″ (1230mm × 1951mm)

HM Dockyard, Plymouth

Plan of the Dockyard. Note the following (in yellow): 'Mould Loft Joiner Shop Etc', 'Working Shed', 'Store House', 'Locks for Stowing Mast'. Other features include 'Temporary Shed for Cable's Rigging', Cinder Pound, Hemp House No. 3. Adjoining Commissioners' gardens, greenhouse, hothouse. 'Pond for the Security of Mast and Yard of Ship Refitting'. Two ships shown alongside yard: *Mary Galley* and *Jersey Breakwater*. New yard wall.

151

'PLAN of His MAJESTY'S Yard PLYMOUTH January 1774 The Black Lines form the Yard in its present State: The yellow are agreeable to the general Plan of Improvement'

'Scale of 40 Feet to 1 Inch' 20 + 200 [= 5.4″] 1: 480

No statement of responsibility

Orientation: E

Dockyard

Ink and watercolour on paper (red, green, yellow, brown, grey)

45″ × 80″ (1144mm × 2032mm)

BL K. Top. 11 88

Plan of the Dockyard. Temporary shed for cable rigging has now become carver's shop. The following additions have been made since **100**: bricklayer's yard, racks for storing sided knees, stone mason's shed, iron house, hatched house, sail field. Occupants of the officers' houses given. Of the alterations proposed on **127**, the following (most of which are on the right-hand side of the yard) have been carried out: two hemphouses, laying house, spinning house, white yarn house, tarring house, black yarn house, hemphouse, mast house, saw pits, slips. The plan also shows how the lay-out of the old yard hindered change: the old yard wall and old pier 'ordered to be taken down'.

The measurements of the yard are summarized thus: 'Length extreme of the Yard from North to South 2779 Feet, Breadth extreme East & West 1673 Feet. Circumference 7453 Feet. Yard contains $62\frac{3}{4}$ Acres'.

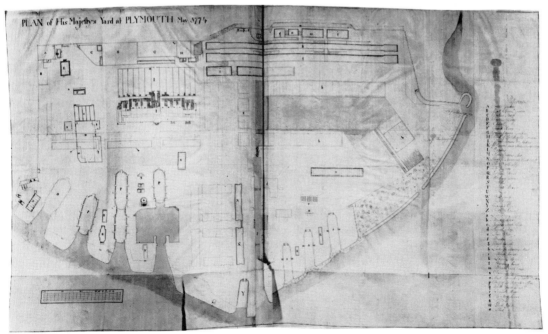

PLAN of His Majesty's Yard at PLYMOUTH Jan. 1774

152

152
'PLAN of His Majesty's Yard at PLYMOUTH
  May 1774'
Scale: '400 feet' [= 5.5″] 1:872
No statement of responsibility
Orientation: E
Dockyard
Ink and watercolour on paper (green, yellow)
22.3″ × 39.3″ (567mm × 999mm)
NMM LAD/11 f. 38

Plan of the Dockyard in May 1774. Key. Note that
the old pier ordered to be taken down and the old
yard wall shown on **151** have now gone.

153
'The Plan of the same Yard with the
  Improvements in 1774'
Scale: 1,200 + 200 [= 6.4″] 1: 2,625
No statement of responsibility
Orientation: E
Dockyard

Ink and watercolour on paper (red, green,
  turquoise, yellow, grey)
9″ × 13.3″ (230mm × 338mm)
BL King's MS 44 ff. 13–14

Plan of the Dockyard (with key) distinguishing
between what has been built and what is proposed
(shown in yellow). The latter ('intended new
Works not yet Executed') include the house
carpenter and joiner's shop, working sheds, rigging
house and storehouses, sail loft, smith's shop, locks
for stowing mast, the second new mast house, four
boat houses, cranes, one more hemphouse and a
proposed new dock.

154
'A DRAUGHT of PLYMOUTH SOUND,
  HAMOAZE and CATWATER shewing all the
  SANDS, ROCKS and SHOALS with the
  SOUNDINGS, MARKS and directions for
  SAILING in and out, also the NUMBER and
  disposition of the HARBOUR MOORINGS
  in HAMOAZE'

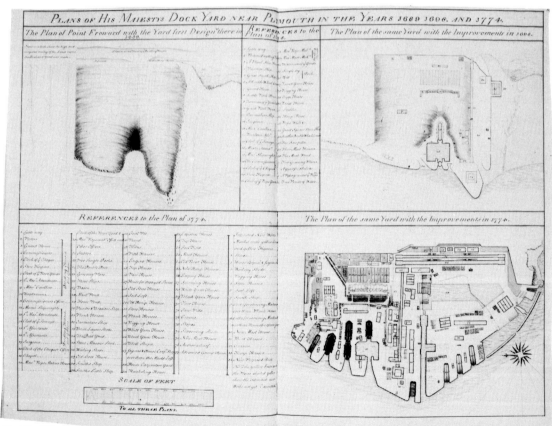

49, 73, 153

154

'A SCALE of ONE MILE' [= 5.3] 'SCALE of
1,000 FEET TO ONE INCH' 5,000 [= 5″]
1:12,000
No statement of responsibility
1774
Rame Head(SW)–Saltash(NW)–Yealm
estuary(SE)
Ink and watercolour on paper (turquoise, green,
red, pale brown, grey wash)
30.8″ × 29.1″ (783mm × 740mm)
BL King's MS 44 f. 15

Chart of Plymouth Sound intended to show the
moorings up the Hamoaze. Landscape around the
Sound shown in detail, although Stonehouse
Bridge omitted and much of Dock town. Dockyard shown in detail. Roads. Rivers. Fields (land
use indicated). Wooded areas. Inter-tidal area.
Soundings. 3-fathom line. Bearings. Sailing
instructions. Table:

PARTICULAR ACCOUNT of the MOORINGS

Fit for what Ships	Number and Nature		
	Chain	Chain & Cable	Total
East Shore			
Ships of the Line	18	3	21
Large Frigates	3	2	5
Total East Shore	21	5	26
West Shore			
Ships of the Line	12	7	19
Large Frigates	2		2
Total West Shore	14	7	21
Middle			
Ships of the Line	5		5
Millbrooke Lake			
Ships of the Line		1	1
Frigate	1		1
Total Mill[broo]ke Lake	1	1	2
St John's Lake			
Frigate	1		1
Grand Total	42	13	55

Abstract of the Moorings

Fit for	
Ships of the Line	46
Frigates	9
Total	55

BL King's MS 44 is a volume entitled 'A SUPPLE-
MENT TO THE BOOK IN HIS MAJESTY'S
POSSESSION WHICH CONTAINETH A
SURVEY OF ALL HIS MAJESTY'S DOCK-
YARDS WITH THE BUILDINGS & THEREIN
TAKEN IN THE YEAR 1698'. The survey covers
Portsmouth, Plymouth, Chatham, Sheerness,
Deptford and Woolwich. Besides plans for each
dockyard in 1689, 1698 and 1774 (reference is made
here to the 1774 models now held at the National
Maritime Museum), it includes a list of all ships in
the Navy on 31 August 1774, an account of the
mobilization of the Navy during the last war and
the present state of timber stores for shipbuilding.
The section devoted to Plymouth comments on the
advantages experienced since 1689 in having a yard
there in time of war. The most considerable
improvements have been those resulting from the
Navy Commissioners' plan of 1764. The original
estimate for these amounted to £379,170 although,
as discussed in the introductory essay above (see p.
61), much of this plan was never implemented.

155
No title
No scale given, but approx. 1:63,000
[M. Mackenzie; NB: Murdoch Mackenzie in this
catalogue refers to Murdoch Mackenzie junior]
[1774]
Porthbury(W)–Wembury(E)
Ink and watercolour on paper (red, blue)
32.1″ × 50.2″ (816mm × 1276mm)
Hydrographic Dept D923/10 Press 1a

Coastal chart from Porthbury to Wembury. Possibly a surveyor's rough. What distinguishes this
chart is the detail supplied about landmarks in and
around Plymouth, several of which are private
houses. Old Church (St Andrew's), New Church
(Charles). Three Holes along Hoe coastline. Sandy
Cove (Millbay). Mr Polby's (Stonehouse), Mrs
Cormick's (Dock), Keyham Point Magazine. Dock

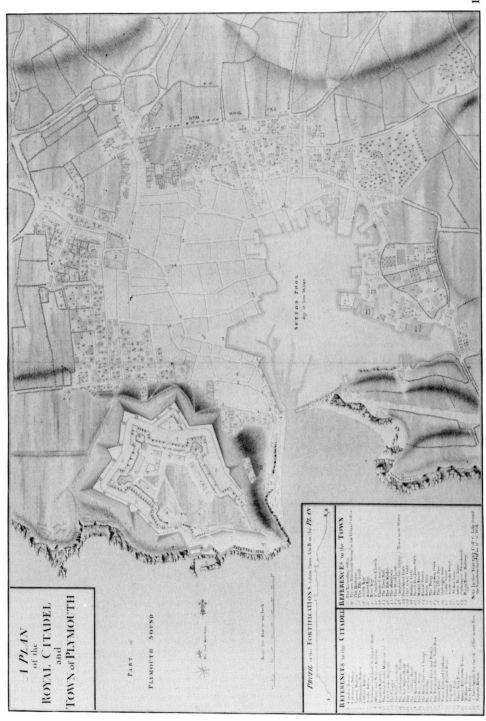

A PLAN
of the
ROYAL CITADEL
and
TOWN of PLYMOUTH

PART of
PLYMOUTH SOUND

Scale Feet to one Inch

SUTTON POOL
dry at low Water

PROFIL of the FORTIFICATIONS taken from A to B in the PLAN

REFERENCES to the CITADEL

REFERENCES to the TOWN

Chapel. Summerhouse at Stoke. Boathouse near Weston Mill Lake. Mr Drew's. Tor House. Mr Harris's House. Round House. Wood House. Mutley Firs. Bowling Green House. Game Keeper's (near Redding Point). 4-fathom line. Inter-tidal area. Soundings.

156

'A PLAN of the ROYAL CITADEL and
   TOWN of PLYMOUTH'
'Scale 200 Feet to an Inch' 100 + 800 [= 4.5"]
   1:2,400
'Drawing by Peter Couture of the 3d Class April
   1776'
Orientation: W
Citadel and Sutton Pool
Ink and watercolour on paper (red, green, grey)
19.4" × 28" (492mm × 708mm)
BL Add MS 60393 C

Plan of the town and Citadel (with keys). Includes a profile of the fortifications taken from north to south of the Citadel. A fresh feature is the new bakehouse belonging to the Victualling Office; otherwise, the plan corresponds closely to **91**. Water system north of Old Town Gate shown. Roads. Fields. Trees. Gardens. Some hills shown in relief. Inter-tidal area. Noted that in 1717 Colonel C. Lilly found the variation to be 11° 15' west. Compass pointer. 'The True Meridian'.

157

'PLYMOUTH' (inset)
on 'A NEW HYDROGRAPHICAL SURVEY
   OF THE BRITISH CHANNEL with PART
   of the ATLANTIC OCEAN as far as CAPE
   CLEAR, Improved from THE LARGE
   CHART of the Late THOMAS JEFFERY'S
   Geographer to the KING'
'London. Published as the Act directs by Robert
   Sayer and John Bennett, 1st August 1777'
Scale: '900 Fathoms' [= 1.3"] 1:49,846
Rame Head(SW)–Torpoint(NW)–Oreston(NE)
   –Yealm estuary(SE)
Printed
6.3" × 7.2" (160mm × 183mm)
NMM 416/12 PB D8506

Chart of the Sound. Maker Church showing signals. Inter-tidal area. Soundings. 4-fathom line. 'Winter Rock 11 Feet', 'Shovel 17 Feet', 'Cobler 12' ft. Compass bearings. 'Tides Flow 5¼ at Full and Change'

See Le Gear *Geographical Atlases* c. 2 9486.

158

As **157** except:
'Printed for Robt Sayer and Jno Bennett No 53,
   Fleet Street as the Act directs, 1 March 1782'
NMM 363/127 PB D8233; PRO MR 948

159

No title
'A Scale of six Inches to an English Mile
   containing 1,760 Yards' [= 6"] 1:10,560; 'A
   Scale of three Cables-length' [= 2"]
Murdoch Mackenzie
1777–9
Rame Head(SW)–St Stephens(NW)–Mutley(NE)
   –Wembury(SE)
Ink and watercolour on paper (red, blue)
63.6" × 50.5" (1614mm × 1283mm)
Hydrographic Dept D881 Press 15b

Chart of the Sound giving precise details as to the area's defensive capabilities in terms of guns. Much information about beacons and buoys. Batteries: Stoke Blockhouse (formerly Stoke Summerhouse): eight 3-pounders, eight 12-pounders in the blockhouse, besides twenty Swivelstocked blunderbuses and musketry and thirteen 18-pounders in the two northernmost faces of the battery; West Hoe: six 18-pounders; Easter King's: four 18-pounders; Wester King's: ten 18-pounders; Devil's Point: four 18-pounders; Old Gun Wharf: six 24-pounders; Mount Wise: eight 32-pounders, two 10-inch mortars; East of Cremyll redoubt: line of musketry, five 6-pounders; near Sandway Point: four 18-pounders; NE of Kingsand: eight 18-pounders; Kingsand: four 18-pounders; St Nicholas Island: four 18-pounders, twenty-one 32-pounders, two 13-inch mortars. Details of beacons and buoys in 1778: Tinker (swinging beacon), Shovel (white buoy), Panther (red buoy), Cobler (swinging beacon). 'NB a short time before we finished the Survey, we discovered the West Nap – by mere accident, and got the Masters to place a black Buoy on it.' Similar details of beacons and buoys supplied for 1780 and May 1791. Note especially 'New Rock in Cawsand Bay 22 feet, or rather 23 feet' (1791). Another note reads: 'Remember that when Mr Mackenzie first came upon this Survey, there was only 1 Beacon [Tinker], and 2 Buoys [Shovel, Panther] in Plymouth Sound . . . he discovered the Nap Rock, only just before he finished the Survey, and got a Black Buoy put on it.' Fresh landmarks: Guildhall; flagstaff; West Sentry Box (Plymouth Hoe); agent's house, near the French prison; Royal Naval Hospital cupola and water engine; Mount Stone; boathouse at Stonehouse; Reed's house (Stoke); summer-houses at Mutley and Cawsand;

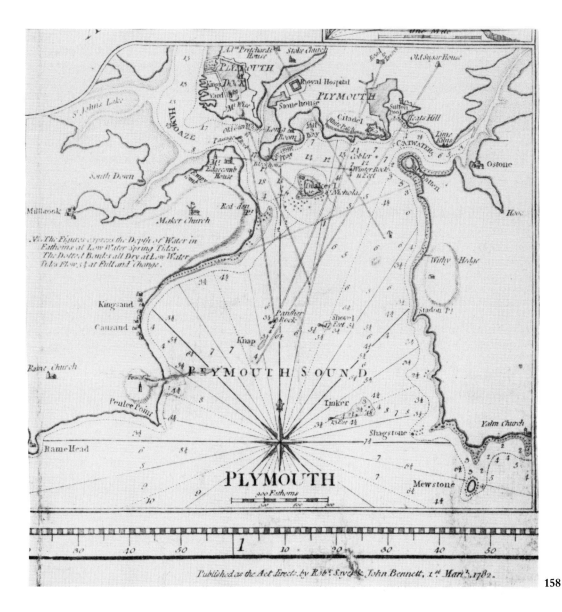

158

'Seaman's barn' (Mutley); Cawsand pier. Rope-walk at Torpoint. Ferries at Mutton Cove and St German's; Heifer Bridge near St John's. Limestone quarries at Cattedown, Millbay, Devil's Point, Easter King's. Ballast pits at Wilcove. Nursery near Lower Anderton. Hatching around fortifications: Cremyll redoubt, Kingsand, Mount Wise, Mount Batten. *Temeraire* (hulk). Coastal area: stones, gravel, beach, hardway, mud. Inter-tidal area. Very numerous soundings. 2-, 4- and 5-fathom lines, also danger line around rocks. Anchorages. Compass bearings. Sailing directions. 'This Survey was begun in 1777. In fact, we measured a . . . line

and took some [horizon]tal angles, and did little work, in the year but as we were then [ordered] to the North Coast [of Kent], it was stopped . . . as above mentioned. This survey was finished in 1778 and part of 1779.'

Another, much more faded, surveyor's rough of this chart has survived.

160

'To his Royal Highness GEORGE AUGUSTUS FREDERICK Prince of Wales, Duke of Cornwall and Rothsay, Earl of Chester, Electoral Prince of Brunswick and Luenburgh,

Earl of Carrick, Baron of Renfrew, Lord of the Isles, Great Steward of Scotland, Captn General of the Artillery Company, Lord High Steward of Plymouth etc This Plan of the Borough of Plymouth and its Environs in the County of Devon is most Humbly Inscribed, by His Royal Highness's Most dutiful Servant Richd Cowl'
'Publish'd as the Act directs, May 17 1779 Paternoster Row Cheapside London'
'A Scale of Feet 770' [= 3.2″] 1:2,887
'Engrav'd by G. Terry Paternoster Row'
Surveyed in 1778
Millbay(W)–Town and Citadel–Cattewater(E)
Printed
26.9″ × 27.9″ (684mm × 709mm)
Bodleian Gough Maps Devonshire 9; Plymouth Proprietary Library; WDRO Acc 157

Plan of the town, showing street pattern and roads leading out of the town, churches, gardens and orchards. Key identifies significant buildings: places of worship (all denominations), civic buildings, public houses, theatre, quays (New Quay described as 'Parade'; South Quay described as 'Barbican Quay'), custom-house, hospitals, prisons. Fields on edge of town shown, and watercourse from Millbay to north-west edge of town. Ships and boats in Sound and Sutton Pool.

161

As **160** except:
'To his Royal Highness . . . This Plan of the TOWN and CITADEL of PLYMOUTH . . . A PLAN of the Town and Citadel of PLYMOUTH Surveyed by Richard Cowl 1778'
'London. Publish'd as the Act directs, May 1st 1780 by Wm Faden corner of St Martins Lane Charing Cross'
BL K. Top. 11 83; BN SH Portefeuille 23 Division 5 Pièce 21; Bodleian C 17 a.3; Service Historique de l'Armée de Terre KII B 3/57

Minor additions: 'New Battery Six 18 P[ounde]rs' marked on West Hoe; Bull Ring marked on East Hoe.

162

As **160** except:
'A Plan of the Town and Citadel of Plymouth Copié au Dépôt des Fortifications, d'après un plan de la Marine en Février 1852'
1779 [1852]
Archives du Génie ART 14: PLYMOUTH/10

163

'Plan de Plymouth sur un projet d'attaque de cette Place Joint à une lettre de M de la Luzerne au comte de Broglie du 23 juin 1779'
'Echelle cent toises' [= 2.1″] 1:3,714
? M de la Luzerne
Orientation: W
Dock
Ink and watercolour on paper (red and brown ink, green wash)
12.5″ × 15.2″ (318mm × 386mm)
Service Historique de l'Armée de Terre MR 1414 no. 47

Simple sketch of Dock town and yard showing lines, barracks and main features in Dockyard.

164

'PLYMOUTH SOUND HAMOAZE CAWSAND BAY and CATWATER Surveyed and navigated by Murdoch Mackenzie Junr 1779'
'SCALE of six Inches to a Mile' [= 6″] 1:10,560
'Scale of three Cable's Length' [= 2″]
Rame Head(SW)–St Stephens(NW)–Mutley(NE) –Wembury(SE)
Printed
60″ × 46.9″ approx. (badly warped); (1525mm x 1192mm)
Hydrographic Dept c88 Shelf 3h

An extremely detailed navigational chart of Plymouth Sound and the Hamoaze. Gun batteries as on **159**, although details of guns at Stoke Summerhouse and St Nicholas Island have been omitted. Mount Edgcumbe battery. Fresh landmarks: Jeffry's House (Coxside), East Sentry Box (Hoe), Devil's House (Stonehouse), Half-way House (Stoke), Mutley Firs, Mount Edgcumbe (Temple, Summerseat, Lodge, Hothouse). Details of existing buoys, including mooring and transporting buoys, and suggestions for additional buoys for the safety and guidance of men-of-war when entering or leaving Plymouth Sound or Cawsand Bay. Key distinguishing between rocky, grassy and clay cliffs; also shores and ledges (rocky, sandy, beachy, stony and muddy, as far as they dry with the spring tide); rocks always above water, those covered and uncovered alternately by the tide, those dry with the spring tide only, and rocky shoals always under water. Sand and gravel banks always below water. Numerous soundings. Chart shows red danger line round rocks, line to show how near ships may stand to shore in 4 fathoms water and water less than 2 fathoms. Best anchorages. Bearings. True and magnetic north. Leading marks to shoals and

165

buoys with their bearings also given. Best channels. Direction of stream of flood, time of high water on days of new and full moon, speed in knots of stream at spring or neap tides. Views along top, left- and right-hand edges of map with some sailing directions.

165

'A SURVEY of PLYMOUTH SOUND
    HAMOAZE, CATWATER, and CAWSAND
    BAY'
'Hydrographical Office. Published according to
    Act of Parliament . . . by Capt Hurd RN
    Hydrographer to the Admiralty'
2 Nautic[al] Miles [= 8.1″] 1:18,026
'Lieutenant Murdoch Mackenzie 1779. J. Walker
    Sculp[*si*]*t*. . . . A few alterations and additions
    have been since made by William Chapman,
    Master RN'
1779 [1810]
Rame Head(SW)–St Stephens(NW)–Mutley(NE)
    –Wembury(SE)
Printed
38.2″ × 24.7″ (971mm × 628mm)
BL SEC 1 (30)

Printed Admiralty chart of Plymouth Sound. Shows landing places and land fortifications in detail, e.g. Spike Point, East and West Sentry Boxes at Citadel, batteries at Staddon, West Hoe, also blockhouses at Stonehouse, Mount Wise Old Gun Wharf, Keyham Point Magazine, Stoke fort. Dockyard shown in detail including telegraph. Rope-walks at Torpoint as well as Coxside. Major rocks in Sound noted including beacons where applicable. Inter-tidal area. Sea-bottom distinguished as muddy, rocky or sandy. Soundings. A few anchorages. Bearings. Magnetic variations. Compass. Sailing Instructions include information on tides, leading-marks for middle, west and north-west channels.

166

As **165** except;
'PLAN DE LA RADE ET DU PORT DE
    PLYMOUTH Levé en 1779 par le Lieutenant
    Murdoch Mackenzie PUBLIE PAR ORDRE
    DU ROI Sous le Ministère de Son Excellence,
    M. le Comte CHABROL DE CROUSOL,
    Pair de France, Secrétaire d'Etat au
    Département de la Marine et des Colonies. Au
    Dépôt-général de la Marine en 1825'
in *NEPTUNE DES ILES BRITANNIQUES*
Scale: '*2 Milles Marins*' [= 7.9″] 1:18,483
37″ × 24.1″ (940mm × 612mm)
BL Maps 147 e 3 36

Guns pointing towards Sound from Stoke fort. 'V' (*vase*) indicates mud, 'R' (*rochers*) rocks along coastline. Fleur-de-lys pointing north.

167

As **166** except:
Scale: '*2 Milles Marins*' [= 7.7″] 1:18,963
27.8″ × 23.5″ (707mm × 597mm)
Archives du Génie ART 14: PLYMOUTH/8

168

'PLAN of ENCAMPMENTS IN THE
    NEIGHBOURHOOD OF PLYMOUTH in
    1779 under LT GENL SIR D LINDSAY and
    in 1780, 1781 and 1782, under LT GENL
    HAVILAND'
'Scale of Yards' 100 + 1,000 [= 4.1″] 1:9,658
Scale of Furlongs 8 [= 6.5″]
[Captain George Morrison, Lieutenant Paterson
    and Captain J.W. Green]
c. 1779–82
Orientation: NW
Rame(SW)–Millbrook(NW)–Ford(NE)–Hoe(SE)
Ink and watercolour on paper (red, green, blue,
    black, turquoise, yellow, brown)
13.7″ × 26.6″ (347mm × 674mm)
BL Add MS 15533 pl.59

Map of the landscape around the mouth of the Hamoaze, showing military encampments at Dock, Maker and Rame during the War of American Independence. Dock: Wiltshire regiment occupying barrack beyond George Square in 1779, Somerset regiment just outside Dock lines in 1780. Cornwall: 1st battalion royal encamped near Maker Church in 1779, while a little farther off were the 2nd battalion (1779), the 1st battalion royal – their second position (1780) – and the Carmarthen 1st battalion royal, the North Devon, Leicester, Somerset and North Gloucester (1781). Between Sollack and Ford were the 50th foot Somerset, North Gloucester and Cornish in 1782; while the North Hants were stationed at Rame in 1779. This map is based on the Drawing Office survey discussed in the introductory essay. Roads. Hills. Fields (land use). Wooded areas. Inter-tidal area. Directional arrow.

169

As **168** except:
'PLAN OF THE ENVIRONS OF
    PLYMOUTH'
Scale: 100 + 2,000 yds [= 7.7″] 1:9,818

1 Mile (= 8 Furlongs) + 1 Mile [= 12.9″]
Cawsand(SW)–Torpoint(NW)–Crabtree(NE)
  –Down Thomas(SE)
BL Add MS 15533 pl.161

Drawing Office map of the landscape around the Sound. Roads. Hills. Fields (land use). Wooded areas. Inter-tidal area.

Both the above plans occur in a volume 'TO THE KING'S MOST EXCELLENT MAJESTY THE FOLLOWING PLANS OF ENCAMPMENTS, and DISPOSITIONS OF THE ARMY in GREAT BRITAIN from 1778 to 1782, are most humbly Presented'. The volume lists officers, stations, strength of battalions and forces for each camp, also plans of all the camps, which is why these maps are included.

170
'A General Plan with a Project for the Defence of the Arsenals of Plymouth, by Lieut: Colonel Dixon Chief Engineer of the Plymouth Division'
'Scale 800 feet to an Inch' 1,000 + 5,000 [= 7.5″]
  1: 9,600
'Revised and Corrected by Geo: Beck January 1780'
Cawsand(SW)–[Torpoint](NW)–Crabtree(NE)
  –Down Thomas(SE)
Ink and watercolour on paper (red, green, yellow, orange, brown, black, blue)
26.7″ × 39.4″ (645mm × 953mm)
BL K. Top. 11 79 2

Neat survey of the landscape around the Sound concentrating upon its defence capability at land and sea. The map is unusual in that altitudes are given. The map was drawn to accompany Lt.-Col. Matthew Dixon's report of 10 January 1780, detailing the guns at the various batteries in the area. These have remained unchanged since Mackenzie's chart of 1777–9 with the exception of Wester King's (now twelve 18-pounders) and Dock lines north-east of the Gun Wharf (seven 12-pounders). Another interesting feature of the map is the positions of ships intended to serve as floating batteries: 1–3 to secure the entrance to Cattewater; 4 to prevent the enemy from landing men in Millbay; 5 to be occasionally sunk to prevent frigates and smaller vessels passing by West Channel; 6 to cooperate with batteries against the enemy's attempt on ships of the line; 7 to defend West Channel; 8 to prevent entry into Stonehouse creek; 9–11 to defend the interior passage near Navy Yard; 12 to enfilade the hollow way between

Mount Pleasant and the Dock lines; 14 to enfilade Keyham creek; 13 and 15 to protect the proposed work at Torpoint. Roads. Hamlets. Farms. Fields (some land use). Limestone quarries and kilns.

171
'A PLAN of the TOWN, CITADEL, DOCK and SOUND OF PLYMOUTH WITH THEIR ENVIRONS Surveyed by RICHD COWL, & Planned by LS DE LA ROCHETTE'
'London. Published as the Act directs, by W. Faden, corner of St Martin's Lane, Charing Cross, Novr 1 1780'
Scale: 'One Mile and a Half' [= 3.7″] 1:25,686
Engraved by Wm Faden, 1780
Rame Head(SW)–Saltash(NW)–Elfordleigh(NE)
  –Erme estuary(SW)
Printed
19.6″ × 27.1″ (498mm × 689mm)
Hydrographic Dept B21 Shelf Qf

Map of the landscape around the Sound, concentrating upon its defence capabilities (key). Guns as **159** except: Citadel: fifteen 42-pounders, twenty-three 32-pounders, twenty-four 18-pounders, twenty-eight 9-pounders; Marine Barracks (intended): six 18-pounders; Wester King redoubt: eight 18-pounders; Devil's Nose [sic]: six 18-pounders; battery near to Mount Wise: six 32-pounders; battery within the lines: six 9-pounders; bridge battery over the Quarry (Dock): six 9-pounders; [Mount Edgcumbe] Obelisk battery: eight 18-pounders; Lord Edgcumbe's battery: twenty-one guns; Cawsand: four 18-pounders; St Nicholas Island: seventy-two guns. The other significant feature about the map is the large number of country houses which are shown, together with their owners' names. Roads. Hatching for hills, which are prominent on this map. Trees and parks shown. Lime-kilns at Cattedown. Reservoir and 'Dead Lake' at Stoke. 'A Hulk' off Barn Pool. 'New Magazine' at Weston Mills. 'Watch Triangular Tower' at Penlee. 'PART OF CORNWALL' at St Budeaux; 'PART OF DEVON' at St John's and on Maker peninsula. 'TAMER RIVER Navigable 20 Miles'. 'Winter Rock 11 Feet', 'Shovel 15 Feet', 'Knapping Rock 15 Feet', 'Tinker 13 Feet'. Soundings. Fathom lines around edge of coastline. Anchorages.

The West Country Studies Library, Exeter has a slightly larger edition of this map (19.6″ × 27.3″; 498mm × 693mm) which may be a later edition of the above map (R31380).

172

'Plan du Dock'

'*Echelle de 3 Milles*' [= 4.5″] 1:42,240

No statement of responsibility

c. 1780

Rame Head(SW)–Carkeel(NW)–Cattewater(NE)
    –Mewstone(SE)

Ink and wash on flimsy paper

7″ × 8.6″ (178mm × 218mm)

Service Historique de la Marine, Vincennes
    Recueil no. 32 (63)

Inaccurate sketch of the landscape around the
Sound, noting Maker encampments ('*redoutes*') and
signal towers at Maker Church and Penlee tower.
Some roads (Maker). Hills (relief).

173

'PLAN of ST NICHOLAS ISLAND with the
    new Battery as also the alterations of the lower
    Line, Projected by Lieut Colonel Dixon, Chief
    Engineer of the Plymouth Division'

Scale: '40 Feet to an Inch 200 Feet' [= 5″] 1:480

'H[enr]y Castleman Draughtsman'

c. 1780

St Nicholas Island

Ink and watercolour on paper (green, pink,
    turquoise, yellow, grey)

28.1″ × 20.2″ (714mm × 513mm)

PRO MPH 727

Plan of St Nicholas Island showing bearings from
point 'A' to Mount Wise, Mount Edgcumbe, Rame
Head, the Eddystone lighthouse, the Mewstone

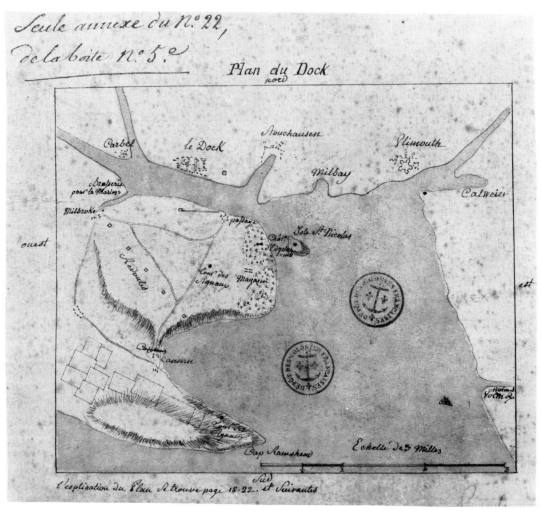

and the Citadel. Magazines. Proposed storehouse and gunner's quarter are noted. In the bottom left- and top right-hand corners of the map are section drawings of the proposed walls showing high water-mark. Direction pointer.

174

No title
'Scale Two Inches to the Mile' 1,000 + 10,000 yds [= 12.8″] 1:31,680
No statement of responsibility
c. 1780
Talland(SW)–Liskeard(NW)–South Brent(NE) –Aveton Gifford(SE)
Ink and watercolour on paper (red, green, yellow)
25.3″ × 59.5″ (variable) (643mm × 1643mm)
BL Add MSS 57638 5

Relief map of the area from Seaton (Cornwall) in the west to Yealmpton in the east and north as far as Roborough Down. Heights above sea-level are given in feet for many places along the coastline.

Some of the major roads have been marked off in miles: Plymouth–Tavistock, Cremyll–Liskeard, and mileages from Ivybridge and Modbury to Plymouth, and from Liskeard to Saltash. Maker encampments. Many individual buildings marked in red ink. Many place-names (especially Cornwall). Names of major landowners have been noted in red ink against their homes . Distances across the sea noted: across Plymouth Sound 3 miles; Cremyll–Mount Wise, 500 yards; Southdown–Dock, 1,400 yards; Torpoint–Dock, 800 yards; Saltash ferry, 500 yards; Looe Island–Rame Head, 9 miles. Rivers. Roads (including the turnpike road from Modbury to Plymouth). Hills. Bridges. Beaches.

The map was presented by Colonel Sir Augustus Frazer KCB RA.

175

'A PLAN of ST NICHOLAS ISLAND near PLYMOUTH'
Scale: '10 [rect. 100] Feet to an Inch' 100 + 300 [= 4″] 1:1,200

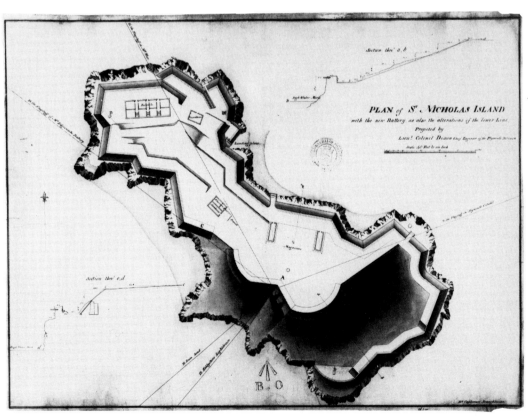

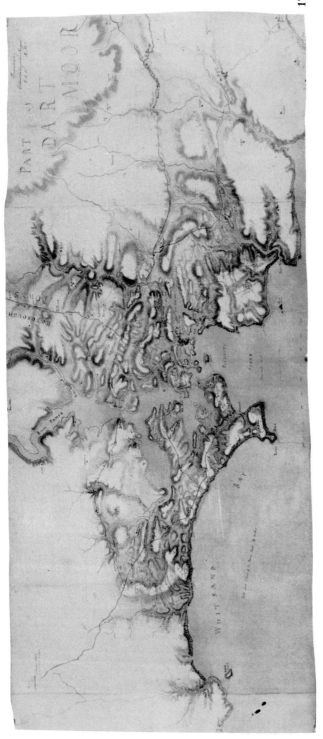

F. Langen
'July 2d 1781'
Orientation: S
St Nicholas Island
Ink and watercolour on paper (green, grey, brown, pink, blue, yellow)
19.4″ × 28.4″ (494mm × 710mm)
Patricia, Viscountess Boyd. Ince Castle, Saltash.

Plan of St Nicholas Island (key). Gun platform and buildings are unchanged from 1725 (**92**), although 'Old Saluting Platform' has been renamed 'Mount Batten platform'. Memorandum that the large rock to the north-west of St Nicholas Island becomes an island itself at high water. Note the dangerline in the sea around the edge of the islands (number of fathoms not given). The top edge of the map shows a view of the north-east prospect of St Nicholas Island, while the bottom edge has section drawings.

Illustrated in Christie's *London Valuable Travel and Natural History Books*, Wed. 26–Thurs. 27 Oct 1988, no. 196, p. 87.

176
'A CHART OF PLYMOUTH SOUND, CATWATER AND HAMOAZE'
'Publish'd as the Act directs 31st July 1782 by J Bew Pater Noster Row'
Scale: 'English Miles 2' [= 3.1″] 1:40,877
'Jno Lodge *Sculp*[*sit*]'
Rame Head(SW)–[Saltash](NW)–Cattedown(NE) –Mewstone Rock(SE)
Printed
8.7″ × 10.6″ (217mm × 267mm)
BL PP 3557v (Reading Room); Plymouth Central Library

Printed chart of Plymouth Sound. Batteries shown on St Nicholas Island (32-pounders), Mount Edgcumbe, Kingsand. Maker tower drawn. Inter-tidal area. Soundings. A few anchorages. Compass.

BL PP 3557v occurs in *The Political Magazine*, 3 (July 1782), p. 408.

177
'PLYMOUTH HARBOUR' (inset)
on 'A MAP of the WESTERN CIRCUIT of England Containing the Counties of CORNWAL, DEVON, DORSET, SOMERSET, WILTS & HANTS Geo-hydrographically Delineated on a Scale of a Quarter of an Inch to a Mile By BENJAMIN DONNE and SON TEACHERS of the Mathematics and Natural Philosophy'
'Publish'd by Benjn Donne, Bristol, as the Act directs April 30 1784'
'To the Right Honourable the Earl of Salisbury to Tho[ma]s Harris Esq[ui]r[e] Alder[ma]n W[illia]m Blake & John Garnet Esq[ui]r[e]s, Mr Clayfield & Mr Aldridge, Merchants in Bristol, To John Baring Esq[ui]r[e] & Mr John Rowe of Exeter, To Messrs Weres & Co Merch[an]ts, Wellington & to Messrs Fox's, Merch[an]ts in Falmouth, for Favours received & To the rest of the Subscribers: this Map is humbly Inscribed. . . .'
Scale: 'One Stat. Mile' [= 1″] 1:63,360; 'One Sea Mile' [= 1.1″]
Rame Head(SW)–Saltash(NW)–Saltram(NE) –Yealm estuary(SE)
Printed
8.4″ × 7.1″ (213mm × 180mm)
BL K 6 66 2 TAB: Bodleian C 17:9 (36); Royal Geographical Society England and Wales S/Div.7

Chart of Plymouth Sound (unoriginal). A few of the gentry's houses marked with owners' names given. Enclaves of Cornwall in Devon, and Devon in Cornwall shown. Major roads shown. 'West Petherel Chapel'. 'White rock' (Winter). Inter-tidal area. Soundings. Fathom line. Anchorages. Compass bearing. The crude style and inaccuracy of the landmarks for Plymouth are an enigma, considering the much more accurate town plan produced by Donn nearly twenty years earlier.

Note on the map: 'The Purchaser is desired to observe that every Genuine Copy is signed by B or H Donne'.

178
'A SURVEY of the COAST LINE of part of the RIVER TAMER [sic] HAMOAZE THE SOUND and CATWATER PLYMOUTH'

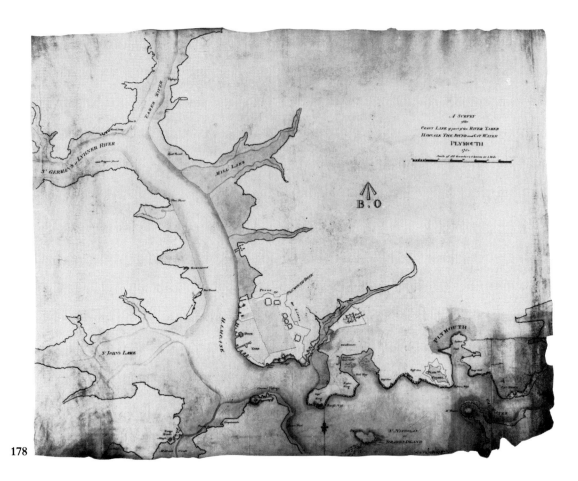

178

'Scale of 80 Gunter's Chains or 1 Mile' 10 + 70
   [= 6″] 1:10,560
Drawing Office
1784 (endorsed)
Millbrook(SW)–Saltash(NW)–Mount Batten
   (SE)
Ink and watercolour on paper (red, blue, pink)
44.3″ × 25.8″ (1,126mm × 656mm)
PRO MPH 378 (WO 78/1488) (PRO Catalogue
   no. 2050)

A detailed survey of coastal indentations in the
Upper Sound and Hamoaze. Marine Barracks,
Stonehouse occur for first time. Note 'St Nicholas
or Drake's Island'. Inter-tidal area. Directional
fleur-de-lys.

179
'Part 1 Plymouth and country 8 miles around – in
   2 parts W. Gardner 1784' (endorsed)

Scale: '6 inches to a mile' ⅛ + 2 miles [= 12.8″]
   1:10,560; 500 + 3,000 yds [= 12″]; 1,000 +
   10,000 ft [= 12.5″]
Crafthole(SW)–Hingston Down(NW)
   –Tavistock(NE)–Shag Stone(SE)
Ink and watercolour on paper (red, black, green,
   sepia, grey)
57.3″ × 110″ (1,456mm × 1896mm)
PRO MR 1199 (Part 1) (WO 78/385) (PRO
   Catalogue no. 2052)

Detailed survey of the landscape on either side of
the Hamoaze. Many place-names. Devonport.
Much detail. Military Hospital, Stonehouse;
powder works at St Budeaux and Pennycross
Chapel noted for first time. Staddon Heights
battery. Roads. Hills. Fields (land use indicated by
differing shades of green). At sea, note 'course of
vessels going up the Hamoaze'. Breakwater pencilled in later. Inter-tidal area. This map has less
detail than **180**.

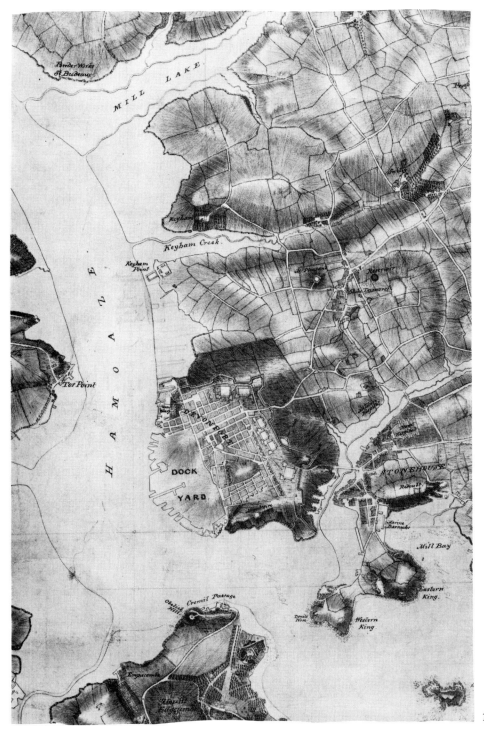

179

180

'An Actual Survey and MEASUREMENT of
  PLYMOUTH and DOCK TOWNS with their
  FORTIFICATIONS and the ADJACENT
  COUNTRY Survey'd by Order of HIS
  GRACE the DUKE of RICHMOND etc
  MASTER GENERAL of the ORDNANCE
  Under the Direction of COLONEL DIXON
  Chief Engineer'
'Scale of 80 Gunter Chains or One Mile' 10 + 70
  [= 6"] 1:10,560; 2,000 yds [= 7.4"]
William Gardner
1784
Rame Head(SW)–Saltash(NW)–Widey(NE)
  –Mount Batten(SE)
Ink and watercolour on paper (red, turquoise)
31.4" × 41.7" (798mm × 1060mm)
PRO MR 1385 (WO 78/857)

Detailed survey of the landscape to the north and
west of the Sound. Many place-names. Much detail
concerning the countryside including individual
buildings such as farms (Keyham Farm, Woodland
Farm, Barn Farm, Moor Farm, Wellarton Farm,
Waverton Farm, Coldridge Farm); vicarages (Stoke
and Egg Buckland); mills etc. Maker encampments. Note that the countryside is shown in relief.
Roads. Fields (some land use). Inter-tidal area.
Compass bearings.

181

'The SOUTH PART of AN accurate SURVEY
  and MEASUREMENT of PLYMOUTH and
  DOCK TOWNS with their Fortifications and
  THE ADJACENT COUNTRY Survey'd by
  ORDER of HIS GRACE the DUKE of
  RICHMOND etc Master General of the
  Ordnance Under the DIRECTION of
  COLONEL DIXON Chief Engineer by
  William Gardner Surveyor In the Years 1784,
  1785 & 1786'
'Scale of 80 Gunters Chains or One Mile' [= 6"]
  1:10,560; '2,000 Yards': 100 + 1,900 [= 6.8"]
Mount Edgcumbe(SW)–Barne Barton(NW)
  –Leigham(NE)–Plymstock(SE)
Ink and watercolour on paper (red, green, pink,
  yellow, brown)
35" × 24" (889mm × 610mm)
PRO OS 5/4 (Part 2)

Another survey by Gardner of the landscape
around the Upper Sound. Many place-names,
particularly for Cornwall, among which are Wivel-
scombe Farm, Orchard Farm, Earth Farm, Earth
Island, Pool Farm; Wacker Mill. Woodford and
Herdwick Farms at Plympton; Marsh Mill. Roads

(including turnpike roads which have been
coloured yellow). Hills (relief). Fields. Keyham
Bridge. Inter-tidal area.

See Yolande Hodson, with introduction by Tony
Campbell, *Ordnance Survey Drawings 1789–c. 1840
(the Original Manuscript Maps of the First Ordnance
Survey of England and Wales from the British Library
Map Library)*, p. 40.

182

As **181** except:
Portwrinkle(SW)–St Germans(NW)–[Fardle](NE]
  –Erme estuary(SE)
49.2" × 105.5" (1040mm × 2663mm)
BL K. Top. 11 80

183

'PLYMOUTH' (inset)
on 'To His Royal Highness Prince William Henry
  This CHART of the BRITISH CHANNEL Is
  most Humbly dedicated by His most Obedient
  and Dutiful Servant John Hamilton Moore'
'London. Publish'd as the Act directs June 27th
  1786 by JOHN HAMILTON MOORE,
  Tower Hill'
'One Mile' [= 1.3"] 1:48,738
Engraved by John Russell.
Rame Head(SW)–Torpoint(NW)
  –[Plympton](NE)–Yealm estuary(SE)
Printed
7.1" × 8" (180mm × 203mm)
BL 1068 (58)

Chart of Plymouth Sound. White Patch on Hoe.
Old Sugar House. Mount Edgcumbe obelisk.
White House at Kingsand. Staddon Farm. Rocks
named, including Shovel (17 ft). Inter-tidal area.
Soundings. A few anchorages. Bearings. Notes on
tides. Instructions for leading marks.

184

'Reconnoissance militaire de la Baie et des Ports
  de Plimouth faite en novembre 1786'
Scale: '600 Toises' [= 1.8"] 1:26,000
No statement of responsibility
Rame Head(SW)–St John's(NW)–Plym
  estuary(NE)–Yealm estuary(SE)
Ink and watercolour on paper (red and brown
  ink; red and blue)
10.1" × 12.1" (258mm × 308mm)
Archives du Génie ART 14: PLYMOUTH/5
  (two copies)

Chart of the Sound giving details of shipping channel ('*route des Vaisseaux pour entrer dans le port du Roi*'), fortifications and depth of water for mooring at low tide in Cattewater. Royal Naval Hospital described erroneously as '*hopital militaire*'. Inter-tidal area. Rocks.

185

'PLAN du Port et de la Baye DE PLIMOUTH Dressé d'après les dernières Observations' on 'NOUVELLE CARTE REDUITE DE LA MANCHE DE BRETAGNE', '*Publiée sous l'Aprobation des Académies des Sciences et de Marine DEDIEE AU COMMERCE PAR LE SR DEGAULLE Ingénieur Hidrographe de la Marine, de l'Académie des Sciences, belles Lettres et Arts de Rouen, Correspondant de l'Académie des Sciences de Paris, et Professeur d'Hidrographie AU HAVRE 1788*' in LE NEPTUNE FRANCOIS, vol. 1

'*Echelle d'un Mile Anglais*' [= 2"] 1:31,680 (inset)
'Bellanger *Sculpsit*'
Rame Head(SW)–[Torpoint](NW)–Crabtree(NE)–Yealm estuary(SE)
Printed
8.7" × 12" (225mm × 305mm)
BN Ge A 642; NMM 209/40–42 PB D8127

Chart of Plymouth Sound. 'Winter *12 pieds de Mer basse*'. 'Shovell *14 pieds de mer basse*'. 'Tinker *16 pieds de mer basse*'. Soundings. A few anchorages. Bearings.

186

'GENERAL PLAN of PLYMOUTH with the situation of the DOCK YARD, CITADEL, MAKER HEIGHTS, and the Environs; Shewing the Soundings in Plymouth Sound, and distances of the Rising Grounds. Drawn by R. STURT, by direction of Lt COL DURNFORD, Commanding Royal Engineer, 1788'

Scale: (i) 'Feet 1000 + 8000' [= 11.4"] 1:9,473
        (ii) 'Yards 1000 + 2000' [= 11.4"]
        (iii) 'Miles 2' [= 13.4"]
Millbrook peninsula(SW)–Lipson Mill(N)–Shag Stone(SE)
Ink and watercolour on paper (red, green, pink, orange, brown, grey)
57.1" × 39.8" (1451mm × 1012mm)
PRO MR 1434

Map of the landscape around the Sound noting the distances in yards between the batteries on the rising grounds as follows: Citadel–Mount Batten 2,670; Citadel–St Nicholas Island 4,662; St Nicholas Island–West Hoe Battery 2,980; St Nicholas Island–Maker Church 7,850; St Nicholas Island–Mount Wise 6,160; St Nicholas Island–Staddon Heights 8,000; Mount Batten–Staddon Heights 6,554; Maker Church–Penlee Tower 8,850; Maker Church–Mount Pleasant 12,910; Hay (Cornwall)–Maker Church 15,250; Staddon Heights–Maker Church 13,732; Staddon Heights–Penlee Tower 16,350; Wester King's–Mount Wise 3,124; Wester King's–Mount Pleasant 7,840; Mount Pleasant–Hay 16,240; Mount Pleasant–Merrifield 12,840; Merrifield–Ince 6,352. Fresh place-names: Berry Hill, Tretball, Keystick, Winnow Farm (Cornwall). New Bridge River (Cattewater). Roads. Hills (relief). Inter-tidal areas up Cattewater. Soundings in Cawsand and Whitsand bays. Compass pointer with fleur-de-lys.

187

'A SURVEY OF PLYMOUTH SOUND Taken in the Year 1788 HUMBLY Dedicated to the Rt Honourable THE EARL OF CHATHAM R HOPKINS ESQ LORD ARDEN LORD HOOD LORD BELGRAVE HON JT TOWNSHEND A GARDNER ESQ LORDS COMMISSIONERS of the ADMIRALTY By Their LORDSHIPS most devoted and most obedient Servant James Fraser'

'A Scale of 1014 Fathoms or one Nautical Mile 1014' [= 7.3"] 1:79,092
Rame Head(SW)–Torpoint(NW)–Plymouth–Yealm estuary(SE)
Ink on paper (brown, black)
42.5" × 42.5" (1080mm × 1080mm)
Hydrographic Dept c91 Press 5h

Chart of Plymouth Sound. Landmarks are shown either as bearings or because of their military significance. Note the emphasis on high ground: Cawsand, Rame, Penlee, Maker and Staddon are all described as heights with altitudes given in red. 'I have deduced the longitude of St Nicholas Island from my observations on the Solar Eclipse in June 1788, having previously determined the error of the Lunar Tables at that time, by a rigorous calculation founded on the observations of Alexander Aubert Esq at Loampit Hill near Greenwich. The Latitude of the Island has been settled by Mr Willm Bayly Head Master of the Royal Academy at Portsmouth with an Astronomical Quadrant before he sailed with Capt Cook, in the year 1772.' Relative situations of the Handeeps and the Eddystone Rocks laid down for the first time, according to Fraser in order to improve the safety of naval ships. St Nicholas Island now commonly called Drake's Island. Sailing directions for line of battle ships.

186   (detail)

Fresh landmarks: Stonehouse Church, a tavern and Capt. Bertie's (Stoke), New Chapel at Dock, Cunney Cove (Mount Wise), old Fish–House (beyond Cawsand), old obelisk (near Raven's Point), Eastern Trees (near Tor House), old mill (NE of Plymouth). Mr Winn's (Cattedown). Two quarries on West and East Hoe respectively (West Hoe erroneously described as Easter King's). Weir House (Torpoint). Hills. The sea: 'Larey Gut' (Laira). Black rocks. Other rocks: Eastern Tinker, Western Tinker, Carlos, Mane, Duke and Adder. Scots Grounds. Foul ground given when appropriate. Some inter-tidal areas (sea-bottom distinguished variously as clay, mud, rocky ground or sandy). Soundings. Compass.

188

As **187** except:

'A SURVEY OF PLYMOUTH SOUND Taken in the Year 1788 by James Fraser Then a Master in His Majesty's Navy with the BREAKWATER and PIER Proposed for the Sheltering of PLYMOUTH SOUND By Messrs Rennie, Hemmans & Whidbey April 22nd 1806'

38.6″ × 38.6″ (981mm × 981mm)

BL Add MS 11818a

Lacks sailing directions given above. Attached is a report written by Rennie in 1806:

There is probably no harbour on the South West Coast of England so well situated as Plymouth for the stationing of His Majesty's Fleets that are to meet the natural Enemies of their Country. The Bay is extensive, the entrance to the Hamoaze is deep, its capacity is very great and the Anchoring Ground excellent. A Fleet of Ships of any size and of any Number, may find ample security there and as the Dock Yard is extensive, it is of infinite consequence as a Naval Station for the resort of His Majesty's Fleets.

The Catwater is also an excellent Harbour; the water is in parts deep and well sheltered, but the retent is small; such however as it is, nothing can be more favourable for the Commerce of this Country.

Possessing so many natural advantages as Plymouth does, it is somewhat remarkable that nothing has hitherto been done to rectify its defects, i.e. to make a proper and secure place in which Ships of War when they go out of the Hamoaze and are bound to Sea, can ride in safety during Storms, or for those who are inward bound and are obliged to anchor until the Tide and Winds will permit them to go into the Harbour . . .'

189

As **188** except:

'A SURVEY OF PLYMOUTH SOUND Taken in the Year 1788, by James Fraser then a Master in HIS MAJESTY'S NAVY, with the BREAKWATER and PIER proposed for the SHELTRING of the SAID SOUND by Messrs Rennie & Whidbey April 22d 1806'

Ink on paper (red, blue, green, brown, grey)

39.4″ × 39.4″ (1002mm × 1002mm)

Duchy of Cornwall DCO Maps & Charts 33

190

'Plymouth Dock & Lines 1789' (endorsed)

Scale: '200 feet to an Inch 100 + 1500' [= 8″]
    1:2,400

[Elias Durnford]

Dockyard and Dock town

Ink and watercolour on paper (red, green, brown, grey, yellow)

24.7″ × 24.4″ (625mm × 600mm)

PRO MR 1427 (WO 78/2581)

A map of Dock giving street pattern and names. Dockyard in outline only. The map shows the boundary wall surrounding the Dockyard and the new boundary wall surrounding south side of Dock town; also drains running along eastern edge of Dock. Letters A–E (no key) relate to wall around road leading out of Dockyard (main *barrière*) to Stoke. F–I relate to section of boundary wall running from near Marlborough Square to Ordnance Wharf. Numbers 1–9 also relate to this new boundary wall, 10–13 relate to road within the lines (section from George Square–Cumberland Square). Note Mutton Cove: new wharf; on corner of Prospect Row and new boundary wall is Royal Artificer Company's Garden. Workshop below stone quarry. Governor's house. Ordnance storehouses along Dock lines noted; also Hospital; Timber pound; Body's Timber Yard above Gun wharf. Guardrooms at main and small *barrière*. Hills (relief). Direction pointer.

191

'Plan of the Town of Plymouth Dock etc'

Scale: '200 feet to an Inch 200 + 1500' [= 8.5″]
    1:2,400

'Lieut.-Col. Elias Durnford, RE'

c. 1789

Dockyard and Dock town

Ink and watercolour on paper (red, green, brown, turquoise, grey, yellow)

23″ × 27″ (585mm × 686mm)

PRO MPH 406 (3) (WO78/1521) (PRO Catalogue no 2059)

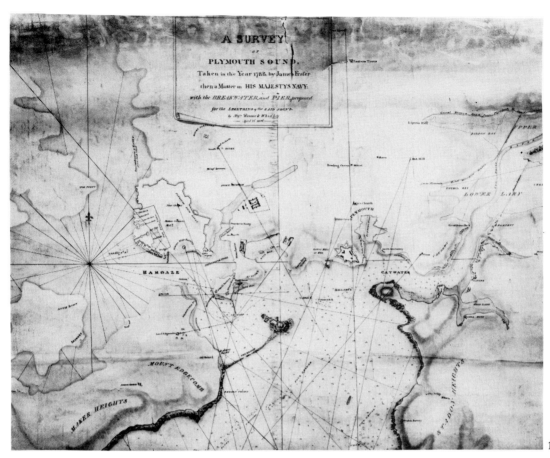

189

A very similar map to the above, endorsed 'Plymouth Dock and Lines showing sites for New Buildings'. Proposed pier and new walk at Mutton Cove; proposed wall above Mount Wise redoubt and below stone quarry. 'Road to the New Horse Ferry' (Torpoint). Ordnance boundary fence. Direction pointer.

Note the description of Plymouth as 'Moorend hills' in the 'appearance of the land as seen from the Hand Deeps'. Governor's house at Dock. Soundings. Danger-line around rocks. Bearings to the Hand Deeps and to the East Rutts. Direction pointer. Loose item bound into volume.

192
No title
'SCALE of MILES 1 + 5' [= 6″] 1:63,360
'J. Smith and S. Hemmans MA'
1791
Horestone Point(W)–Prawle Point(E)
Ink and watercolour on paper (blue, yellow, grey)
21.4″ × 28.6″ (544mm × 727mm)
BL Add MSS 38076 A1

Small-scale chart of the coastline from Looe to Salcombe showing the Hand Deeps and East Rutts.

193
As **192** except:
'J[ame]s Smith and S[amue]l Hemmans'
Ink and watercolour on paper (red, yellow, blue)
21.1″ × 28.4″ (536mm × 722mm)
Hydrographic Dept k19 Shelf Od

194
'Plan of Plymouth and its Environs'
'Scale of Feet 1500 + 4500' [= 6.7″] 1:10,746
'Scale of Yards 1000 + 3000' [= 13.4″]
'Scale of Miles 1 + 2' [= 18.6″]

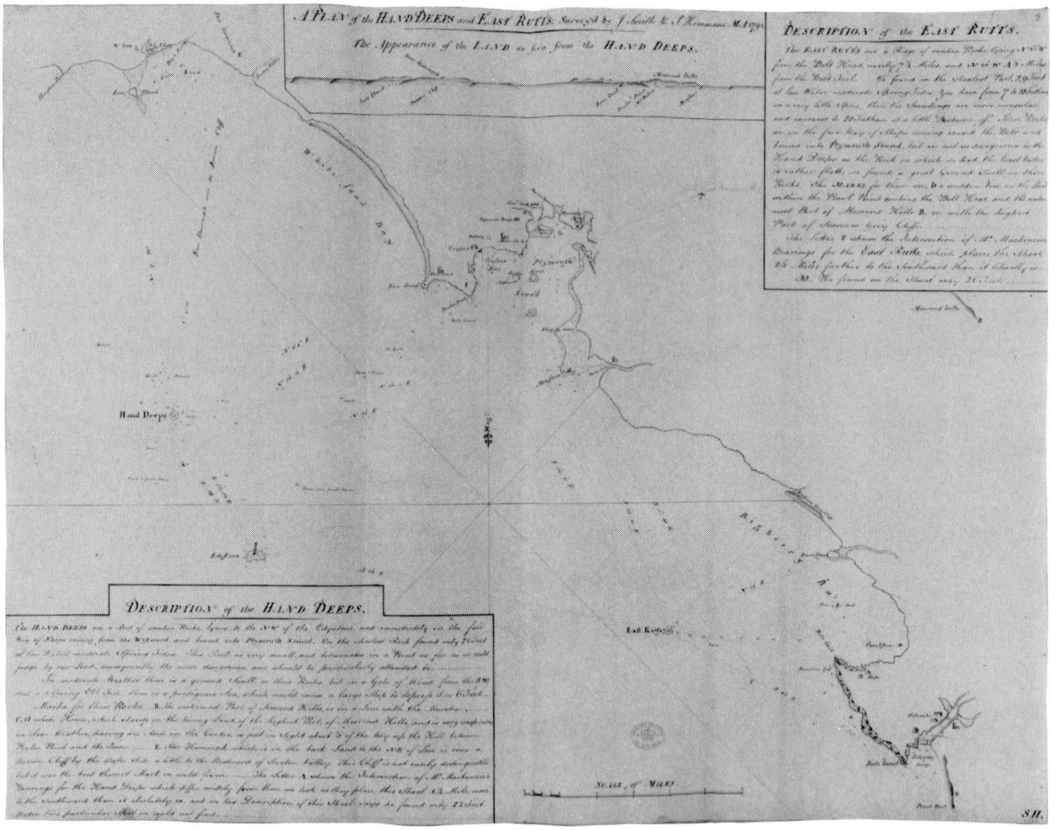

192

'Drawn by R. Sturt and A. Spicer'
1793
Portwrinkle(SW)–Polbathic(NW)–Boringdon
Park(NE)–Revelstoke(SE)
Ink and watercolour on paper (red and black ink,
green wash)
82.5″ × 48.8″ (1897mm × 1240mm)
PRO MR 1176 (WO 78/345) (PRO Catalogue
no. 2062)

Detailed survey of the landscape around Plymouth
Sound and beyond showing hills in relief. Many
place-names. Outlying churches, villages, hamlets,
farms, mills, shown and marked. Large country
houses and parks accurately depicted: Port Eliot,
Mount Edgcumbe, Saltram. Estuaries marked and
rivers shown. Roads shown; turnpike roads stained
brown. Field boundaries shown, also distinction
between wooded areas and other ground. Inter-
tidal area. Direction pointer.

195

'A PLAN and SURVEY of the Tract of a Stream
   of WATER proposed to be conveyed from the
   River Walkham in Dartmoor to the Lines of
   Plymouth Dock'
Scale: 'Two Miles' [= 3.9″] 1:32,492
'Matthew Dixon Colonel of Engineers'
c. 1793
Merrifield Bridge(NE)–Dock(SW)
Ink and watercolour on paper (red, green, grey,
yellow)
28.6″ × 18.1″ (726mm × 460mm)
BL Add MSS 50008 B f. 18

Plan of the proposed leat from the River Walkham
to Plymouth Dock. Powers to build a leat up to 10
ft wide for the purpose of supplying water were
granted to Plymouth Dock Waterworks Company
in 1793 (C. Gill (ed.) *Dartmoor: A New Study*, 1970,
p. 262). The plan is a line-drawing, giving landmarks along the route from the intended weir near

Mis Tor until Granby Square at Dock. On Dartmoor, these landmarks are tors (named), brooks, houses until Walkhampton Church, when the leat runs parallel with the road into Dock. Other landmarks are the boundary stones between the parishes of Bickleigh and Buckland Monachorum, the houses of known individuals (Franklin's house, Garland's house) and military landmarks such as camp ground, 'Devon Militia's Mess House', inns, turnpike gates. Widey mills. Pennycross Chapel. Names of owners of land adjoining proposed leat given where known. Roads. Houses. Barns. Huts. Gates.

196

'A Plan of the Marsh adjoining Stonehouse Lane in the borough of Plymouth belonging to the Mayor and Commonalty of the borough of Plymouth survey'd the 22d of August 1794 by Granville Smith Teacher of the Mathematicks and Land Surveyor in Plymouth'
'A Scale of Chains 66 feet each Statute Measure' 10 [= 5"] 1:1,584
Orientation: S
Salt-marsh above Millbay
Ink and watercolour on paper (red, green, brown)
20.9" × 25.8" (531mm × 656mm)
WDRO W281

A plan of the salt-marsh which extended in a triangle from Old Mills at Millbay to the road running from Plymouth to Stonehouse (base line of the triangle). The plan notes the buildings at Millbay with their size measured in perches (paper mills, Mr Dunsterville's house and yard, miller's house and court). The marsh itself is measured as 26½ acres statute measure, hedges not included. The plan also shows boundaries around the edge of the marsh, and notes land belonging to the mayor and commonalty of Plymouth and to the Earl of Mount Edgcumbe. Gates. Wells. Direction pointer.

W. Dunsterville leased a paper mill in 1779 (Worth *Calendar of Plymouth Municipal Records*, p. 284).

197
No title
'Scale of Feet' 80 + 400 [= 6"] 1:960
No statement of responsibility
? Post-1794
Citadel and East Hoe
Ink and watercolour on paper (pink, green, turquoise, yellow, sepia, grey)
38.4" × 21.1" (976mm × 536mm)
PRO MPHH 61 (2) (WO 78/1244) (PRO Catalogue no. 2063)

Plan of the Citadel and adjoining land distinguishing boundaries and occupation. Boundary

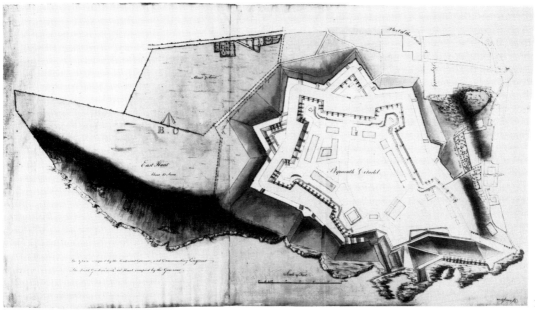

197

wall of Victualling Office. Fence surrounding Citadel noting that the area within and the glacis are occupied by the Lieutenant governor and commanding engineer, while the governor occupies the fields, gardens and East Hoe. Acreage of East Hoe (13 acres) and field north (7 acres) considerably less than in **30**. Note the quarry north of the Victualling Office which is shown for the first time.

198

'TO THE Right Honorable the Master, Wardens & Elder Brethren of the Trinity House, THIS CHART OF PLYMOUTH SOUND is most respectfully Dedicated by their humble Servant W. HEATHER'
'London. Published as the Act directs, July 12 1798 by HEATHER and WILLIAMS, at the Navigation Warehouse, No 157 Leadenhall Street'
'Scale of Two Miles' [= 4.8″] 1:26,400
Rame head(SW)–Saltash(NW)–Yealm estuary(SE)
Printed
25.1″ × 15.5″ (638mm × 394mm)
Archives Nationales Marine 6 JJ 68; BL Maps 151 f. 1 (3a); BN SH Portefeuille 23 Division 5 Pièce 23; Naval Historical Library Vf 11/11

Chart of Plymouth Sound. White House due north of Plymouth. Mill dam at Millbridge. 'Assembly' at Long Room. Telegraph near Maker Church; also 'Government Ground'. Hatching for hills. Inter-tidal area. Soundings. Anchorages including notes on whether suitable for large or small ships. Compass rose.

199

As **198** except:
'A New Edition. Corrected by J.W. Norie, 1829'
'Stephenson *sculp*[*sit*]'
BL 2127 (5)

200

No title
Scale: 'Fathoms 1,200' [= 2.3″] 1:37,565
J.B. Warren
July 1798
Maker(SW)–Torpoint(NW)–Plymouth–Mewstone(SE)
Ink and watercolour on paper (red, green, yellow, brown, grey)
7.8″ × 12″ (198mm × 305mm)
PRO Adm 1/2686 no W79a (PRO Catalogue no. 2067)

A rudimentary sketch of the Sound showing where the pier proposed by J.B. Warren to the Admiralty in the accompanying letter might be built. Inter-tidal area. Soundings. Compass. 'The Bay of Cawsand is the best Anchorage for Ships of War and has the greatest depth of Water of any near, and further to the Westward than any other place in the Channel either for bringing Squadrons or Convoys . . .' Warren's proposal was for a pier to be run out from Penlee Point. The pier would have a curve of $\frac{3}{4}$ to 1 mile to break the force of the sea. It would be composed of rough stone, seaweed and old hulks filled with stones and sunk. He estimated that such a task could be completed in two years if undertaken by a thousand men encamped on Maker Heights. Alternatively, four to five hundred convicts could do the work, which would be unlikely to cost more than £30,000. The benefits would be considerable, enabling a fleet or convoy of twenty ships of the line to be sheltered from the wind.

201

'PLYMOUTH SOUND, HAMOAZE and CATWATER with the LEADING MARKS and VIEWS of LAND'
'Published by LAURIE & WHITTLE Fleet Street 12 Octr 1800'
'SCALE OF ONE MILE or 2,040 Yards' [= 4.5″] 1:16,320
'Wm PRICE MASTER in the ROYAL NAVY 1798 LONDON'
Penlee Point(SW)–Thanks(NW)–[Plympton](NE)–Yealm estuary(SE)
Printed
36.5″ × 25.5″ (928mm × 648mm)
BL K.MAR III 75; BN SH Portefeuille 23 Division 5 Pièce 24; Hydrographic Dept B320/1–2 Shelf Qf

Printed chart of Plymouth Sound. Many of the land features have been drawn in perspective in miniature, such as: Wembury Church, Staddon Farm, Tan Chapel, Cattedown lime-kiln, Old Sugar House, New Church, Stone beacons on Hoe, Royal Naval Hospital (chapel used as a landmark) Stoke Church, Pritchard's house, Plymouth Mill and New Chapel at Dock, Admiral Graves's house at Thanks, Mount Edgcumbe obelisk, Mount Edgcumbe house, Maker Church and parsonage. Roads on Maker peninsula. Track from Stoke Church to Dock. Mount Edgcumbe park. Major rocks with beacons and buoys given (key). Distinction between rocks under water and those dry at low water. Inter-tidal area. Soundings. Anchorages. Compass with many bearings, especially to Old Church (St Andrew's). Sailing instructions. Many coastal profiles.

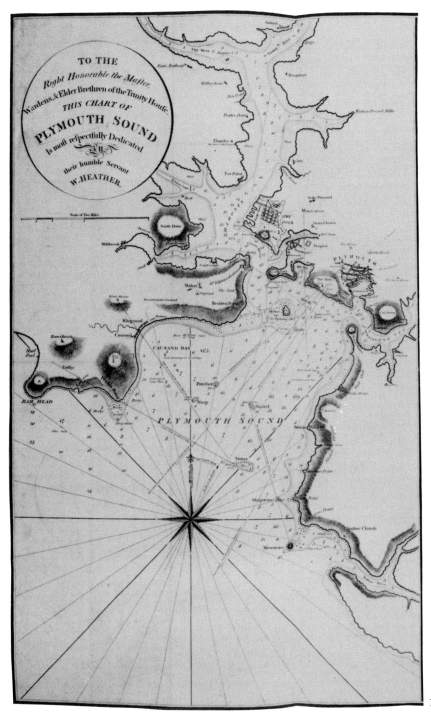

198

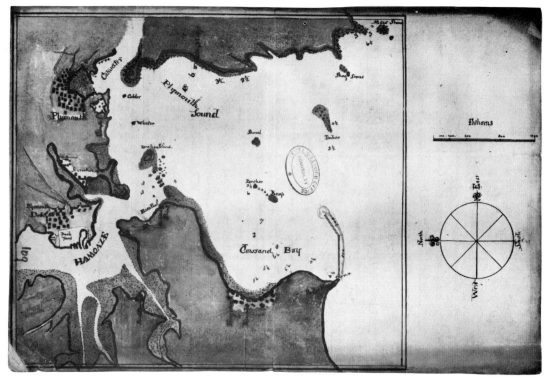

200

202

'A CHART of the COAST of DEVONSHIRE
FROM EXMOUTH TO RAME HEAD:
Containing TOR BAY, START BAY,
PLYMOUTH SOUND &ca by WILLIAM
PRICE, Master of His Majesty's Ship
THESEUS'

'LONDON Published by LAURIE & WHITTLE
No 53 Fleet Street Jany 1st 1799'

No scale given

Engraved by George Allen, no. 19 Shoe Lane,
Fleet Street, London

Rame Head(W)–Exmouth(E)

Printed

24.1″ × 30.5″ (including insets) (614mm x
775mm)

NMM 379/10 PB D8240

A printed chart of the coastline from Exmouth to
Rame Head. Inter-tidal area. Soundings. Note the
views of the high land over Plymouth, and appear-
ance of the land to the eastward of Plymouth.
Insets: marks to run into the Hamoaze between
Drake's Island and Redding Point; marks for the
Shovel, Panther, Tinker, Knap, etc.

See Le Gear *Geographical Atlases*, c. 11 9488.

Undated Maps

203

'Plan de la Rade de Plymouth'

No scale given, but approx. 1:17,500 (variable)

No statement of responsibility

Late seventeenth century

Plymouth Sound

Ink on paper (black, red, brown, green)

14.4″ × 18.8″ (366mm × 478mm)

BN SH Portefeuille 23 Division 5 Pièce 3

Vague sketch of Plymouth Sound including
lengthy key. The plan was probably made with
invasion in mind since the chief land features are the
fort on St Nicholas Island, Citadel and towers at
Mount Batten and Penlee. The key describes how
Plymouth is situated behind the hill on which the
Citadel is built, thus completely hiding it from the
Sound. Drake's Island is described as a sugar loaf
('*pin de sucre*') with two perimeter roads around it
containing about sixty pieces of cannon; above the
rock is a powder tower. The Citadel contains
nearly seventy pieces of cannon, but since it stands
high above the sea, as soon as a ship approaches the
guns become useless to prevent entry into the
Hamoaze. Soundings. Brief sailing directions on

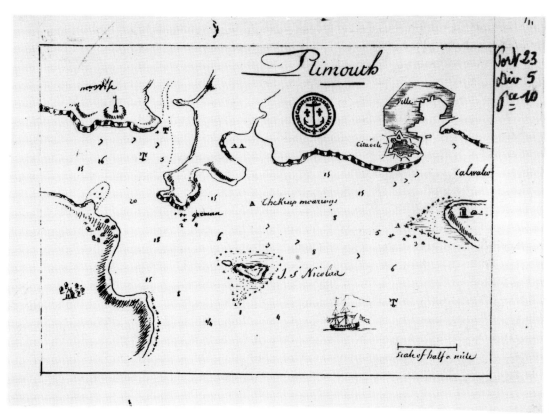

204

how to avoid running into rocks on entering the Cattewater.

204
'Plimouth'
'scale of half a mile' [= 1.3″] 1:24,369
No statement of responsibility
Late seventeenth century
Plymouth Sound
Ink on paper
7″ × 9.8″ (178mm × 249mm)
BN SH Portefeuille 23 Division 5 Pièce 10

Vague sketch of Plymouth Sound. 'The King's moarings' south of Millbay. Rough passage up the Hamoaze drawn in. A few soundings. Anchorages.

205
[Vue de Plymouth]
No scale given, but approx. 1:6,840
No statement of responsibility
? Early eighteenth century
Orientation: S

[Kingsand](SW)–[Torpoint](NW)–Plymouth(NE) –[Mount Batten](SE)
Ink and watercolour on paper (red, green, brown)
17.7″ × 24″ (variable) (450mm × 610mm)
BN SH Portefeuille 23 Division 5 Pièce 1

Bird's-eye-view pictorial map of landscape around the Sound, as seen from beyond Stoke Church. The town of Plymouth is shown surrounded by a wall, and the town gates and quay clearly depicted. Dockyard much in evidence, also gun batteries and the blockhouse at Cawsand suggesting that this map was drawn for military reasons. A key to the map notes two prisons beyond the town of Plymouth to the north-east. Stonehouse is described as *'ville franc'* and Mount Edgcumbe as *'maison de Cromwel'*. Roads. Land use shown in general terms.

206
'Idee du Port de Plymout En Angleterre'
'Echelle d'une Lieue françoise' [= 6.2″] 1:28,205
No statement of responsibility
? Mid-eighteenth century

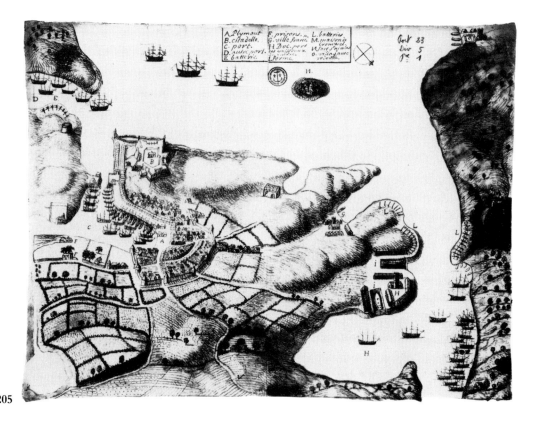

205

Rame Head(SW)–[Saltash](NW)–Cattewater(NE)
  –[Yealm estuary](SE)
Ink and watercolour on paper (red, green,
  brown, grey)
19.7″ × 29.8″ (500mm × 757mm)
BN SH Portefeuille 23 Division 5 Pièce 11

Sparse chart of Plymouth Sound. Key. Town of
Plymouth described as hidden by the Citadel.
Includes much detail on guns: Pigg's Point
described as a battery of seven cannons, Mount
Batten as a gun-tower, Drake's Island as having a
perimeter wall with two rows of guns and
Stonehouse as '*Bourg de Pescheurs où il y a une batterie
Suite de gasons de 18 canons*'. Reference to Saltash as
'*Peuplade de Religionnaires François*' and to Maker as
a display tower for signals to ships. Large hospital
drawn immediately north of the town of Ply-
mouth.

207
'CARTE des Environs de la Ville et Port DE
  PLYMOUTH' (inset)
on 'TABLEAU HIDROGRAPHIQUE QUI
  CONTIENT LE DETAIL MARITIME DES

PRINCIPAUX PORTS . . . Fait d'après des
Manuscrits précieux que possède le Che[valie]r
de Beaurain Géographe ordinaire DE SA
MAJESTE et Ci-devant de l'Education de
Monseigneur le Dauphin Avec Privilège du
Roy'
'*Echelle de trois Miles d'Angleterre*' [= 3″] 1:63,360
Mid-eighteenth century
Rame Head(SW)–Torpoint(NW)–Oreston(NE)
  –Yealm estuary(SE)
Printed
4.5″ × 5.6″ (115mm × 145mm)
NMM DUC 223: 2/51

Printed chart of the Sound. '*Pour la Sureté du Havre,
en tems de Guerre l'on tend une Grosse Chaine.*' Notes
in French, but Dutch place-names.

208
'Carte particulière de la Baye et Ports [sic] de
  Plimouth'
Scale: '*0.064 ¼ de lieue marine ½ li*' [= 5″] 1:17,280
  (endorsement)
No statement of responsibility
Eighteenth century

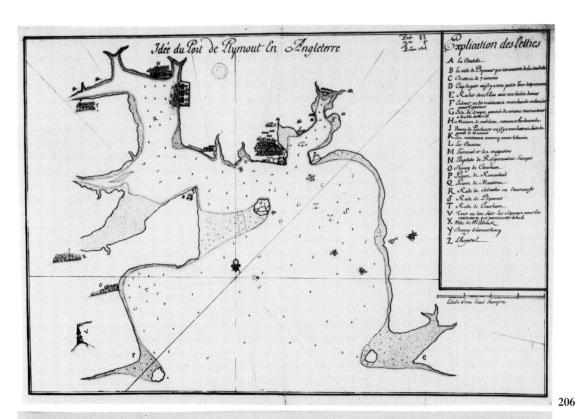

206

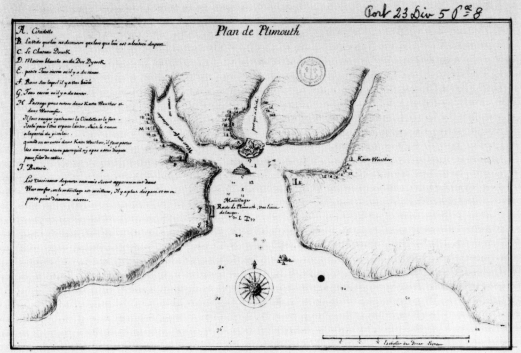

210

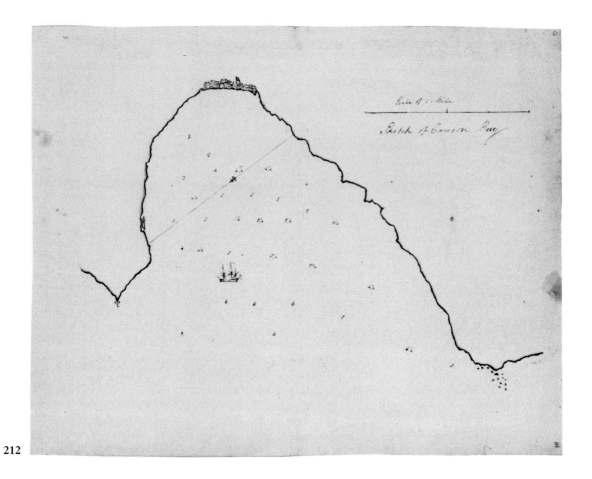

212

Rame Head(SW)–Saltash(NW)–Plymouth(NE)
  –Yealm estuary(SE)
Ink and watercolour on paper (red and black ink;
  turquoise, green, brown, grey)
26.2″ × 22.6″ (666mm × 574mm)
Archives du Génie ART 14: PLYMOUTH/1

Chart of Plymouth Sound. Inter-tidal area. Soundings. Anchorages. Compasses.

209
As **208** except:
26″ × 22.8″ (661mm × 579mm)
BN SH Portefeuille 23 Division 5 Pièce 14

210
'Plan de Plimouth'
'*Echelle de Deux Lieux*' 1 + 1 [= 4.8″] 1:71,280

No statement of responsibility
Eighteenth century
Plymouth Sound. Survey so poor that it would
  be misleading to attempt precision
Ink on paper
10.1″ × 16″ (251mm × 407mm)
BN SH Portefeuille 23 Division 5 Pièce 8

Rough and inaccurate sketch of Plymouth Sound,
possibly drawn later from memory. The Sound
itself described as a league across. Key. Town of
Plymouth noted as '*La ville que l'on ne découvre que
lors l'on est à l'entrée du port*'. Mount Edgcumbe
house described as '*Maison blanche ou du Duc
Dyorck*'. Mount Batten described as '*petite tour
carrée où il y a du canon*'; Penlee Tower similarly.
Passages for entering Cattewater and Hamoaze
given. Note that enemy warships lie in Hamoaze
because the anchorage is better there.

211
'RADE DE PLIMOUTH'
'*Lieus Marines de France et d'angleterre de vingt au
    Degré 8*' [= 14"] 1:97,755
No statement of responsibility
Eighteenth century
Talland Bay(SW)–Bodmin(NW)–Plympton(NE)
    –Bigbury(SE)
Ink and watercolour on paper (yellow and green
    wash)
15" × 21.2" (381mm × 539mm)
BN SH Portefeuille 23 Division 5 Pièce 15

Distorted and rather confused map of the coastal
area from Talland Bay to Bigbury, probably
designed to show communications in the event of
invasion. The map highlights the river estuaries and
their course inland from West Looe in the west to the
Dart in the east. Some errors have crept in: the River
Plym is wrongly noted as flowing into the Hamoaze, while two non-existent estuaries (the Rivers
Bott and Balmer) have been inserted between the
Rivers Yealm and Avon. A signal noted between
Liskeard and Looe; another above the River Yealm.
The map also notes main roads, particularly the road
to London via Exeter. Hills. Land use. Note above
Liskeard that although the ground is cultivated, it is
hilly. Boggy ground noted near Bigbury; park
beyond Liskeard. Notes on rocks and a garbled
version of how to enter the Hamoaze. Inter-tidal
area. Soundings. A few anchorages.

212
'Sketch of Causon Bay'
'Scale of 1 Mile' [= 5"] 1:12,672
No statement of responsibility
Eighteenth century
Orientation: W
Cawsand Bay
Ink on paper
12.6" × 16.2" (320mm × 412mm)
NMM LAD/11 f. 61

Sketch of the shoreline around Cawsand Bay.
Soundings. Direction pointer.

213
No title
Scale: 'One Mile to an Inch' 1:63,360
No statement of responsibility
Late eighteenth century
Portwrinkle(SW)–St Germans estuary(NW)–Laira
    estuary(NE)–Revelstoke(SE)
Ink on paper (red and black)
15.2" × 19.2" (386mm × 488mm)
PRO MPH 729 (PRO Catalogue no. 2065)

Sketch-map of the coastline around Plymouth
Sound. Place-names but little other detail. Road
from Crafthole to Torpoint via Anthony noted.
Eddystone lighthouse.

Supplement I: Additional Maps, Charts and Plans

The following maps were documented after completion of the catalogue.

A1
'PLYMOUTH' (inset)
On 'A New and Correct Draught of the CHANNELL between ENGLAND & FRANCE Shewing ye Sands, Shoales, depth of Water and Anchorage on ye Said Coasts with the Setting of the Tydes and ye Time of High Water as observed by Capt Edm Halley'
'Sold by Saml Thornton Hydrograp[he]r at the signe of England Scotland and Ireland in the Minories LONDON'
Scale: 'One Mile' [= 5″] 1:12,672
Rame Head (SW)–[Torpoint](NW)–Lipson(NE)–Mewstone(SE)
3.4″ × 3″ (85mm × 76mm)
NMM 426/187 (SEL 27); Plymouth City Museum

A2
'THE PLAN OR MAP to which THE Annex't Deed refers'
'A Scale of Feet' 100 + 500 [= 6″] approx. 1:1,200
14 June 1758
Site of Royal Naval Hospital, Stonehouse
24″ × 20″ approx. (608mm × 508mm)
Present location unknown (map not examined)

Plan on deed of conveyance showing site of Royal Naval Hospital. Land shown as fields (names, acreages and in some cases names of owners of fields given). The fields are bounded by Stonehouse Creek, the road running from Stonehouse to Plymouth and by a new road. Plym Bound Stones marked. Mill. Mill pond. Stream of fresh water. Compass.

The plan has been reproduced by P.D.Gordon Pugh in 'History of the Royal Naval Hospital, Plymouth, Part 1: The Life and Times of Captain Richard Creyke', *Journals of the Royal Naval Medical Service*, 58 (1972), pp. 78–94, 207–26.

The information regarding scale and size was recorded by Miss M. Lattimore before the disappearance of this item.

A3
'PLAN DES VILLE PORTS RADE ET CITADELLE DE PLIMOUTH' (inset)
on 'CARTE DE L'ENTREE DE LA MANCHE QUI CONTIENT LE DETAIL DES MANOEUVRES DE L'ARMEE COMBINEE DE FRANCE ET D'ESPAGNE SOUS LE COMMANDEMENT DE MR LE COMTE D'ORVILLIER PENDANT LE COURANT DU MOIS D'AOUST DE L'ANNEE 1779'
'*Echelle de trois milles*' [= 2.8″] 1:67,885 (inset)
'*Echelle de 10 Lieues Marine*' [= 3″] 1:5,829,120 (main chart)
Paradès
1779
Ink and watercolour on paper (red, green, yellow)
6.4″ × 6.7″ (163mm × 173mm) (inset)
18.5″ × 26.5″ (467mm × 673mm) (main chart)
Service Historique de la Marine, Vincennes G190

Inset of Plymouth Sound on a chart of the Channel. The chart shows routes taken by the combined army (France and Spain) from 14 August, when it left France (the Spanish contingent having arrived off the French coast on 6 August) and chased the rearguard of the English squadron; 17 August when the fleet stood off Plymouth (and the English ship the *Ardent* was taken by three French frigates); 18–23 August and manoeuvres on 31 August.

This chart is at the back of Paradès's 'Relation abrégée de la conduite et des operations de M. DE ROBERT PARADÈS, mestre de camp à la suite de la cavalerie, à commencer du premier janvier 1778 jusqu'à la paix, 1782'.

A4

'A plan of Sutton Pool with the adjacent Keys
  and Buildings, 1786'
'The Scale': 100 + 500 ft [= 4.2″] 1:1,714
William Simpson, Surveyor
Sutton Pool
Ink and watercolour on parchment (red, blue,
  grey)
11.2″ × 25.4″ (29.6mm × 64.3mm) (variable)
Duchy of Cornwall DCO Maps and Charts 741

Plan of Sutton Pool with named quays, streets and
buildings, especially South Quay, Smarts Quay
and New Quay. Key giving descriptions, rents,
dates when leases expire, improved rent and
comments, particularly amounts expended by lessees and buildings erected by them. Notes where
property has become dilapidated. Compass
pointer.

Early nineteenth-century annotations in red ink,
probably by Thomas Davis (I owe this suggestion
to Graham Haslam).

A5

(On dorse of **A4**)
'A PLAN of SUTTON POOL and the adjacent
  Parts 1788'
'A Scale of Feet 660' [= 3.2″] 1:2,475
Sutton Pool and its entrance from Cattewater
Ink and watercolour on parchment (red, blue,
  yellow, grey)
Size as **A4** except plan does not extend to the
  whole

Plan of Sutton Pool showing its entrance from the
Cattewater. Site of the Fish-House marked in
section A/B; inset of Sutton Pool showing proposed swing-gate. Diagram showing NE and SW
winds 'Swell coming in from the Sound with the
Tide'. Queens Battery and Mount Batten drawn.
Rocks around edge of coastline shown. Compass
pointer.

Supplement II: Articles Worthy of Mention

The following are maps and similar items which do not qualify for inclusion in the catalogue but which are worthy of mention.

WM1
'PLEMUE'
in *Le Grand Routier: pillotage et Entrage de mer . . .*

Pierre Garcie
Poitiers
1542
NMM Unique Item no. E2632

Simple woodcut diagram showing the entry to Plymouth Sound.

WM2
'EXPEDITIONIS HISPANORUM IN Angliam vera descriptio ANNO D MDLXXXVIII [1588]'
Robert Adams; engraved by Augustine Ryther
1589/90
London
BL Maps C.7 c.1. NMM PB D8529. Many other copies available.

Ten charts covering the course of the Spanish Armada around the British Isles; four show Plymouth.

See Henry Yates Thompson (ed.) *LORD HOWARD OF EFFINGHAM AND THE SPANISH ARMADA*, printed for the Roxburghe Club, 1919.

WM3
'De Canaal tusschen Enghelandt en Vranckrijck'
in *THE LIGHT OF NAVIGATION*
William Johnson [Willem J. Blaeu]
Amsterdam
1620
NMM BLA 10 PB D8259

Chart showing this area of the coastline, including 'Pleymuye', 'Limehouse', 'Vissersdorp'.

WM4
'Carta particolare dell canale Fra Inghilterra è Francia . . .'
in *ARCANO DEL MARE*, vol. 2
Robert Dudley, Duke of Northumberland and Earl of Warwick
Florence
1661 (first publ. 1646/7)
NMM COL 04 PB D8260

Chart including this area of the coastline. 'Limehous', 'Frierio' (Friary).

WM5
'A Prospect of Plymouth and ye Sound, as it is Seen between ye Ram head and Mewstone a League from ye Citadel, with a view of Hamoze and Catwater, Sutton Pool And all ye Remarkable Points etc . . .'
c. 1713
BL Maps C.10 c.15; BN SH Porte feuille 23 Division 5 Pièce 2

Bird's-eye pictorial view of the Sound with notable landmarks dotted about the hills.

A smaller version also occurs in *RECUEIL des VILLES PORTS D'ANGLETERRE*, 'tiré des Grands Plans de Rocque et du Portuland de l'Angleterre du Sr Belin, 1759'.

WM6
'DE'MONSTRATION DE PLEMUE'
in *Le Petit Flambeau de la Mer, ou le Veritable Guide des Pilotes Cotiers*
'Sieur Bougard, *Lieutenant sur les Vaisseaux du Roi . . . Au Havre*'
1731
Royal Geographical Society Library 165.B

Crude woodcut chart of Plymouth Sound.

WM7
'A SURVEY of the SOUTH COAST of
ENGLAND from PLYMOUTH TO THE
LIZARD BY Lieut Murdoch Mackenzie, 1773',
published 1809.
Duchy of Cornwall 1488; NMM G223:2/42

Printed map with brief detail on Plymouth Sound.

WM8
Model of Plymouth Dockyard
January 1774

NMM ADM/Y/PD 8 has references to the model.
The parts painted yellow on the model represent
proposed improvements (see **150** and **153**).

WM9
'PLAN OF THE ENCAMPMENT ON
BUCKLAND DOWN NEAR PLYMOUTH
from 14 July to 22 Octr 1778'
BL Add MS 15533 pl.41

Shows turnpike road from Plymouth to Tavistock;
also roads to Plympton, Shaugh and Thornbury.

WM10
'A ROUGH PLAN of Buckland Down with the
Late Encampment and the invirons or Lands
Round in the County of Devon'
William Blackamore
BL Add MS 15534

Much detail on the countryside: woods, orchards,
lakes, wells, quarries, pits and springs.

WM11
'PLAN OF THE ENCAMPMENT ON
ROBOROUGH DOWN UNDER THE
COMMAND OF MAJ: GEN GREY from 7th
June to 6th Novr 1781'
BL Add MS 15533 pl.101

Shows Exeter Gate near Warleigh Lake; rivers
leading into Warleigh Lake and Plymouth Lake;
bridges beneath Plymouth to Tavistock road.

WM12
'SKETCH of the ENCAMPMENT on
ROBOROUGH DOWN, Sept 1782'
BL Add MS 15534

Regiments encamped are 75th Foot, Derbyshire,
Devon Foot, Worcestershire, Oxfordshire, Devon
South, Carmarthen.

WM13
'A Chart showing the true Situations of the
Eddystone Lighthouse and Rocks, and the
Handeeps, and East Rutt Shoals; first Surveyed
by Murdoch Mackenzie Junr in the year 1774;
and Protracted anew from Mr Mackenzie's
original angles by Graeme Spence, in the year
1807 in order to illustrate their Nautical
Description; which shows that the Compass
Bearings of the Handeeps given by the Masters
attendant to the Navy Board in the year 1791,
are wrong, and ought to be Corrected.'
Hydrographic Dept D 923/3 Shelf Qa

WM14
Watercolour sketches of headlands (atlas of thirty
coastal views of English Channel)
Staples, W
1796
NMM STA 01/8,10–11,18

Appendix I
Institutions Holding Maps of Plymouth

London

Main Institutions

1   British Library, Great Russell Street, WC1B 3DG
2   Public Record Office, Chancery Lane, WC2 1AH; Ruskin Avenue, Kew, Richmond, Surrey, TW9 4DU
3   National Maritime Museum, Romney Road, Greenwich, SE10 9NF

Others

4   Duchy of Cornwall, 10 Buckingham Gate, SW1E 6LA
5   Naval Historical Library, Ministry of Defence, Whitehall Library, 3–5 Great Scotland Yard, SW1A 2HW (closed access)
6   Royal Geographical Society, 1 Kensington Gore, SW7 2AR

Oxford

7   Ashmolean Museum, University of Oxford, Beaumont Street, OX1 2PH
8   Bodleian Library, University of Oxford, OX1 3BG

Taunton

9   Hydrographic Department, Ministry of Defence, TA1 2DN

Plymouth

10   West Devon Record Office, Unit 3, Clare Place, Coxside, PL4 OJW
11   Plymouth Central Library, Drake Circus PL4 8AL
12   Plymouth City Museum, Drake Circus PL4 8AJ
13   HM Dockyard PL1 4SG
14   Plymouth Proprietary Library (Private Lending Library), 111 North Hill PL4 8JY

Exeter

15   Devon Record Office, Castle Street, EX4 3PU
16   West Country Studies Library, Castle Street EX4 3PQ

Private Owners

17 Boughton House (The Duke of Buccleuch), Kettering, Northants. NN14 1BJ
18 Hatfield House (The Marquess of Salisbury), Hatfield, Herts. AL9 5NF
19 Ince Castle (Patricia, Viscountess Boyd), Saltash, Cornwall, PL12 4RN
20 Longleat House (The Marquess of Bath), Warminster, Wilts. BA12 7NN

Paris

21 Bibliothèque Nationale, 58 rue Richelieu, 75084
22 Archives Nationales, 60 rue des Francs Bourgeois, 75141
23 Archives du Génie, Château de Vincennes, 75997
24 Service Historique de l'Armée de Terre, Château de Vincennes, 75997
25 Service Historique de la Marine, Château de Vincennes, 75997

Madrid

26 Archivo Histórico Nacional, Serrano 115, Madrid 6

Appendix II
Index of Maps by Location

The entries to this appendix are listed in the sequence: catalogue number, reference, title.

1 British Library, Department of Manuscripts

Cotton MSS Augustus

One of the foundation collections of the Department. Collected by Sir Robert Cotton, who died in 1631, and presented to the nation by his grandson in 1700; transferred to the British Museum in 1753.

5	Cotton MS Augustus I i 6	'A Plott of all the Coast of Cornwall and Devonshire . . . 1588'
1	Cotton MS Augustus I i 35–36, 38–39	South-west peninsula, *c.* 1539
15	Cotton MS Augustus I i 40	'Il novo recinto della fortification . . .', 1601–2
9	Cotton MS Augustus I i 41	Leat map
16	Cotton MS Augustus I i 42	'Plimouth Forte', *c.* 1601–2

Add MSS

This collection consists of nearly all the manuscripts acquired by donation, purchase or bequest since 1756.

41	Add MS 5415 E art 2	Citadel, 1677
65	Add MS 9329 f. 170	'The Barton of Mount Wise'
60	Add MS 9329 f. 171	'First Draught The Plot of the Ground about Point Froward'
63	Add MS 9329 ff. 172–73	'Second Draught. The Yard and Docks Compleat'
188	Add MS 11818a	'A Survey of Plymouth Sound', 1788, James Fraser
168	Add MS 15533 pl.59	'Plan of Encampments in the neighbourhood of Plymouth', 1779–82
WM11	Add MS 15533 pl.101	'Plan of the Encampment on Roborough Down', 1781

169	Add MS 15533 pl.161	'Plan of the Environs of Plymouth'
WM10	Add MS 15534	'A Rough plan of Buckland Down with the late Encampment'
WM12	Add MS 15534	'Sketch of the Encampment on Roborough Down, Sept 1782'
22	Add MS 15737 f. 24v	'Plimouth', *c.* 1646
25	Add MS 16370 f. 41	'Plymouth Harbour Containing the Sounde, Causen Bay CatWater Hamause Mill Bay . . .'
26	Add MS 16370 f. 43	'Plan van de Harbour of Pleymouth with the niewe Cittadeel upon the How 1665'
27	Add MS 16370 f. 45	Plymouth Sound
29	Add MS 16371 D	'Plane of the Royal Cittadel of Pleymouth', 1668
45	Add MS 18989 f. 5	'Thus sheweth Plimouth sound when you are at an Anker . . .', 1689
101	Add MS 22875 f. 20	'Plan of the Cittadel of Plymouth', between 1750 and 1752
102	Add MS 22875 f. 21	'Plan of St Nicholas Island', between 1750 and 1752
103	Add MS 22875 f. 22	'Plan of the Gun Wharf and the King's Dock Yard', between 1750 and 1752
192	Add MS 38076 A1	Chart of coastline from Looe to Salcombe, 1791
195	Add MS 50008 B f. 18	'A Plan and Survey of the Tract of a Stream of Water . . . from the R. Walkham . . . to the lines of Plymouth Dock', *c.* 1793
174	Add MS 57638 5	Plymouth Sound, *c.* 1780
124	Add MS 57638 6	'Plymouth Sound', mid–late eighteenth century
156	Add MS 60393 C	'A Plan of the Royal Citadel and Town of Plymouth', 1776

King's MSS

Collected by George III and transferred to the British Museum in 1823 by George IV. Manuscript maps from this collection are kept in the Map Library as King's Topographical Collection (see below).

43	King's MS 40 f. 8	'The Plain or Plott of Plymouth Sound, Ham Oaze and Catt water'

69	King's MS 43 ff. 125–26	'A Plan of Plymouth Sound. . .', 1698
68	King's MS 43 f. 127	'A View of Plymouth Sound. . .', 1697
47	King's MS 43 f. 130	'The Plan of Point Froward with ye Yard Designed therein in [16]89'
70	King's MS 43 f. 130	'A View of His Majesties Dockyard at Plymouth . . .', 1698
71	King's MS 43 f. 130	'The same Plan as it Appears . . . 1698'
49	King's MS 44 ff. 13–14	'The Plan of Point Froward with the Yard first Design'd there in 1689'
73	King's MS 44 ff. 13–14	'The Plan of the same Yard with the Improvements in 1698'
153	King's MS 44 ff. 13–14	'The Plan of the same Yard with the Improvements in 1774'
154	King's MS 44 f. 15	'A Draught of Plymouth Sound, Hamoaze and Catwater', 1774
80	King's MS 45 f. 34	'The East Prospect of Plymouth', 1714–17
81	King's MS 45 f. 34	'A Generall Plan of Plymouth Harbour'
83	King's MS 45 f. 34	'A Plan of the Royall Citadell of Plymouth', 1715
59	Lansdowne 847 f. 80	'The First Draught' (Dockyard)
62	Lansdowne 847 f. 82	'Second Draught Representing the Yard Complete', 1694

Reading Room

176	PP 3557v	'A chart of Plymouth Sound, Catwater and Hamoaze', 1782

Map Library

King's Topographical Collection

51	K. Top. 11 74 1	Plymouth Sound, ? 1692–4
52	K. Top. 11 74 2	'Plymouth', ? 1692–4
89	K. Top. 11 75	'A plan of the Town, Citadel and Harbour of Plymouth . . .', 1724
85	K. Top. 11 76	'A General Plan of the Ports of Hamouse and Plymouth . . .', post-1719
114	K. Top. 11 77	'Plan of the Town, Citadel, Dock and country round Plymouth', John Manson, 1756

115	K. Top. 11 78 1	'Plan of the Town, Citadel, Dock and country round Plymouth', Abraham d'Aubant, 1756
117	K. Top. 11 78 2	'Plymouth Sound', copied by Thomas Smart, 1765
170	K. Top. 11 79 2	'A General Plan with a Project for the Defence of the Arsenals of Plymouth . . .', Lt.-Col. Dixon, revised 1780
182	K. Top. 11 80	'The South Part of an accurate Survey and Measurement of Plymouth and Dock Towns', William Gardner, 1784–6
40	K. Top. 11 81	'Plymouth'
91	K. Top. 11 82	'An Exact Plan of the Royal Citadel and Town', 1725
161	K. Top. 11 83	'Plan of the Town and Citadel of Plymouth', Richard Cowl, 1780
110	K. Top. 11 85	'A Geometrical Plan and West Prospect of Stoke Town . . . with HM Dock Yard and Ordnance Wharfe', pre-1756
109	K. Top. 11 86	'Plan of the Lines round Plymouth Dock . . .' D. Slack, pre-1756
112	K. Top. 11 87	'A Geometrical Plan and West Elevation of HM Dockyard near Plymouth with the Ordnance Wharfe etc', 1756
151	K. Top. 11 88	'Plan of His Majesty's Yard Plymouth Jan 1774'
92	K. Top. 11 91	'St Nicholas Island', 1725

King George III's Maritime Collection

Charts and sea atlases presented to the Admiralty in 1828 and then to the British Museum at various dates from 1844 to 1953.

129	K. MAR I 12	'Carte de la Baye et Port de Plimouth', ? 1764
67	K. MAR III 74	'Plymouth Sound, Catwater and Ham Ouse', 1695
201	K. MAR III 75	'Plymouth Sound, Hamoaze and Catwater . . .', 1800

Others

| 183 | 1068 (58) | 'PLYMOUTH' |
| 111 | 2123 (53) | 'A Geometrical Plan and West Prospect |

		of Stoke Town in the County of Devon . . .', ? pre-1756
199	2127 (5)	Chart of Plymouth Sound, 1829 edition
95	2140 (25)	'Plymouth Sound'
126	2147 (6)	'An Exact Plan of the Ground humbly proposed to be purchased at the Dock of Plymouth', ? 1759
WM2	Maps C.7 c.1	'Expeditionis Hispanorum in Angliam vera descriptio', Adams, 1589/90
53	Maps C.8 d.7	'Plymouth to the Rt. Honble Arthur Earle of Torrington . . .', Greenvile Collins, 1693
149	Maps C.10 d.7	'Plymouth Sound, Ham Oaze and Catwater', 1798
WM5	Maps C.10 c.15	'A Prospect of Plymouth and ye Sound . . .', *c.* 1713
104	Maps C.10 d.18	'A Plan of the Town and Citadel of Plymouth', Emmanuel Bowen, 1754
93	Maps C.11 a.5	'Plimouth Sound', in *Atlas Maritimus et Commercialis*
141	Maps C.11 b.7	'Plymouth Sound, Ham Oaze and Catwater . . . 1770'
131	Maps C.11 c.7	'A Plan of the Town and Citadel of Plymouth', B. Donn, 1765
86	Maps C.26 f. 22(7)	'A Correct Draught of Plymouth Sound Catt Water and Ham Owse'
18	E 31 (15)	'A True Mapp and Description of the Towne of Plymouth and the Fortifications thereof . . . 1643'
166	Maps 147 e 3 36	'Plan de la Rade et du Port de Plymouth Levé en 1779 par le Lieutenant Murdoch Mackenzie'
148	Maps 151 f. 1 (3)	'Plymouth Sound, Ham Oaze and Catwater', 1797
198	Maps 151 f. 1 (3a)	'Chart of Plymouth Sound', Heather, 1798
138	MT 11 h.1 (8)	'Plymouth Sound surveyed by Joseph Gilbert . . .', 1769
140	MT 11 h.1 (9)	'Plymouth Sound, Ham Oaze and Cat Water', 1770
165	SEC I (30)	'A Survey of Plymouth Sound, Hamoaze, Catwater and Cawsand Bay', 1779

| 177 | K 6 66 2 TAB | 'Plymouth Harbour', B. Donn, 1784 |

2 Public Record Office

Chancery Lane

37	E178/6198	Sketch-map of the Lambhay, 1672
33	MPE 363	Plan showing ownership of the Hoe
30	MPE 436	Plan showing ownership of the Hoe, *c.* 1671
4	MPF 6	'Sir Ric[hard] Grenvyle for the fortifying of Plymm[outh]', *c.* 1586–8
14	MPF 262	'Platt of Plimowth by [Si]r Ferd[inando] Gorges', 1596
12	SP 12/245 f. 31	'The platte of ye forte upon ye hoo of Plimouthe', Adams, 1593
13	SP 12/245 f. 32	Copy of above, probably by Simon Basil

Kew

31	MPH 374	1814 copy of seventeenth century plan showing ownership of the Hoe
178	MPH 378	'A Survey of the coast line of part of the River Tamer . . .', 1784
191	MPH 406 (3)	'Plan of the town of Plymouth Dock', *c.* 1789
34	MPH 539	1814 copy of plan showing ownership of the Hoe
173	MPH 727	'Plan of St Nicholas Island', *c.* 1780
96	MPH 728	Citadel, ? 1741
213	MPH 729	Plymouth Sound, late eighteenth century
197	MPHH 61 (2)	Citadel and East Hoe, ? post-1794
116, 118–23	MPHH 129	'Plymouth Sound', 1756 and mid–late eighteenth century
97	MPHH 223/2	'Plan of the Royal Citadel at Plymouth', 1812 (copy of 1741 map)
32	MPHH 223/4	Plan of the East Hoe
35	MPHH 223/5	1814 copy of plan showing ownership of the Hoe

99	MP1 253	Harbour chart of the Hamoaze intended to show suitable sites for moorings, 1747
90	MR 902 (2)	'A Plan of the Town, Citadel and Harbour of Plymouth', 1725
158	MR 948	Plymouth inset on 'A New Hydrographical Survey of the British Channel', 1782
135	MR 1111	'Plan de la Ville, des Ports, de la Citadelle et des Chantiers de Plymouth', 1768
194	MR 1176	'Plan of Plymouth and its Environs', 1793
179	MR 1199 (Part 1)	'Plymouth and Country about 8 miles around', W. Gardner, 1784
180	MR 1385	'An Actual Survey and Measurement of Plymouth and Dock Towns . . . by order of . . . the Duke of Richmond', W. Gardner, 1784
190	MR 1427	'Plymouth Dock and Lines 1789'
186	MR 1434	'General Plan of Plymouth', R. Sturt, 1788
181	OS 5/4 (Part 2)	'The South part of an accurate Survey and Measurement of Plymouth and Dock Towns . . . by order of . . . the Duke of Richmond . . . by W. Gardner', 1784–6
36	T1/382/70	Diagram showing ownership of the Lambhay, 1672 [1758]
200	Adm 1/2686 no. W79a	Sketch of the Sound relating to the proposed breakwater in Cawsand Bay, 1798

3 National Maritime Museum, London

79	ADM/Y/PD 1	'The Ground Platt of HM Dockyard at Hamose', *c.* 1712
100	ADM/Y/PD 2	'A Plan of HM Dockyard near Plymouth, 1748'
128	ADM/Y/PD 3	'Plan of Plymouth Yard with the Estimat for the several Buildings', *c.* 1764
WM8	ADM/Y/PD 8	References for model of Plymouth Dockyard, January 1774

152	LAD/11 f. 38	'Plan of His Majesty's Yard at Plymouth May 1774'
127	LAD/11 f. 39	'A Plan of HM Yard Plymouth . . . 1761'
139	LAD/11 f. 40	'Plymouth Sound, Ham Oaze and Cat Water', ?1769–70
212	LAD/11 f. 61	'Sketch of Causon Bay', eighteenth century
134	LAD/11 f. 67	'A Plan of Catwater . . .', 1767
46	LAD/11 f. 70	'The Original Plat of Ground on which Plymouth Yard now stands . . .', ?1689/90
20	LAD/11 f. 71	'A True Map and Description of the Town of Plymouth . . .', 1643 [post-1828]
48	LAD/11 f. 72	'Plan of Point Froward with the Yard first Designed there in 1689'
72	LAD/11 f. 72	'Plan of the same Yard with the improvements in 1698'
28	P/45	Citadel and part of Plymouth, de Gomme, 1666/7
38	P/45	Cattewater, Citadel, part of Town of Plymouth, de Gomme, 1672
23	101/59 JAC 01 PB D8258	Plymouth Sound [1654]
185	209/40–42 PB D8127	'Plan du Port et de la Baye de Plimouth dressé d'après les dernières Observations', 1788
129	211/483 PB D8194	'Carte de la Baye et Port de Plimouth', ? 1764
130	211/484	'Plan des Ville et Citadelle de Plymouth'
53	335/8 (GRC 01) PB D8205	'Plymouth to the Rt Honble Arthur Earle of Torrington . . .', Greenvile Collins, 1693
86	336/49 (GRC 03)	'A Correct Draught of Plymouth Sound Catt Water and Ham Owse'
55	340/54 (GRC 09) PB D8198	'Plymouth . . .', Greenvile Collins, 1792 edition
88	340/54 (GRC 09) PB D8198	'A New and Correct large Draught of Plymouth Sound Cattwater and Hamoaze', 1792 edition
93	341/9 (DDC 01/9) PB D8196	'Plimouth Sound', 1728
158	363/127 PB D8233	'Plymouth', publ 1782

202	379/10 PB D8240	'A Chart of the Coast of Devonshire from Exmouth to Rame Head. . .', 1799
149	379/72 LAW 03	'Plymouth Sound, Hamoaze and Catwater surveyed in 1797', 1798
67	382/18 (LEA 01) PB E7505	'Plymouth Sound Catwater and Ham Ouse', 1695
142	416/12 PB D8506	'Plymouth Sound, Ham Oaze and Catwater . . .'
157	416/12 PB D8506	'Plymouth', 1777
146	419/111 PB D8407	'Plymouth Sound, Ham Oaze and Catwater surveyed in 1786'
75	423/69–71 (SEL 03) PB E6863	'Plymouth Harbour', 1701
A1	426/187 (SEL 27)	'Plymouth'
207	DUC 223:2/51	'Carte des Environs de la Ville et Port de Plymouth', mid-eighteenth century
94	VKE 19/38,40 PB D8039	'Nieuwe Afteekening van het Inkoomen van Plymouth'
WM1	Unique item no. E2632	'Plemue'
WM3	BLA 10 PB D8259	'De Canaal tusschen Enghelandt en Vranckrijck'
WM4	COL 04 PB D8260	'Carta particolare dell canale Fra Inghilterra e Francia . . .'
126	MS 80/046	'An Exact Plan of the Ground humbly proposed to be purchased at the Dock of Plymouth', ? 1759

4 *Duchy of Cornwall, London*

| 189 | DCO Maps and Charts 33 | 'A Survey of Plymouth Sound . . .' James Fraser, 1788 |
| A4–A5 | DCO Maps and Charts 741 | Survey by William Simpson, 1786, 1788 |

5 *Naval Historical Library, London*

141	Ve 33	'Plymouth Sound, Ham Oaze and Catwater Survey'd in 1770', 1779
53	Ve 44	'Plymouth to the Rt Honble Arthur Earle of Torrington', Greenvile Collins, 1693
147	Ve 34	'Plymouth Sound, Hamoaze and Catwater Surveyed in 1786'
149	Vf 11/9 and 10	'Plymouth Sound, Hamoaze and Catwater Surveyed in 1797'

| 198 | Vf 11/11 | '. . . Chart of Plymouth Sound . . . by W. Heather', 1798 |

6 Royal Geographical Society, London

131	England and Wales D. 15	'A Plan of the Town and Citadel of Plymouth', Donn, 1765
133	England and Wales D. 15	'A Plan of Stoke Town and Plymouth Dock', Donn, 1765
77	England and Wales S. 107	'Plymouth Harbour laid down from a Survey'
86	England and Wales S. 178	'A Correct Draught of Plymouth Sound Catt Water and Ham Owse', 1723
177	England and Wales S/Div. 7	'Plymouth Harbour', 1784
5	1 c 211	Printed version of map **5**, published by J. Pine in 1740
WM6	165.B	'De'monstration de Plemue', 1731

7 Ashmolean Museum, Oxford

| 18 | C II 304 | 'A True Mapp and Description of the Towne of Plymouth . . . Seige 1643' |

8 Bodleian Library, Oxford

Richard Gough (1735–1809) devoted much of his life to a study of British topography; his topographical collections, including maps, were left to the Bodleian Library.

19	Gough Maps 5 f. 9B	'A True Mapp and Description of ye Towne of Plymouth . . .', 1643 [eighteenth century]
95	Gough Maps 5 f. 10B	'Plymouth Sound'
84	Gough Maps 5 f. 21B	'A General Plan of Plymouth Harbours', 1718
82	Gough Maps 5 f. 25B	Survey of Dockyard and town
67	Gough Maps 83	'Plymouth Sound, Catwater and Ham Ouse', 1695
53	Gough Maps 86	'PLYMOUTH to the Rt Honble ARTHUR Earle of Torrington . . .', Greenvile Collins, 1693
131	Gough Maps Devonshire 3	'A Plan of the Town and Citadel of Plymouth', B. Donn, 1765
112	Gough Maps Devonshire 7	'A Geometrical Plan and West Elevation of HM Dockyard', 1756

111	Gough Maps Devonshire 8	'A Geometrical Plan and West Prospect of Stoke Town . . .'
160	Gough Maps Devonshire 9	'Plan of the Borough of Plymouth and its Environs', R. Cowl, 1778
141	Gough Maps Devonshire 10	'Plymouth Sound, Ham Oaze and Catwater Survey'd in 1770'
108	Hope Adds 410	'A Plan of the Town and Citadel of Plymouth', 1755
177	C 17:9 (36)	'Plymouth Harbour', Donn, 1784
104	(E) C17:25 (8)	'A plan of the town and citadel of Plymouth', Bowen, 1754
161	C 17 a.3	'. . . Plan of the town and Citadel of Plymouth', R. Cowl, 1780

9 Hydrographic Department, Taunton

171	B21 Shelf Qf	'A Plan of the Town, Citadel, Dock and Sound of Plymouth with their Environs . . .', R. Cowl, 1780
149	B315 Shelf Dk	'Plymouth Sound, Hamoaze and Catwater Surveyed in 1797', 1798
201	B320/1–2 Shelf Qf	'Plymouth Sound, Hamoaze and Catwater . . .', William Price, 1798
164	c88 Shelf 3h	'Plymouth Sound Hamoaze Cawsand Bay and Catwater Surveyed and navigated by M Mackenzie, 1779'
187	c91 Press 5h	'A Survey of Plymouth Sound', James Fraser, 1788
159	D881 Press 15b	Plymouth Sound and Hamoaze, M. Mackenzie, 1777–9
WM13	D923/3 Shelf Qa	'A Chart showing the true Situations of the Eddystone Lighthouse and Rocks, and the Handeeps and East Rutt Shoals', G. Spence, 1807
155	D923/10 Press 1a	Coastal chart from Porthbury to Wembury, [1774]
193	k19 Shelf Od	Chart of the coastline from Looe to Salcombe, 1791
141	k93 Shelf Dk	'Plymouth Sound, Hamoaze and Catwater Survey'd in 1770', 1779
21	L1290 Shelf Od	'A Map and Description of the Town of Plymouth . . . Seige 1643', [nineteenth century]

10 West Devon Record Office, Plymouth

17	W489	Map showing mills and water system, early seventeenth century
24	72/1204/Ai	Plan of the Lambhay, pre-1665
39	72/1204/Aii	Sketch-map of the Lambhay, *c.* 1672
125	W467	'The Plan or Particular to which the Annexed Certificate of Edward Bayntun Esq . . . doth refer 1757'
160	Acc 157	'. . . Plan of the Borough of Plymouth and its Environs . . . by Richard Cowl . . .', 1779
196	W281	'A Plan of the Marsh adjoining Stonehouse Lane . . . survey'd . . . by Granville Smith . . .', 1794

11 Plymouth Central Library

94	—	'Nieuwe Afteekening van het Inkoomen van Plymouth . . .', G. van Keulen
98	—	'Plymouth Sound', 1744–7
141	—	'Plymouth Sound, Hamoaze and Catwater Survey'd in 1770'
149	—	'Plymouth Sound, Hamoaze and Catwater Survey'd in 1797'
176	—	'A Chart of Plymouth Sound, Catwater and Hamoaze', 1782

12 Plymouth City Museum

53	'Plymouth to the Rt Honble Arthur Earle of Torrington . . .', Greenvile Collins, 1693 (two copies)
131	'A Plan of the Town and Citadel of Plymouth', B. Donn, 1765
149	'Plymouth Sound, Hamoaze and Catwater . . . 1797'
A1	'Plymouth'

13 HM Dockyard, Plymouth

150	'Plan of His Majesty's Yard at Plymouth . . . 1771 . . .'

14 Plymouth Proprietary Library

18	—	'A True Mapp and Description of the Towne of Plymouth . . . Seige 1643'

15 Devon Record Office, Exeter

44	1120Z/F247	'The Mannour of Stonehouse Surveyed and Plotted . . .', Jerom Roch, 1682/3
113	L1258/Maps: Road 3	'A Plan of the Great and Cross Roads about Plymouth and Dock . . .', 1756

16 West Country Studies Library, Exeter

171	R31380	'A Plan of the Town, Citadel, Dock Sound of Plymouth with their Environs', R. Cowl and L.S. de La Rochette

17 Boughton House, Kettering

50		'Plymouth Harbour with all the Rivers . . .', Jerom Roch, *c.* 1690
74		'Plan of the Town and Cittadel of Plymouth . . .', between 1698 and 1712

18 Hatfield House, Hatfield

11	CPM I 35	'Plat of Plymoth', ? 1592
2	CPM I 36	'Plat of Plymo[uth]', ? pre-1549
6	CPM I 41	'discriptio[n] of a Tow[n]', *c.* 1590/1
8	CPM I 60	Leat map, *c.* 1591
10	CPM II 31	Sa[in]t Nicholas Ilande by Plimmouthe', Adams, 1592
7	CPM Supp 10	Plymouth Sound, ? 1590/1

19 Ince Castle, Saltash

175	—	'A Plan of St. Nicholas Island near Plymouth', 1781

20 Longleat House, Warminster

3	—	Harbour chart of the Sound, post-1553

21 *Bibliothèque Nationale, Paris*

185	Ge A 642	'Plan du Port et de la Baye de Plimouth . . .', 1788
53	Ge DD 1172 (23)	'Plymouth to the Rt Honble Arthur Earle of Torrington . . .', Greenvile Collins, 1693
131	Ge DD 1488	'A Plan of the Town and Citadel of Plymouth', B. Donn, 1765
129	Ge FF 4496 pl.10	'Carte de la Baye et Port de Plimouth', ? 1764
130	Ge FF 4696 pl.11	'Plan des ville et Citadelle de Plymouth', ? 1764

Département des Cartes et Plans

Maps in the 'Service Hydrographique' were separated from other series in 1947; no clue as to their provenance remains.

205	SH Portefeuille 23 Division 5 Pièce 1	'Vue de Plymouth', ? early eighteenth century
WM5	SH Portefeuille 23 Division 5 Pièce 2	'A Prospect of Plymouth and ye Sound . . .', *c.* 1713
203	SH Portefeuille 23 Division 5 Pièce 3	'Plan de la Rade de Plymouth', late seventeenth century
57	SH Portefeuille 23 Division 5 Pièce 4/1	'Carte de Plimouth'
56	SH Portefeuille 23 Division 5 Pièce 5	'Plan de la Rade de Plymouth . . .'
58	SH Portefeuille 23 Division 5 Pièce 6	'A Chart of the Harbour of Plymouth from Capt Collins's Survey'
210	SH Portefeuille 23 Division 5 Pièce 8	'Plan de Plimouth'
76	SH Portefeuille 23 Division 5 Pièce 9	'Plan Particulier du Port et Rade de Plemme où les Sondes sont en Brasses'
204	SH Portefeuille 23 Division 5 Pièce 10	'Plimouth'
206	SH Portefeuille 23 Division 5 Pièce 11	'Idée du Port de Plymout En Angleterre'
88	SH Portefeuille 23 Division 5 Pièce 12	'A New and Correct Large Draught of Plymouth Sound Cattwater and Hamoaze'
61	SH Portefeuille 23 Division 5 Pièce 13	'Plan des ouvrages du Port de Plymouth 10 Pièces 1745'
64	SH Portefeuille 23 Division 5 Pièce 13	'2nd Draught The Yard and Dock Compleat'
66	SH Portefeuille 23 Division 5 Pièce 13	'9th [Draught] The Barton of Mount Wise'

209	SH Portefeuille 23 Division 5 Pièce 14	'Carte particulière de la Baye et Ports de Plimouth'
211	SH Portefeuille 23 Division 5 Pièce 15	'Rade de Plimouth', eighteenth century
78	SH Portefeuille 23 Division 5 Pièce 16	'A New Chart of the Plymouth Sound observed by Capt Edmund Halley'
112	SH Portefeuille 23 Division 5 Pièce 17	'A Geometrical Plan and West Elevation of His Majesty's DockYard near Plymouth . . .' 1756
110	SH Portefeuille 23 Division 5 Pièce 18	'A Geometrical Plan and West Prospect of Stoke Town . . .'
95	SH Portefeuille 23 Division 5 Pièce 19	'Plymouth Sound'
141	SH Portefeuille 23 Division 5 Pièce 20	'Plymouth Sound, Hamoaze and Catwater Survey'd in 1770', 1779
161	SH Portefeuille 23 Division 5 Pièce 21	'. . . Plan of the Town and Citadel of Plymouth . . .', 1780
198	SH Portefeuille 23 Division 5 Pièce 23	'. . . Chart of Plymouth Sound . . . by W. Heather', 1798
201	SH Portefeuille 23 Division 5 Pièce 24	'Plymouth Sound, Hamoaze and Catwater', William Price, 1800

22 Archives Nationales, Paris

| 144 | Marine 6 JJ 32 Pièce 54 | 'Plymouth Sound, Hamoaze and Catwater surveyed in 1770', *c.* 1779 |
| 198 | Marine 6 JJ 68 | 'Chart of Plymouth Sound', W. Heather, 1798 |

23 Archives du Génie, Paris

208	ART 14: PLYMOUTH/1	'Carte particulière de la Baye et Ports [sic] de Plimouth'
95	ART 14: PLYMOUTH/2	'Plymouth Sound', S. Mace, 1737
136	ART 14: PLYMOUTH/3	'Plan de la Ville, des Ports, de la Citadelle et des Chantiers de Plymouth'
143	ART 14: PLYMOUTH/4	'Plymouth Sound hamoaze et Catwater mesuré en 1770', *c.* 1779
145	ART 14: PLYMOUTH/4	'Plymouth Sound Hamoaze and Catwater Surveyed in 1770', *c.* 1779
184	ART 14: PLYMOUTH/5	'Reconnaissance militaire de la Baie et des Ports de Plimouth . . . 1786'
132	ART 14: PLYMOUTH/6	'Carte de la Citadelle de Plymouth pris Sur la Carte du Devon par Dunn'

167	ART 14: PLYMOUTH/8	Chart of Plymouth Sound
162	ART 14: PLYMOUTH/10	'A Plan of the Town and Citadel of Plymouth Copié au Dépôt des Fortifications, d'après un plan de la Marine en Février 1852'

24 *Service Historique de l'Armée de Terre, Paris*

104	KII B 2 3	'A Plan of the Town and Citadel of Plymouth', E. Bowen, 1754
161	KII B 3/57	'. . . Plan of the Town and Citadel of Plymouth . . .', R. Cowl, 1780
137	L1 C 61	'Plan de la Ville, des Ports, de la Citadelle et des Chantiers de Plymouth . . . 1768'
163	MR 1414 no. 47	'Plan de Plymouth sur un projet d'attaque de cette Place Joint à une lettre de M de la Luzerne au comte de Broglie du 23 juin 1779'

25 *Service Historique de la Marine, Paris*

42	Recueil no. 32 (62)	'The Royall Cittadell, Plymouth', *c.* 1677
172	Recueil no. 32 (63)	'Plan du Dock', *c.* 1780
A3	G190	'Plan des Ville Ports Rade et Citadelle de Plimouth' (inset)

26 *Archivo Histórico Nacional, Madrid*

105	Leg 4218 Sa 182	'A plan of the town and citadel of Plymouth', *c.* 1779
106–7	Leg 4218 Sa 183–84	'A plan of the town and citadel of Plymouth', *c.* 1779
54	Leg 4218 Sa 193	'Port de Plymouth', *c.* 1779
87	Leg 4218 Sa 194	'A Correct Draught of Plymouth Sound, Catt Water and Ham Ouze', *c.* 1779

Appendix III
Biographical Notes on Selected Map-makers

These notes are compiled from the following sources, for which full titles are given in the bibliography: Bryan, Dyer, Eden, Foster, Hodson, Marshall, Porter, Ravenhill, Taylor. The *Dictionary of National Biography* and the National Maritime Museum, *Catalogue of the Library*, also provided material. The phrase 'other maps known (Tooley)' means that further maps by this map-maker are cited in R.V. Tooley, *Dictionary of Mapmakers*, 1979, Alan R. Liss Inc. and Meridian Publishing Company.

'AD'. Responsible for **101** and **102**. ? Augustus Durnford (*fl.* 1750–3).

ADAMS, Robert (1540–95). 'Rob[erto] Adamo *authore*' (**12**). Also responsible for **10** and **WM2**. Appointed Surveyor of Works and Buildings to Queen Elizabeth I in 1594. (Bryan; Eden; Taylor.) Other maps known (Tooley).

ANDERSON, J.W. (*fl.* 1800–14). 'Copied by JW Anderson RMS & D [Royal Military Surveyor & Draughtsman] . . .' (**35**).

BAYNTUN, Edward. 'Edward Bayntun Esq His Majesty's Surveyer [sic] General of the Dutchy [sic] of Cornwall . . . 1757'. Responsible for **125**.

BECK, George (*fl.* 1778–80). 'Revised and Corrected by Geo Beck January 1780' (**170**). Ordnance draughtsman.

BELLANGER. 'Bellanger *Sculpsit*' (**185**). Possibly J.A. Bellanger (Bryan).

BLACKAMORE, William. Responsible for **WM10**.

BOWEN, Emmanuel (*c.* 1720–67). 'Eman: Bowen Geogr[apher] to His Majesty' (**104**). Engraver, print-seller and publisher in London. Died poor and nearly blind. Other maps known (Tooley).

CANOT, Pierre Charles (*c.* 1710–77). 'PC Canot *Sculp*[*sit*]' (**112**). French engraver who came to England in 1730; elected Associate Engraver of Royal Academy, 1777. (Bryan.) Other maps known (Tooley).

CASTLEMAN, Henry (*fl.* 1776–98). 'H[enr]y Castleman Draughtsman' (**173**). Ordnance draughtsman. (Marshal.)

CHAPMAN, William, Master RN (1749–1832). 'A few alterations and additions have been since made BY William Chapman, Master RN' (**165**). Admiralty surveyor. (Eden.) Other maps known (Tooley).

CLEVELEY, I. 'Shipping by I. Cleveley' (**112**). Probably John Cleveley senior (*ex inf.* Francis Herbert).

COLLINS, Greenvile (*fl.* 1677–94). 'Ct G Collins Hydrogr[apher] to the KING. . . . Captain Greenvile Collins Hydrographer in Ordinary to the King and Queens most Excellent Majesties' (**53**). Also responsible for **86**. Commander in RN, 1679–94 . Wrote a 'Journal' in 1676. In 1681 he was ordered by the king to survey the sea-coasts of England; the results were published in 1693 as *Great Britain's Coasting Pilot*. Financial problems due partly to an underestimate of the cost of making the survey meant that Collins was unable to do the work as satisfactorily as he would have liked, and after publication the work was criticized. Despite this, however, it was reissued many times until 1792 with occasional revisions and additions. (Eden; Dyer; Taylor.)

COUTURE, Peter (*fl.* 1773–8). Ordnance draughtsman. 'Drawing by Peter Couture of the 3d Class April 1776' (**156**).

COWL, Richard. 'Surveyed by Richard Cowl' (**161**). Also responsible for **160** and **171**. Schoolmaster (married 16 October 1777 in Plymouth, died 1789). See W. Ravenhill 'Richard Cowl's proposals for making a new County Map of Devon in 1787', *Devon and Cornwall Notes and Queries* XXXV.ix (Spring 1986), pp. 338–44. (Eden; Ravenhill.)

D'AUBANT, Abraham (*fl.* 1754–9). 'Abr[aha]m D'Aubant *delin[eavi]t*' (**115**). Ordnance draughtsman, practitioner and ensign. (Marshal; Porter.) Other maps known (Tooley).

DE BÉVILLE, (*fl.* 1768). 'M de Béville *Lieuten[an]t Colonel de Dragonees*' (**135–7**).

DE GOMME, Sir Bernard (1620–85). Responsible for **25–30**, **38**. A Dutch engineer, who became Surveyor of Ordnance to Charles II. (Eden; *DNB*; Taylor; Hodson; Porter.) Numerous other maps (Tooley).

DE LA LUZERNE (*fl.* 1779). Possibly responsible for **163**.

DE LA ROCHETTE, Louis Stanislas (1731–1802). 'Planned by LS de la Rochette', cartographer and engraver (**171**). Other maps known (Tooley).

DEGAULLE, J.B. (1732–1810). 'SR DEGAULLE, *Ingénieur Hidrographe de la Marine, de l'Académie des Sciences, belles Lettres et Arts de Rouen, Correspondant de l'Académie des Sciences de Paris, et Professeur d'Hidrographie AU HAVRE 1788 . . . Se Vend à Honfleur ches l'Auteur*' (**185**). Other maps known (Tooley).

DELAHAYE, Gabriel (*fl.* 1712). Possibly responsible for **74**.

DESMARETZ, Colonel John Paul (*c.* 1685–1768). Responsible for **116**. Engineer. Born abroad but joined English army in 1709; later became Chief Ordnance Draughtsman. (Eden; Hodson.) Other maps known (Tooley).

DIXON, Matthew (*fl.* 1784–8). 'Survey'd . . . Under the Direction of Colonel Dixon Chief Engineer' (**180**); 'Projected by Lieut Colonel Dixon, Chief Engineer of the Plymouth Division' (**173**); 'Matthew Dixon Colonel of Engineers' (**195**). Also responsible for **170**. Ordnance draughtsman.

DONN, Benjamin (1729–98). 'Delineated from an ACTUAL SURVEY . . . By BENJAMIN DONN . . . Printed for the AUTHOR', 'B. Donn, Teacher of the Mathematics etc late of Bideford, now of the City of Bristol' (**131**); 'Geohydrographically Delineated . . . by BENJAMIN DONNE and SON TEACHERS of the Mathematics and Natural Philosophy . . .' (**177**). Born in Bideford, Devon, Donn is one of the few local men in this catalogue. Other maps known (Tooley).

DUDLEY, Sir Robert (1573–1649). Responsible for **WM4**. Naval commander and inventor. Son of Robert Dudley, Earl of Leicester, probably illegitimate. Settled in Florence and was made Duke of Northumberland and Earl of Warwick by the Emperor in 1620.

DUMMER, Edmund (*fl.* 1677–1713). Responsible for **43**, possibly also **68–70**. Sent to Tangier as a midshipman extraordinary in 1682. Appointed Surveyor of the Navy in 1692. (Eden; Hodson.) Other maps known (Tooley).

DURNFORD, Elias (member of Corps of Royal Engineers 1759–94). 'Drawn . . . by direction of Lt Col DURNFORD, Commanding Royal Engineer, 1788' (**186**); 'Elias Durnford Lieut-Col, RE' (**191**). Possibly responsible for **190**. Member of a family well represented in the Royal Engineers. Elias served much abroad. (Porter.) Other maps known (Tooley).

FADEN, William (1750–1836). 'Engraved by William Faden' (**171**). Also a publisher (**161**) and cartographer. (Eden.) Other maps known (Tooley).

FOURDRINIER, Peter (*fl.* 1720–58 in London). 'P Fourdrinier *Sculp*[*sit*]' (**111**). Engraver, publisher and map-seller of French origin. (Bryan.) Other maps known (Tooley).

FRASER, James (*fl.* 1788). 'James Fraser Then a Master in His Majesty's Navy' (**187–9**).

GARDNER, William (*fl.* 1762–1800). 'William Gardner Surveyor' (**181**). Also responsible for **179–80**. Worked for Duke of Richmond from *c.* 1767; later became Chief Draughtsman in the Drawing Office at the Treasury (1794–1800). (Eden; Marshal.) Other maps known (Tooley).

GASCOYNE, Joel (*fl.* 1668–1703). Possibly responsible for **75**. Topographical draughtsman.

GENIBELLI, Federico (*fl.* 1601–2). Responsible for **15** and probably **16**.

GILBERT, Joseph (*fl.* 1769). 'Surveyd by Joseph Gilbert Master of His Majesty's ship *The Pearl*' (**138**). Also responsible for **139**. Other maps known (Tooley).

GORGES, Sir Ferdinando (?1566–1647). Responsible for **14**. Governor of Plymouth.

GOULD, Francis (*fl.* 1760–1801). Copied **118**. Ordnance draughtsman.

GREEN, Captain J.W. (*fl.* 1778–82). Possibly responsible for **168**.

GRENVYLE, Sir Richard (?1541–91). Responsible for **4**. Naval commander who organized coastal defences in the south-west (1586–88). Another map known (Tooley).

HALLEY, Edmund (1656–1742). See **77–8**, **86**. Hydrographer, Gazetted Captain in the Navy (1698), Astronomer Royal and Geographer. Other maps known (Tooley).

HEMMANS, Samuel, MA, (*fl.* 1791). Responsible for **192–3**. Another map known (Tooley).

HODDLE, Robert. 'Copied by R[ober]t Hoddle Oct 15 1812' (**97**).

HOLLAR, Wenceslas (1607–77). Engraved **18**. Born in Prague, brought to England by the Earl of Arundel and appointed drawing teacher to the prince (later Charles II).

HURD, Capt (?1757–1823). 'Capt Hurd RN Hydrographer to the Admiralty' (**165**). Other maps known (Tooley).

JACOBSZ, Theunis (*fl.* 1654). Responsible for **23**. Well-known Amsterdam family in the publishing and printing trade. Theunis and son Jacob were cartographers, while the other son, Caspar, was a printer and publisher. (NMM Catalogue.)

JEFFERYS, Thomas (?1710–71) 'Engraved by Thos Jefferys' (**126**). Geographer to George III, engraver and publisher. Went bankrupt in 1765, and much of his business was bought by Sayer and Bennet, who are also represented in the catalogue. Later resumed business and joined by William Faden, who took over from him and who also occurs in the catalogue. (Eden.) Other maps known (Tooley).

'JH'. Responsible for **103**. ? Joseph Heath (*fl.* 1750–9), Ordnance draughtsman.

'JR'. ? Jerome Roch (**41**).

LANGEN, F. (*fl.* 1781). Responsible for **175**.

LEA, Philip (*fl.* 1666–1700). 'P. Lea at the Atlas and Hercules in Cheapside 1695 . . . Sold by Philip Lea Globe-maker at the Atlas and Hercules in Cheapside near Fryday Street end London' (**67**). (Eden; Taylor.) Other maps known (Tooley).

LEICESTER, Earl of. *See* DUDLEY, Robert.

LENNOX, Charles, Duke of Richmond (1735–1806). 'Survey'd by Order of His Grace the Duke of Richmond etc Master-General of the Ordnance' (**180–1**). Entered the army as a young man. Appointed Master-General of the Ordnance in 1782. Promoted a national Trigonometrical Survey. Dismissed as Master-General in 1795.

LILLY, Christian (1685–1738). 'Col Christian Lilly, one of his Majesties Ingeniers, 1715' (**83**). Also responsible for **80–1, 84**. Served much abroad. As 3rd Engineer, Plymouth Division, Lilly was involved in the survey of fortifications, barracks and storehouses in the country ordered by the Duke of Marlborough in the early eighteenth century. (Eden; Porter.) Other maps known (Tooley).

LODGE, John (*fl.* 1754–96). 'Jno Lodge *Sculp*[*sit*]' (**176**). Geographer and engraver. (Bryan.) Other maps known (Tooley).

MACE, Sandford (*fl.* 1737). 'S. Mace *Del*[*ineavit*]' (**95**).

MACKENZIE, Murdoch, junior (1743–1829) 'Surveyed and navigated by Murdoch Mackenzie Junr' (**164**); '*Levé par le Lieutenant Murdoch Mackenzie*' (**166**). Also reponsible for **155, 159, 165**. See also **WM13**. Murdoch Mackenzie succeeded his uncle and namesake as Maritime Surveyor at the Admiralty. His maps have a particular significance in this catalogue because of their accuracy. (Eden; Hodson.) Other maps known (Tooley).

MADGETT, Robert (*fl.* seventeenth–eighteenth centuries). 'Robertus Madgett *Delineavit*' (**96**).

MANSON, John (*fl.* 1748–57). 'Drawn by John Manson Ens[ign] 1756' (**114**). Military engineer who worked much abroad. (Eden; Hodson; Marshal; Porter.) Another map known (Tooley).

MILTON, Bro (*fl.* 1756). 'Bro Milton *inv[eni]t*' (**110**). (Eden.)

MILTON, Thomas (1743–1827). 'T Milton *Surv[?] et delin[eavit]*' (**111–12**). Draughtsman and engraver who practised in London and Dublin; governor of Society of Engravers. (Bryan.) Other maps known (Tooley).

MOORE, John Hamilton (d. 1801). 'Humbly dedicated by His most Obedient and Dutiful Servant John Hamilton Moore . . . Publish'd . . . by JOHN HAMILTON MOORE, Tower Hill . . . Sold by Mr Moore in London' (**183**). Founded the family firm in 1763. Other maps known (Tooley).

MORRISON, Captain George (*fl.* 1778–82). Responsible for **168**.

MOSLEY, Charles (*fl.* 1737–70). 'Cha[rles] Mosley *sculp[sit]*' (**95**). Engraver who lived in London and was chiefly employed by booksellers. (Bryan.) Other maps known (Tooley).

PATERSON, Lieutenant (*fl.* 1778–82). Responsible for **168**.

PRICE, William (*fl.* 1794–1801). 'W[illia]m PRICE MASTER in the ROYAL NAVY 1798 LONDON' (**201**). Master, HMS *Theseus*. Other maps known (Tooley).

RICHMOND, Duke of. *See* LENNOX, Charles.

ROCH, Jerome (*fl.* 1682–3). 'Surveyed & Plotted . . . By Jerom Roch Jr' (**44**); 'Hydrographically describ'd by Jerom Roch' (**50**). Responsible for original of **43**. Was Alexander Roch (**37**) a member of the same family? *See also* 'JR'.

RUSSELL, John (*fl.* 1733–79). 'Engraved by John Russell' (**183**). Also a draughtsman. (Bryan.) Other maps known (Tooley).

RYTHER, Augustine (*fl.* 1576–95). Responsible for **WM2**. Engraver and instrument-maker.

'SB'. 'SB *authore*' (**13**). ? Simon Basil (*fl.* 1590–1608), apprentice of Robert Adams, Surveyor of Works (1606–15).

SEALE, R.W. 'RW Seale *del[ineavit] et sculp[sit]*' (**98**).

SEARLE, R. 'Copied by R Searle June 1814' (**31–2**).

SIMPSON, William (1759–93). 'Surveyor' (**A4/5**). Lived at Bath towards the end of his life. (Eden.)

SLACK, Daniel (*fl.* 1755–9). 'D Slack *Delin[eavit]*' (**109**). Ordnance draughtsman. (Eden; Marshal; Porter.)

SLADE, B. (*fl.* 1747). Responsible for **99**.

SMART, Thomas (*fl.* 1758–84). 'Copy'd by Thomas Smart' (**117**). Ordnance draughtsman. (Marshal; Porter.)

SMITH, Granville (*fl.* 1794). 'Granville Smith Teacher of the Mathematicks and Land Surveyor in Plymouth' (**196**). (Eden.)

SMITH, I.S. (*fl.* 1767). Responsible for **134**.

SMITH, James (*fl.* 1791). Responsible for **192–3**. Possibly the James Smith, Master, RN, listed in Tooley.

SPARKES, Jonathan (*fl.* 1660–85). Responsible for **33**. (Eden.)

SPENCE, Graeme (*fl.* 1807). Responsible for **WM13**. Apprentice to Murdoch Mackenzie junior.

SPICER, Alexander (*fl.* 1780–93). 'Drawn by . . . A Spicer' (**194**). Ordnance draughtsman. (Marshal.)

STEPHENSON. 'Stephenson *sculp*[*sit*]' (**199**).

STURT, Robert (1780–1801). 'Drawn by R. Sturt by direction of Lt Col Durnford' (**186**); 'Drawn by R. Sturt and A. Spicer' (**194**). Ordnance draughtsman. (Marshal.)

TERRY, Garnet (1775–94). 'Engrav'd by G. Terry Paternoster Row Cheapside London' (**160**). Also a jeweller. (Bryan.) Other maps known (Tooley).

TEST, William (*fl.* 1759–1814). Certified **31–2**, **34–5** as Chief Royal Military Surveyor and Draughtsman in 1814. Copied **119**. Other maps known (Tooley).

VAN KEULEN, Gerard. Responsible for **94**.

WALKER, John (1759–1830). 'J. Walker *Sculp*[*si*]*t*' (**165**). Admiralty engraver. Other maps known (Tooley).

WARD, Jacob (*fl.* 1689–93). Probably responsible for **45**.

WARD, John (*fl.* 1638–60s). Responsible for **33** (Eden). Parliamentary Surveyor of Crown Lands.

WARREN, J.B. (*fl.* 1798). Responsible for **200**.

WILDE, Charles (*fl.* 1646). Possibly responsible for **22** (Foster).

Appendix IV
Features Within the Town of Plymouth

First sightings on maps are given in these notes. However, it should be borne in mind that there can be wide variations between the date when a feature first occurs upon the landscape and the date when it is first shown on a map. The number for each feature corresponds to that given on the chart of Sutton Pool overleaf.

1 PIGG'S POINT / later QUEEN ANNE'S BATTERY. Shown on **27** as 'hogg's peck point', *c.* 1665. In 1689/90, £88 18s. 1d. were spent on fortifications at Pigg's Point and Mount Batten because the French fleet were on the coast (W133 f. 153). According to **80**, it had fourteen guns *c.* 1714–17.

2 ROPEWALK. Shown on **91**, 1725. A long covered walk, or a long building over smooth ground, where ropes were manufactured.

3 ORDNANCE STOREHOUSES. Shown on **81**, *c.* 1714–17 as Ordnance storehouses. By 1757 (**125**) they are described as a hospital for sick and hurt seamen.

4 COXSIDE GATE / FRIARY GREEN GATE / NEW TOWN GATE. Shown on **11**, *c.* 1592. According to R.N. Worth, it was removed soon after 1809 (*History of Plymouth*, p. 417).

5 FRIARY GATE. Shown on **15**, 1601/2. According to R.N. Worth, it was removed in 1763 (*History of Plymouth*, p. 417).

6 FRIARY. Occupies a prominent position on **1**, *c.* 1539. According to Worth, it was founded in 1313 by the Carmelites or White Friars. At the Dissolution, it was destroyed and the site may have passed to the mayor and corporation. In 1794, the buildings were converted into a hospital for sick soldiers (*History of Plymouth*, p. 227).

7 GASCOIGNE GATE / NORTH GATE. Shown on **91**, 1725. According to R.N. Worth, it was removed in 1768 (*History of Plymouth*, p. 417).

8 SALT-HOUSE. Shown on only one map, of 1757 (**125**).

9 CHARLES CHURCH. Among the municipal records survives part of a draft petition of the mayor and inhabitants of Plymouth to Charles I for permission to erect a new church, since St Andrew's was insufficient (W359/69). Licence to build this new church and to divide the parish of Plymouth into two separate parishes was granted in 1641/2, the church to be built at the cost of the inhabitants (W11). The Act for building the new church was passed in 1640. The church was finished in 1657. Charles Church is sometimes referred to on charts as 'New Church'. Map **148** mentions 'Plymouth New Church which has a Spire Steeple'.

Chart of Sutton Pool, indicating features within the town of Plymouth

10 MARTIN'S GATE / EAST GATE. Shown on **91**, 1725. A lease of 1656 among the municipal records refers to it as having been recently built by the mayor and commonalty; the lease was to John Martyn, whose property it adjoined. The gate had three rooms above it, measured 18 ft 4 in from east to west and 14 ft 6 in from north to south (W635). According to R.N. Worth, it was removed in 1789 because of an accident to a servant of one of the royal princes who was hurt while passing under it (*History of Plymouth*, p. 417).

11 THE GREAT TREE. Shown on only two maps, **91** (1725) and the copy of it made in 1776 (**156**). The 'Great Tree att Brittayne side' is referred to in 1604 in the Black Book (WDRO W46 f. 10).

12 OLD TOWN GATE. Shown on **11**, *c.* 1592. There are several references to it among the municipal records: in 1607/8, the gate was amended (W132 f. 159). It is shown quite prominently on **17**. However, it was apparently rebuilt in the mid-seventeenth century, since a lease of 1656 refers to it as 'lately erected and builte by the . . . Maior and Commonalty'. The gate measured 42 ft from east to west, 18 ft from north to south at this date (W636). According to R.N. Worth, this gate was rebuilt again in 1759 and taken down in 1809 (*History of Plymouth*, p. 417).

13a–e TOWN MILLS. Shown on **11** (*c.* 1592), but shown in much more detail on **17** (early seventeenth century), where 13a was used as a tucking mill, 13b known as the Lower Mill, 13c as the Malt Mill, 13d as the Middle Mill, and 13e as the Higher Mill. Several of these mills were built by Sir Francis Drake, *c.* 1590–1 (W46 f. 8). A reference to the malt mill as having been lately erected occurs in a commission of 1603 to settle a dispute concerning the ground on which it was built (W46 f. 80v). The White Book contains a constitution enacting that all inhabitants of the borough were to get their corn ground at the Town Mills except in time of frost, 1614 (W48 f. 82). Mill account books have survived covering the period 1627–31 (W496–98) and 1729–92 (W500); also mill leases for 1612–1819 (W531–51).

14 FRANKFURT GATE. Shown on **11**, *c.* 1592. Apparently rebuilt in the mid-seventeenth century, because a lease of 1652 refers to it as 'that new built howse . . . lately called . . . the Guarde howse att Franke Ffort' (W632). According to R.N. Worth, it was removed in 1783 but since it is not shown on **160**, it was probably demolished between 1765 (**131**) and 1778.

15 SHAMBLES. Shown on only three maps (**91**, **156** and **160**). Although there are frequent references to the Shambles among the municipal records, it is probable that at least two different places are referred to. Thus in 1605/6, £794 8s. 1d. was spent on building the flesh Shambles and Guildhall (W132 f. 155v), but in July 1606 it was agreed that the flesh Shambles should be removed and re-erected next to the churchyard (W361/47), and a decree of 1637 referred to the Shambles in the churchyard at that date (W373: long since missing). It is possible that the Shambles shown on **91** are those referred to by R.N. Worth, a long narrow range of buildings measuring 200 ft by 12 ft, built in 1656 (*History of Plymouth*, p. 348). Bids made in October 1807 refer to the Old Shambles adjoining the old Church Yard and weighing house, the Shambles in Old Town Street as far as the Leatherhole, and the Leatherhole and Shambles under (W362/41/2).

16 ST ANDREW'S CHURCH. Shown prominently on the earliest map in this catalogue, and the best reference point for the town throughout this period. Appropriately, the earliest account book (1481–1583) to have survived among the municipal records relates largely to St Andrew's Church, in particular to the building of the south aisle, 1481–5 (W129). As mentioned by R.N. Worth, the history of the borough and of its main parish church are inextricably intertwined (*History of Plymouth*, pp. 237–8, 380–3). St Andrew's tower is often referred to on

charts as 'Old Church Tower'; **149** mentions 'The Tower of Plymouth Old Church, which is square, and has four Pinnacles on it'.

17 FISH MARKET. Shown on only three maps (**91, 156** and **160**). As in the case of the Shambles, there are several references to the fish market amongst the municipal records and it is possible these refer to more than one site. The receivers' accounts show that £18 19s. 3d. was paid in 1601/2 for building a fish market against the churchyard wall (W132 f. 139). R.N. Worth refers to the construction of Fish Shambles in Whimple Street in 1693 (*History of Plymouth*, p. 349): this could well be the same site since Whimple Street adjoined the churchyard. A payment of £40 for building Fish Shambles in 1713/14 may refer to this site or to somewhere else (W133 f. 280v). However, the removal of the fish market in 1789 when George III visited the town certainly refers to this site (*History of Plymouth*, p. 382).

18 WORKHOUSE. Shown on only three maps (**91, 156** and **160**). Reference to a workhouse recently built near the churchyard is made in an account of 1628/9 (W132 f. 218v). In 1707 the town procured a new Act of Parliament to erect a workhouse (W46 f. 21v).

19a MARKET-CROSS. The market-cross is shown on only a few maps of the sixteenth century(**1, 6, 11**). There are several references to it among the municipal records. It was mended in 1565/6 (W131 f. 30v) and again in 1571/2 (W132 f. 10). As for its significance in the life of the town, beer and bread were distributed to the poor from there (W132 f. 79v) and James I was proclaimed as king from 'the Market Crosse here in Plymouth' (W46 f. 9v) in 1602. It seems likely that the Guildhall was erected on the site of the former market-cross. Certainly, there appear to be no more references to it, and R.N. Worth thought that the granite pillars of the market-cross were bought by James Bagg for 40s. in 1610 (*History of Plymouth*, p. 348). Celia Fiennes referred to a 'fine stone Crosse' in 1698 but it seems unlikely in view of the above that this can have been the market-cross.

19b GUILDHALL. Documentary evidence shows that the Guildhall was built in 1605/6 (W132 f. 155v); an account of the building costs has survived, 1606/7 (W137). The Guildhall stood at the head of the High Street and is possibly the building shown on **25**. It may also be the 'Long Market House set on stone pillars' referred to by Celia Fiennes in 1698, since it is known that a butter and poultry market was held underneath it. The Guildhall was probably erected on the site of the former market-cross; the Guildhall was demolished in 1800.

20 CUSTOM-HOUSE. Shown on **160**. According to R.N. Worth, this building was erected in the seventeenth century (*History of Plymouth*, p. 341), although payment was made in 1586/7 for work on an earlier custom-house (W132 f. 70). A new custom-house was built in 1820.

21 NEW QUAY. Shown on **28**, 1666/7. The municipal records note a payment of £58 1s. 5d. in 1601/2 for building the New Quay (W132 f. 139v). Likewise, an entry in the Black Book that the quay by John Smart's door was made in 1601 (W46 f. 9v) presumably refers to New Quay rather than Smart's Quay. In 1634/5, the Quay was paved and edged with moorstone (W132 f. 235). In the mid-seventeenth century, a certain William Jennens and John Warren, merchants, challenged the corporation to show that the New Quay had been built before 1576 (R.N. Worth *History of Plymouth*, p. 330). In 1694 James Yonge 'filled up the New Key, and paved it all over, by which it became such a fine walk as now it is' (*The Journal of James Yonge* (ed. Poynter), p. 206). Celia Fiennes, writing four years later, described the New Quay as 'a broad space which leads you up into the broad streete and is used in manner of an exchange for the merchants meeteing . . .' (*Illustrated Journeys*, p. 201). New Quay is described as 'Parade' on **160**.

22 SMART'S QUAY. Shown on **28**, 1666/7. In 1598/9, a Captain Cooper paid the town 10s. for digging a dock by Smart's Quay (W132 f. 124v).

23 SOUTH QUAY / SOUTHSIDE QUAY / BARBICAN QUAY. Shown on **28**, 1666/7. A note in the Black Book records that in 1572 'the kaye on southesyde whereof the southe ende adjoineth to the Barbygan underneth the Castell, was Builded by the towne under full sea marcke, and Contayneth in lengethe one hundred and Thurtie Foot and in Bredethe fourtie and fower foot' (W46 f. 7). South Quay is described as Barbican Quay on **160**.

24 CASTLE. Shown prominently on the earliest map in this catalogue, *c.* 1539. The Black Book records that in 1548 the castle of Plymouth was valiantly defended and kept from the rebels during the Western Rebellion; however, 'then was our stepell burnt with all the townes evydence' (W46 f. 5v). The municipal records include a reference to the castle lately demolished in 1666/7 (W133 f. 37). From **28** (1666/7) onwards, the site of the castle is recorded.

25 SOUTH GATE / BARBICAN GATE. Shown on **8**, *c.* 1591. A lease of 1654 refers to the dwelling-house 'latly raised and built over and on each syde of the Barbican Gate' (W633). James Barber states that the gate was demolished in 1831.

26 FISH-HOUSE AND CAWSEY. The Cawsey or causeway across the mouth of Sutton Pool is clearly shown on **1**, *c.* 1539. As Leland wrote in the 1530s, 'the mouth of the gulph wherein the shippes of Plymouth lyith is waullid on eche side and chainid over in tyme of necessite'. There are frequent references to the cawsey among the municipal records, beginning in the late fifteenth century (W130). In the early years its upkeep was funded at least partly by taxes on hake, and the activities of boats moored within the cawsey were closely watched. There are various references to the chain across the cawsey which is clearly shown on **1** (W130 f. 153v–56). In 1584 stairs were built so that a boat could be entered at low tide (W46 f. 7v); in 1626/7, payment was made for raising the old Cawsey higher so that boats could not come over it (W132 f. 213v). The municipal records do not appear to record when the Fish-House or Cage which stood at the entrance to Sutton Pool was built, although it is shown from the late sixteenth century onwards (**11**). Although a very high tide in 1744 threw the Fish House down (R.N. Worth *History of Plymouth*, p. 330), it was presumably rebuilt, since it is referred to on later maps (**104**, **125**). By 1778, however, there is no breakwater or building at the entrance to the Pool (**160**). As to why it was called the Fish-House, Harris records: 'whether [it] was built for the purpose of curing and storing fish for exportation, or for its being deposited there anciently in order to receive King's and Town's Customs thereon, is now uncertain. . . .' (Harris *An Essay Toward the History of Plymouth*, vol. I, p. 27).

27 HOE GATE. Shown on **26**, 1665. An entry in the receivers' accounts for 1549/50 refers to the making of the Hoe Gate (W132 f.277v). A later reference in the same volume relating to 1656/7 refers to the Hoe Gate near the castle 'lately erected and new built' (W132 f.297). The Hoe Gate was demolished in 1863 (R.N. Worth, *History of Plymouth*, p. 417).

28 WEST HOE BEACON. Shown on only a few maps (**8–9**, **11**, **33–5**). Map **33** refers to 'West Beacon Field'; the beacon stood on a hill. The purpose of the beacon was presumably to signal the approach of danger. The receivers' accounts for 1593/4 record payment of £10 for building the watchhouse at the beacon upon the West Hoe (W132 f.101). Map **15** shows a beacon puffing clouds of smoke into the air, but it is wrongly situated for this beacon, since it is in front of the fort. A further payment of 11s. 7d. is recorded in 1618/19 for repairing the beacon (W132 f. 187).

29 GALLOWS UPON THE HOE (various places). Shown on a few sixteenth-century maps

(**2**, **3** and **6**). Worth suggests 'gibbets were commonly erected on the Hoe' (*History of Plymouth*, p. 152).

30 CITADEL. Frequently shown on maps from **26**, 1665, onwards; also frequently the subject of maps. See pp. 55–8. Celia Fiennes wrote in 1698: 'The fine and only thing in Plymouth town is the Cittadell which stands very high above the town . . . [it] lookes nobly, all marble [i.e. limestone] full of towers . . .' (*Illustrated Journeys*, p. 201).

31 HOE CHAPEL. Shown on only a few sixteenth century maps (**1**, **2**, **6**, **8–10**). The municipal records include a reference to the mending of the Hoe Chapel in 1564/5 (W131 f.16). R.N. Worth suggests that this was originally probably a votive chapel which may also have served the function of a medieval lighthouse. The Chapel remained in use until nearly the end of the sixteenth century (*History of Plymouth*, pp. 233–4).

32 VICTUALLING OFFICE. Shown on **83**, *c.* 1714–17. Previously, storehouses owned by Sir George Cartaret stood on this site. The spy, de Béville, thought that the Victualling Office might provide a useful route for penetrating into the Citadel: '*on entre facilement dans les magasins du Roy qui sont au pied d'un mur fort élevé qui fait partie de l'enceinte de la Citadelle*' (**135**).

33 FORT. Shown on sixteenth- and early seventeenth-century maps (**12**, **14**, **15**, **16**, **25–6**, **19**, **21**). See pp. 31–2.

34 LOWER FORT. Shown on some sixteenth-century and several seventeenth-century maps. The last map to show it is **91** (1725) and its copy, **156**.

Appendix V
Features Around Plymouth Sound

The number for each feature corresponds to that given on the chart of Plymouth Sound overleaf.

1 WEMBURY CHURCH. Shown mainly on printed charts, where it is sometimes described as 'Yealm church' or even 'Wembury Yealme church' (**141**).

2 STADDON BEACON. Shown on both printed and manuscript maps from 1693 (**53**) until 1784 (**177**).

3 STADDON HEIGHTS BATTERY. Shown mainly on late eighteenth-century maps (**179**, **181**, **186–7**).

4 WITHY HEDGE ON STADDON HEIGHTS. Frequently shown on charts from **53** onwards because of its usefulness to sailors. Map **183** mentions Staddon Farm, which is drawn on **201**.

5 MOUNT BATTEN FORT. Frequently shown on these maps. Map **4** refers to a 'new bulworke'; previously this promontory was known as 'howe stert'. **29** shows a battery in front of a round fort in front of a deep valley; a French map describes it as a square tower however ('*petite tour carrée*', **210**) and another describes it as having four cannon (**206**). Its defensive role was enhanced by the fact that ships had to pass this side of St Nicholas Island. In 1689/90, £88 18s. 1d. was spent on fortifications at Piggs Point and Mount Batten because the French fleet were on the coast (W133 f. 153). R.N. Worth says Mount Batten tower was built in the reign of Charles II on the site of one of the old forts erected during the Siege (*History of Plymouth*, p. 421).

6 ORESTON NAVAL POWDER MAGAZINE. Shown on only two maps of the early eighteenth century (**81**, **84**).

7 CATTEDOWN–ORESTON PASSAGE. Shown on **8–9** and continues to be marked on late eighteenth-century maps as Oreston ferry (**174**).

8 RADFORD HOUSE. Shown on **4**: 'Radforde Mr [Christo]pher Harrys his howse and he a sufficient gentillman to take charge to defend this quarter w[i]th thinhabitants of Plimpton hundred.'

9 POMPHLETT MILL. Shown on **18**, although likely to be much older.

10 SALTRAM. Shown on **18**. Two maps refer to Saltram Quay (**69** and **94**).

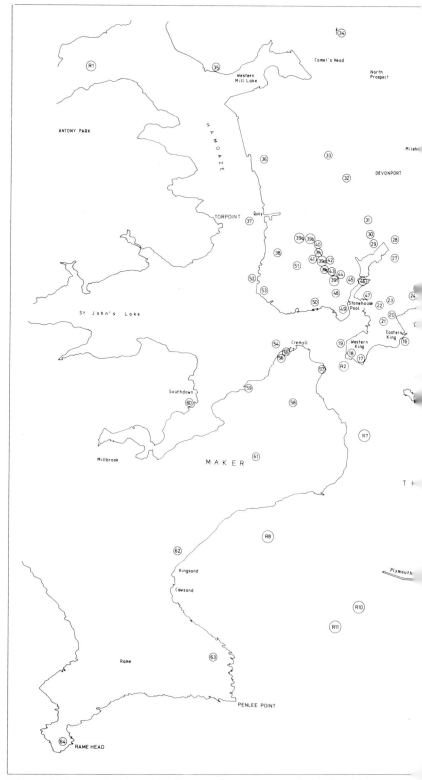

Chart of Plymouth Sound, indicating features around the Sound

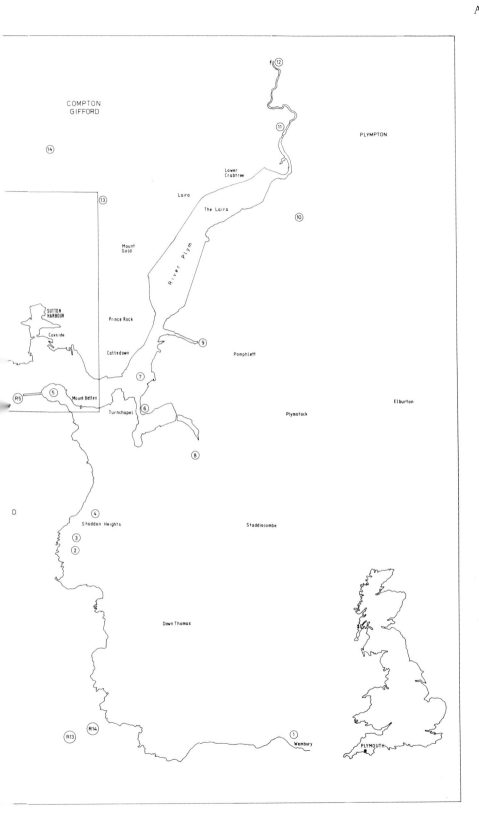

COMPTON
GIFFORD

PLYMPTON

(14)

(13)

Lower
Crabtree

Laira

The Laira

Mount
Gold

(10)

(12)

(11)

River Plym

SUTTON
HARBOUR

Coxside

Prince Rock

(9)

Pomphlett

Cattedown

(7)

R5   (5)   Mount Batten

Elburton

(6)

Turnchapel

Plymstock

(8)

D

(4)

Staddon Heights

Staddiscombe

(3)

(2)

Down Thomas

R14

R13

(1)   Wembury

PLYMOUTH

11 NEW BRIDGE (now MARSH MILLS). Shown on **27**, *c.* 1665. This is almost certainly the stone bridge in Plympton Marsh which was built in 1618/19 (W132 f. 187).

12 PLYM BRIDGE. Shown on **8**.

13 LIPSON MILL. Shown on **18**.

14 MUTLEY FIRS. Shown only rarely on maps of the late eighteenth century; shown on **155**.

15 WEST HOE FORTIFICATIONS. A fort is shown from the earliest map in this catalogue and on many of the sixteenth-century maps (**1**, **4**, **6**, **8**, **15**) until *c.* 1665 (**25**). On late eighteenth-century maps, a gun battery is recorded (**159**, **164**, **171**). This had six 18-pounders.

16 FIRESTONE BAY / EASTER KING FORT. A fort is shown on **6** and continues to be shown into the late eighteenth century: **187** refers to the blockhouse in Firestone Bay in its sailing directions, 1788. The battery at Easter King had four 18-pounder guns by 1777–80 (**159** and **171**).

17 WESTER KING'S FORTIFICATIONS. A fort is first recorded on **6**. Late eighteenth-century maps give details as to the battery: on **159** it is recorded as having ten 18-pounders, while in a report accompanying **170** Lt.-Col. Dixon intended that the twelve 18-pounders marked on his map at Wester King should be used to give additional fire to the north and west channels; he had also removed the guns pointing towards the mainland on St Nicholas Island so that they could not be used to fire on Wester King battery. On **171**, however, Wester King redoubt is recorded as having only eight 18-pounders.

18 DEVIL'S POINT FORTIFICATIONS (STONEHOUSE BATTERY). A fort is shown on the earliest map in this catalogue on the site of what was later to be Stonehouse battery. The fort is still there *c.* 1770 (**140**), but by 1777–9 Devil's Point had four 18-pounders (**159**) and a year or two later it had six (**171**).

19 CREMYLL FERRY. Shown on **8**, *c.* 1591, and frequently thereafter. A map of 1724 notes it as a 'horse ferry' (**89**) and, like some other maps, notes the passage house. As noted by R.N. Worth, for many generations this would have been the chief route from this area into Cornwall (*History of Plymouth*, p. 21). Celia Fiennes in 1698 found it hard going: 'I was at least an hour going over, it was about a mile but indeed in some places, notwithstanding there was 5 men row'd and I sett my own men to row alsoe I do believe we made not a step of way for almost a quarter of an hour.'

20 STONEHOUSE BATHS. These are shown only on **135–7**, made in 1768, soon after the baths had been built. A print of 1766 (not included in this catalogue) is entitled 'A View of the New Baths and Long Room near Plymouth' (WDRO Ph 330).

21 LONG ROOM, STONEHOUSE. Shown on **139**, *c.* 1769/70, probably soon after it was built. Shown on a print of 1766 (WDRO Ph 330).

22 ROYAL MARINE BARRACKS, STONEHOUSE. Shown on a map of 1780 (**171**). The key notes that the intended Marine Barracks will have six 18-pounder guns.

23 STONEHOUSE BLOCKHOUSE. Shown mainly on eighteenth-century maps (**114–15**, **116**, **117**, **148**, **155**, **168–9**). Sometimes referred to as 'Old Blockhouse'.

24 OLD MILLS. Shown on the earliest of the maps in this catalogue and a frequent landmark on maps throughout this period. The Black Book notes details of a grant by Ralph de Valletort to the canons at Plympton of the right to erect a mill at a place near Sourpool and claim mill toll within the manor of Sutton (W46 f. 68v). Later, this was to constitute an important part of the town's income: in 1564, residents were obliged to have their corn ground at Millbay by an order forbidding them to buy meal brought to town (R.N. Worth *History of Plymouth*, p. 344), while a further order of 1570 directed that no one was to grind their corn away from the mills (W48 f. 28). One of the lessees of these mills was Sir Francis Drake who was to build six further mills in connection with the leat: two at Egg Buckland and a further four near the town about 1590/1 (W46 f. 8).

25 FRENCH PRISON / MILL PRISON. Shown on **84** (1718) and frequently thereafter throughout the eighteenth century. Presumably this was called the French prison because the majority of prisoners were French.

26 SALTMARSH (SOURPOOL). Sourpool was the inner reach beyond Millbay; in the Middle Ages the canons at Plympton had held a fishery there. Map **11** records that when Sir Francis Drake built the Plymouth leat and mills, 'this poole was made drie for a medow'. The salt-marsh stretched in a triangle from Millbay (the point marked on the chart) to Stonehouse to the western edge of the town of Plymouth. As there are no seventeenth-century maps of this area, it is not shown until **89**, and not marked as such until **114**, although presumably it had been there much longer. **196** is a plan of the salt-marsh made in 1794 by a local man. At that date, it measured 26½ acres. R.N. Worth, describing the salt-marsh of the late eighteenth century wrote: 'The water had been banked out to some extent; by slow degrees the pool had silted up; and the growth of acquatic plants had so far completed reclamation that the bulk of the ground was . . . a rough pasture . . . intersected by numerous streams' (*History of Plymouth*, p. 368).

27 ROYAL NAVAL HOSPITAL, STONEHOUSE. Shown on **135** (1768) and frequently thereafter. On one map (**184**), it is erroneously referred to as '*hôpital militaire*'. An Order in Council for the building of Haslar Hospital at Portsmouth included mention of a hospital at Plymouth; the land was bought in 1756 and 1758. Although the initial estimate was for only 600 patients, this rose to 1,500 (as noted on **135**). Despite a fire in 1762, the hospital was completed in the early 1770's. See J. Coad 'Historic Architecture of HM Naval Base Devonport 1689–1850', in *Mariner's Mirror* 69.4, pp. 341–92, and J. Coad *The Royal Dockyards, 1690–1850*, Scolar Press, 1989, pp. 297–301. The hospital chapel is used as a landmark on **201**. The hospital cupola and water engine are both shown on **159**.

28 MILLBRIDGE (until 1767, STONEHOUSE BRIDGE). Shown on the earliest map in this catalogue. Until 1767, this was known as Stonehouse Bridge.

29 MILITARY HOSPITAL, STONEHOUSE. Shown on only one map (**179**).

30 STOKE CHURCH. Shown on **2**. A frequent landmark on these maps.

31 STOKE QUINT. Shown on **114** and on several other maps. This was probably a quintain, which was a form of tilting board.

32 MOUNT PLEASANT / STOKE BLOCKHOUSE / SUMMERHOUSE. Shown on **114** (1756). **159** has gun details: eight 3-pounders, eight 12-pounders in the blockhouse, besides twenty Swivelstocked blunderbuses and musketry and thirteen 18-pounders in the two northmost faces of the battery.

33 KEYHAM BRIDGE. Shown on only two maps (**181** and **186**).

34 WESTON MILLS. Marked on **18** (1643).

35 ST BUDEAUX POWDER WORKS. Shown on only one map (**179**).

36 KEYHAM POINT MAGAZINE. Marked on **155**, although the date of this map is 1774 and the site for the powder magazine was apparently not bought until April 1775 (J. Coad, *Royal Dockyards*, p. 255).

37 TORPOINT FERRY (NEW HORSE FERRY). 'Road to the New Horse Ferry' (Torpoint) marked on **191**. An Act for authorizing the Earl of Mount Edgcumbe and Reginald Pole Carew to build and maintain the ferry was passed in 1790.

38 MORICE YARD GUN WHARF. Shown on **89** and frequently thereafter. In 1719 land north of the dockyard was leased from Sir Nicholas Morice. Work began in 1720 and a wharf and two semi-circular basins were made. By 1724, the yard was partly functional. (J. Coad 'Historic Architecture . . .', pp. 367–75).

39a–f DOCK BARRACKS AND LINES (39a = Marlborough Square; 39b = Granby Square; 39c = Frederick Square; 39d = Ligonier Square; 39e = Cumberland Square; 39f = George Square). The lines of fortifications on the north, south and east boundaries of Dock town are shown on **109** which indicates the proposed barracks. Map **114** shows the barracks and lines as built (1756). The key to this map makes clear that there were thirty guns round the lines. De Béville described the lines thus: '*ces retranchemens consistent en un parapet en terre peu élevé et peu épais précédé d'un fossé sec non revêtu sans fraise ni palissade*' (**135**). The barracks consisted of two large squares (39a, 39f) of barracks for four companies each and four lesser (39b–e) for three companies each (**114**). The best maps of this area are **190–1**.

40 MAIN *BARRIÈRE* (DOCK TOWN). Shown on **114–15**, 1756. This was a barrier gate in the lines of fortifications; it led to Morice Town.

41 DOCK CHAPEL. Dock Chapel is shown on **155** (1774) and on a few other maps. St Aubyn's Chapel was consecrated in 1771; the Original Book of Records, containing the names of the proprietors, 1772–1819, and the register of their pews has survived (WDRO 358/1/4). Another chapel ('New Chapel') is shown on **187** (1788).

42 PLACE OF ARMS / MAGAZINE. This is shown on only a few maps (**114–15**, **164** and **191**).

43 DOCK HORSE MILL. Shown on only a few maps (**114–15**, **126**).

44 DOCK WINDMILL. Shown on **114** and on several maps thereafter.

45 SMALL *BARRIÈRE* (DOCK TOWN). Shown on only a few maps (**114–15** and **135–7**). This was the second barrier gate in the lines of fortifications.

46 STONEHOUSE BRIDGE. Until the bridge was built, there was a passage from Stonehouse to Dock which is shown on several maps (**114–15**, for example). Indeed, some of the Drawing Office maps, presumably made in London and without a fresh survey, continue to show this passage although the bridge had been built by then (**168–9**). The bridge is shown on **135** where it is described as a new stone bridge. The Act enabling the Earl of Mount Edgcumbe

and Sir John St Aubyn to build the bridge was passed in 1767. It noted that Stonehouse Creek ferry could only be used by foot passengers, whereas what was needed was a carriage bridge (WDRO 720/4). The bridge was finished in 1773, and in 1784 an act for constituting a turnpike was passed (R.N. Worth *History of Plymouth*, p. 336).

47 WHITE HALL, STONEHOUSE. Shown on a few maps (**69**, **93–4**, **109**, **117**, **168–9**). A mill is shown on **69**.

48 GOVERNOR'S HOUSE. Shown on **190–1** (1789). Government House was built between *c*. 1789 and 1793 as a residence for the commanding officer of the Western District (J. Coad 'Historic Architecture . . .', p. 375).

49 OLD GUN WHARF (MOUNT WISE). Shown on **90** (1725).

50 MOUNT WISE REDOUBT. Shown on **85** (post-1719) and quite frequently thereafter. According to **159**, there were eight 32-pounders and two 10-inch mortars there in 1777–9. According to Lt.-Col. Dixon's report of 1780 (**170**), 'the redouted battery on Mount Wise . . . is intended to defend the passage within Wester-King and to command the obelisk redout on the side of Mount Edgecumbe, to which ground it has been suggested by many Officers, that an Enemy, after having made a landing, either in Cawsand or Whitesand bay, could transport their Guns, Mortars and Stores in order to erect batteries to destroy the Navy yard'.

51 DOCK MARKET. Shown on **133** (1765) and also on **191**.

52 *BERWICK* HULK. Shown on **99** (1747); moorings had apparently been laid below it.

53 DOCKYARD. Frequently shown on maps from the late seventeenth century onwards (**46**); also frequently the subject of maps. See pp. 58–63.

54 *TEMERAIRE* HULK. Shown on **159** (1777–9).

55 CREMYLL REDOUBT. Shown on a few maps from **159** onwards (1777–9).

56 MOUNT EDGCUMBE OBELISK. Shown from **135** (1768) onwards. Mentioned in sailing directions (**140**).

57 MOUNT EDGCUMBE BATTERY. Shown on **164** (1779).

58 MOUNT EDGCUMBE HOUSE. Shown on **3** and quite frequently thereafter.

59 EMPACOMBE. 'Empy Combe' is clearly shown on **84** although there is no mention of the Victualling Office established there in 1707. See J. Coad *Royal Dockyards*, p. 282.

60 SOUTHDOWN NAVAL BREWHOUSE. This is shown frequently on maps from **84** onwards (1718). An Admiralty Board visit there in the late 1740s noted: 'Proceeded to view the brewhouses and other victualling storehouses erected at South Downe in Hamoaze. Found two complete brewhouses, a cooperage and several storehouses which were very conveniently situated for the purpose and in exceeding good order'. See J. Coad 'Historic Architecture . . .', p. 383.

61 MAKER CHURCH. Another landmark feature frequently shown on the maps in this

catalogue from the earliest map onwards. Some maps show signals on the church tower (**157**, **201**, **206**). **198** has a telegraph near the church.

62 AMHERST BATTERY (KINGSAND). Shown on **148** and **171**. In 1797 there were twelve 18-pounders, an increase of four since 1780.

63 PENLEE TOWER. Shown on **139** (*c.* 1769/70). A French map refers to it as '*tour carrée où il y a du canon*' (**210**). Map **171** refers to it as 'Watch Triangular Tower'.

64 RAME HEAD BEACON. Shown most often on printed charts from the seventeenth century onwards, though probably the beacon would have been a longstanding feature and is still shown in 1786 (**184**). The municipal accounts record regular payments to the watchman at Rame in the sixteenth century, and on at least two occasions there are references to the beacon. In 1543/4, for example, the watchman was paid 4d. 'when the bekenys were burnyd' (W130 f. 225v).

65 ST NICHOLAS ISLAND (DRAKE'S ISLAND). Shown on **1** and very frequently thereafter. In 1547/8, a fort was authorized there (W130 f. 246). In order to build the fort, the votive chapel of St Michael which had stood there previously and which is shown on **1**, had to be pulled down (R.N. Worth *History of Plymouth*, pp. 233–4, 408–11). The municipal records include various payments concerning the island's fortifications: £8 13s. 6d. spent in 1573/4 (W132 ff. 19v-20); £279 14s. 4d. in 1583/4 (W132 f. 59); and £115 13s. 11d. in 1589/90 (W132 f. 86). Letters patent of 22 June 1585 provide for an annual pension of £39 10s. 10d. out of the customs of the port of Plymouth to be spent on the wages of four gunners at the fort on St Nicholas Island (W2) 'for the wythstandyng of anye forrayne attempte'.

Appendix VI
Rocks, Sandbanks and Shoals around Plymouth Sound

The reference for each item corresponds to that given on the chart of Plymouth Sound on pp. 200–1.

R1 BEGGAR'S ISLAND. Shown on **8**, *c*. 1591

R2 GERMAN. Sailing Directions in *The English Pilot*, 1701 (**75**): 'About half a Cable's length to the Eastward of the Passage going into Hamouze, lieth a sunken Rock, called the German, about two Ships length from the shore, which at low water hath not above four foot on it. When you come near this Rock going into Hamouse, either with the Flood or Ebb (for the tide will set you right upon it, if it be calm) therefore to avoid it, give this Rock a good birth . . .' **148** (1797): German Rock 'mostly Dry at Low Water Spring Tides'.

R3 ASIA KNOLL.

R4 WINTER. Varying depths under water are given for this as for other rocks, presumably dependent upon the state of the tide and other considerations. Map **4** (*c*. 1586–8) shows 'a rock 12 foote under water called winters stone'. Map **185** (1788) refers to '*Winter 12 pieds de Mer basse*'. Map **157**, however, notes 'Winter Rock 11 feet' (1777), while **94** (1734) mentions '*14 Voet*'.

R5 COBLER. 'Cobler 12' ft under water (**157**).

R6 MELAMPUS.

R7 THE BRIDGE. *The Coasting Pilot*, 1769, notes: 'to the Westward of [St Nicholas] Island is all foul Ground, and sunken Rocks, that the Passage is very difficult, except for small Vessels, or those that are well acquainted' (NMM MAP 05). Shortly after the period covered by this catalogue ends, John Harris wrote in 1811: 'the strait calld the Bridge . . . is as fatal to ships' boats in a squall of wind, particularly from SSE as the strait between Scylla and Charybdis in the Mediterranean. In the course of the last 12 years, by endeavouring to pass this dangerous passage, no less than 15 men-of-wars' boats of different description have been swamped and lost' (Harris *An Essay Toward the History of Plymouth*, vol. I, p. 75).

R8 NEW ROCK. A note of May 1791 on **159** reads: 'New Rock in Cawsand Bay 22 feet or rather 23 feet'.

R9 SHOVEL. **93** (1728) states that this rock was 'call'd so from Sir Cloudesly Shovel, who order'd a Buoy to be put upon it; it lies sunk in 16 Foot Water'. Other estimates of depth below water for Shovel vary between 14 and 17 ft: **185** (1788): '*Shovell 14 pieds de mer basse*'; **94** (1734): '*15 Voet*'; **53** (1693): Shovel 'where is but 16 foot water at low water'; **157** (1777): 'Shovel 17

Feet'; **183** (1786): '17 F'; **149** (1797): 'On the West End of The Shovel in 17 feet water is a White Perch, Buoy or Beacon with its name thereon.'

R10 PANTHER. 'On this Rock is a Black Perch Buoy or Beacon with a Yellow Globe upon it, lying . . . about half a mile from the Shovel 1¼ mile from the Tinker'(**149**).

R11 KNAP. **159** (1777–9): 'a short time before we [Murdoch Mackenzie and others] finished the Survey, we discovered the West Nap – by mere accident, and got the Masters to place a black Buoy on it'. **149** (1797): 'On the South West End of the Knap about SW ½ W by Compass and nearly half a mile from the Panther. Beacon is a similar Black Beacon with a White Globe. From this Beacon the Shoal extends about a Cable's length towards the Panther and has 21 feet on it at low water.'

R12 TINKER. *Great Britain's Coasting Pilot*, 1693, notes: 'There lyeth another Rock near the Shagstone, called the Tinkershears or Swiftsure and hath seventeen foot at low water' (BL Maps C8 d7). Other estimates for depth below water vary from 14 ft, however: **149** (1797) states: 'On the West End of the Tinker in 14 feet water is a White Perch, Buoy or Beacon with an Iron Vane.' At least two maps refer to Tinker as 16 ft below water: **93** (1728), 'Tinker 16 foot', and **185** (1788), '*Tinker 16 pieds de mer basse*'.

R13 SHAG STONE. Shown on a number of printed charts from **53** (1693) onwards.

R14 RENNEY ROCKS.

Bibliography

Unless otherwise stated place of publication is London.

Charts

Day, A. *The Admiralty Hydrographic Service*, 1795–1919, 1967 edition

Dyer, F.E. 'The Journal of Grenvill Collins', *Mariner's Mirror*, XIV.3 (July 1928)

Foster, W. 'A Seventeenth Century Cartographer', *Geographical Journal*, 1914

Howse, D. and Sanderson, M. *The Sea Chart*, David and Charles, Newton Abbot, 1973

Hydrographic Department, Taunton *A Summary of Selected Manuscript Documents of Historic Importance preserved in the Archives of the Department*, 1950

Mackenzie, Murdoch, senior *A Treatise on Marine Surveying, 1774* (1819 edition)

Mollat du Jourdin, M. *Sea Charts of the Early Explorers, 13th–17th Centuries*, Thames and Hudson, 1984

Robinson, A.H.W. 'The Evolution of the English Nautical Chart', *International Hydrographic Review* XXX.1 (May 1953)

Robinson, A.H.W. *Marine Cartography in Britain*, OUP, 1962

Skelton, R.A. 'The Hydrographic Collections of the British Museum', *Journal of the Institute of Navigation*, IX (1956)

Waters, D.W. *The Art of Navigation in England in Elizabethan and early Stuart Times*, 1958

Military Surveying

Close, C. *The Early Years of the Ordnance Survey*, ed. J.B. Harley, New York, 1969

Marshal, D. 'Military Maps of the 18th Century and the Tower of London Drawing Room', *Imago Mundi*, 32 (1980), pp. 21–44

O'Donoghue, Y. *William Roy, Pioneer of the Ordnance Survey, 1726–90*

Skelton, R.A. 'The Origins of the Ordnance Survey of Great Britain', *Geographical Journal*, CXXVIII (1962)

Historical Maps

Bryan's Dictionary of Painters and Engravers, new edition, 1930, revised by George C. Williamson

Campbell, T. 'Understanding Engraved Maps', *The Map Collector*, 46 (Spring 1989)

Chubb, T. *The Printed Maps in the Atlases of Great Britain and Ireland, 1579–1870*, Dawsons, 1974 reprint

Dainville, F. de *La Cartographie Reflet de L'Histoire*, editions Slatkine, Geneva Paris, 1986

Eden, P. (ed.) *Dictionary of Land Surveyors of Great Britain and Ireland 1550–1850*, Dawsons, 1975

Elliot, J. *The City in Maps; urban mapping to 1900*, British Library, 1987

Gurevich, A.J. *Categories of Medieval Culture*, Routledge and Kegan Paul, 1985

Harley, J.B. 'The Evaluation of early maps: towards a methodology', *Imago Mundi*, 22 (1968)

Harley, J.B. *Maps for the Local Historian: A Guide to the British Sources*, 1972, reprinted 1977

Harley, J.B. and Woodward, David (eds) *The History of Cartography*, vol. I, University of Chicago, 1987

Lynam, E. *British Maps and Mapmakers*, 1944

Lynam, E. 'English Maps and Mapmakers of the 16th Century', *Geographical Journal*, CXVI (1950)

Lynam, E. *Proceedings of the B.R.A.*, vol. IV, 1939

Porter, E. *History of the Corps of Royal Engineers*

Skelton, R.A. *The Land Surveyor in English History*, 1962

Skelton, R.A. *Maps: A Historical Survey of their Study and Collecting*, Chicago, 1972

Taylor, E.G.R. *Mathematical Practitioners of Tudor and Stuart England*, Cambridge, 1954

Taylor, E.G.R. *The Surveyor*

Taylor, E.G.R. *Tudor Geography, 1485–1583*, 1930

Tooley, R.V. *Dictionary of Mapmakers*, 1979, Alan R. Liss Inc. and Meridian Publishing Company

Tyacke, S. (ed.) *English Map-making, 1500–1650*, British Library, 1983

Tyacke, S. and Huddy, J. *Christopher Saxton and Tudor Map-making*, BL series no. 2, 1980

Cataloguing and Cartobibliography

Anglo-American Cataloguing Rules, 2nd edition, 1984

British Standards Institution *BS 5195: Recommendations for Bibliographical References to Maps and Charts*

Ehrenberg, R.E. *Archives and Manuscripts: Maps and Architectural Drawings*, SAA Basic Manual Series, Chicago, 1982

Hodson, D. *Maps of Portsmouth before 1801* Portsmouth Record Series, Portsmouth, 1978

Karrow, R.W., junior *The Role of Cartobibliography in the History of Cartography*, 11th International Conference on the History of Cartography, Ottawa, Canada, 8–12 July 1985

Koeman, C. *Collections of Maps and Atlases in the Netherlands*, 1961

Koeman, C. *Atlantes Neerlandici*, Amsterdam, 1967

Le Gear, C. *Geographical Atlases*, Library of Congress, 1963

Pastoureau, M. *Les Atlas Français, XVI–XVII siècles: répertoire bibliographique et étude*, Bibliothèque Nationale, Paris, 1984

Verner, C. 'Captain Collins' Coasting Pilot: A Carto-Bibliographical analysis', *The Map Collector's Circle*, 58 (1969)

Local Historical Material

Barber, J. 'New light on Old Plymouth' *Proceedings of the Plymouth Athenaeum*, vol. IV

Coad, J. 'Historic Architecture of HM Naval Base Devonport 1689–1850, *Mariner's Mirror*, 69. 4

Coad, J. *The Royal Dockyards 1690–1850*, Scolar Press, 1989

Oppenheim, M.M. *The Maritime History of Devon*, University of Exeter, 1968

Patterson, A. Temple *The Other Armada: the Franco-Spanish attempt to invade Britain in 1779*, Manchester University Press, 1960

Worth, R.N. *History of Plymouth from the Earliest Period to the Present Time*, Plymouth, 1890

Worth, R.N. *Calendar of the Plymouth Municipal Records*, Plymouth, 1893

Contemporary Diaries

Fiennes, Celia *The Illustrated Journeys of Celia Fiennes, 1685–c. 1712*, ed. Christopher Morris, Macdonald and Co., 1982

Leland, John *The Itinerary of John Leland in or about the Years 1535–43*, parts I–III, ed. L. Toulmin Smith, 1907

Paradès, Robert, Count de *Secret Memoirs of Robert, Count de Paradès, written by himself on coming out of the Bastille*, 1791

Yonge, James *The Journal of James Yonge, Plymouth Surgeon, 1647–1721* (ed. F.N.L. Poynter), 1963

General

Tenison, E.M. *Elizabethan England; Being the History of this Country . . . from original manuscripts . . . many hitherto unpublished . . .* , vol. VIII, Leamington Spa, 1947